2-9-70

91726
1526

Isotope Effects
in Chemical Processes

Based on a symposium

sponsored by the Division

of Nuclear Chemistry and

Technology at the 153rd

Meeting of the American

Chemical Society, Miami

Beach, Fla., April 11, 1967.

William Spindel,

Symposium Chairman

ADVANCES IN CHEMISTRY SERIES 89

AMERICAN CHEMICAL SOCIETY

WASHINGTON, D. C.   1969

Advances in Chemistry Series

Robert F. Gould, *Editor*

AMERICAN CHEMICAL SOCIETY | PUBLICATIONS

FOREWORD

ADVANCES IN CHEMISTRY SERIES was founded in 1949 by the American Chemical Society as an outlet for symposia and collections of data in special areas of topical interest that could not be accommodated in the Society's journals. It provides a medium for symposia that would otherwise be fragmented, their papers distributed among several journals or not published at all. Papers are refereed critically according to ACS editorial standards and receive the careful attention and processing characteristic of ACS publications. Papers published in ADVANCES IN CHEMISTRY SERIES are original contributions not published elsewhere in whole or major part and include reports of research as well as reviews since symposia may embrace both types of presentation.

Errata:

1. Last sentence on page 249 should read $m_- =$ electronic mass instead of $m =$ electronic mass.

2. In Table III on page 252 $\mu°_{\text{Li}}$ should read $-\mu°_{\text{Li}}$.

3. In the second line of Table IX on page 258 the number 0.087 should be 0.187.

4. Next to the last line of text on page 190 number 23.9 cm.$^{-1}$ should be -23.9 cm.$^{-1}$.

CONTENTS

v

PREFACE

This symposium was organized for the Division of Nuclear Chemistry and Technology of the American Chemical Society under the title "Separation of Stable Isotopes by Chemical Methods." Its major purpose was to acquaint chemists with the variety of chemical methods currently available for separating isotopes of the lighter elements and for separating isotopically labelled molecules.

Papers in this volume outline the principles involved, and the scope of technology required, to concentrate isotopes by chemical exchange, distillation, gas chromatography, electromigration, and photochemical processes. They clearly indicate the implications of the single-stage fractionation factor, the exchange rate, and the reflux operations required, for evaluating the overall suitability of any particular chemical process for application to isotope separation. Well established methods are reviewed, and novel recent methods are examined for fractionating isotopes of the elements: hydrogen, lithium, boron, carbon, and nitrogen. An analysis is made of the factors which are particularly significant for laboratory scale isotope separation, as contrasted to large scale industrial production.

Several papers in this volume deal with transport in various kinds of liquids; others examine critically the fundamental statistical-mechanical theory determining isotope effects for both equilibrium and kinetic processes in condensed as well as gaseous systems. These studies are of interest not only because they serve as a framework for comparing the merits of different isotope separation processes, but they provide powerful tools for using isotope effect data to obtain an understanding of inter-molecular forces in condensed and adsorbed phases and changes in intramolecular forces in isolated molecules. The title of this volume has accordingly been broadened from that of the symposium to reflect the wider scope of its contents.

The papers by A. Klemm and K. Heinzinger and by A. Lodding were not presented at the symposium. I am particularly appreciative to these authors for agreeing to include their contributions in this collection in order to enhance its usefulness to scientists working on isotope effects. I should also like to express my thanks to all the authors, and especially to Jacob Bigeleisen for his assistance in chairing and moderating one of the sessions.

New York, N. Y. WILLIAM SPINDEL
February 1969

Isotope Separation Practice

JACOB BIGELEISEN[1]

Chemistry Department, Brookhaven National Laboratory,
Upton, Long Island, N. Y. 11973

A survey is presented of isotope separation processes. A distinction is made between processes suitable for laboratory scale isotope separation and large scale processes. Examples of laboratory scale separation by the electromagnetic separator, thermal diffusion, distillation, and chemical exchange are discussed. Large scale processes must be designed and operated in accord with cascade principles. These are discussed and illustrated by their implications to the production of heavy water by various processes. The cost of reflux operations in distillation and exchange processes is stressed. Thermal reflux can be achieved in chemical exchange systems by the dual temperature and exchange distillation processes.

Interest in the separation of isotopes started as a scientific curiosity. The question arose as to whether it was indeed at all feasible or possible to separate isotopes. After this question was answered in the affirmative (*24*), it became of interest to separate isotopes on a laboratory scale for use in scientific research. A few examples show the range of utility of separated isotopes. Deuterium has attained widespread use as a biochemical and chemical tracer. It is now abundantly available and is used as freely as any cheap chemical reagent. ^{3}He has opened up an entirely new field of research in low temperature physics and has important applications in the production of temperatures below 1°K. ^{10}B, with a thermal neutron cross section of 4,000 barns, has found wide use in nuclear particle detectors—neutron proportional counters. ^{13}C still finds use as a tracer, but in recent years its most frequent use has been in electron spin and nuclear magnetic resonance spectroscopy. ^{15}N occupies a unique position as the only usable tracer for nitrogen. ^{18}O finds application as a

[1] Present address: Univ. of Rochester, Rochester, N. Y. 14627.

chemical tracer, while the less abundant isotope ^{17}O is the only oxygen istotope with a nuclear magnetic moment. ^{17}O is scarce and much sought after for nuclear magnetic resonance studies of oxygen compounds.

Separated isotopes have played an important role in the production of nuclear power and in the development of nuclear energy. The importance of separated isotopes in this field can be seen at once by considering the thermal neutron cross sections of those isotopes which have become important in the nuclear industry. A few of these are given in Table I. The very small neutron absorption cross section of deuterium, compared with protium, together with its excellent moderating power, has made heavy water a very important reactor moderator. ^{10}B has found wide-

Table I. Thermal Neutron Cross Sections of Some Isotopes Useful for Nuclear Energy Production

Isotope	Natural Abundance (%)	σ (barns)	
^{1}H	99.99	0.33	
^{2}H	0.015	0.0005	
^{10}B	19	4000.	
^{11}B	81	<0.05	
^{14}N	99.6	1.8	
^{15}N	.37	.00002	
^{235}U	0.7	580	(fission)
		107	(capture)
^{238}U	99.3	2.8	

spread use in reactor control and reactor shielding because of its high cross section. Of the naturally occurring isotopes of uranium, only ^{235}U undergoes slow neutron fission. It is the all important isotope for reactors which utilize uranium fuel.

In this discussion we shall divide isotope separation processes into two categories: (1) those which are primarily useful as laboratory scale processes, and (2) those which are useful for large scale separation processes. For laboratory scale operation, the electromagnetic separator, thermal diffusion columns, chemical exchange processes, and distillation have proven useful and show considerable versatility. Only the following processes have proven to be sufficiently economical for large scale production of separated isotopes: chemical exchange, distillation, and gaseous diffusion. Although the ultra-centrifuge is still in the development stage, it does have potential for large scale separation of isotopes of the heavy elements. In this paper we shall give a brief discussion of the principles of the separation processes together with examples from operating practice.

Laboratory Scale Processes

Electromagnetic Separator. The mass spectrograph was developed in the early 1940's for the production of gram to kilogram quantities of separated isotopes. Such separators were often called calutrons in recognition of their development at the University of California Radiation Laboratory. The separator operates by magnetic resolution of a beam of accelerated ions, formed in an ion source by electron bombardment. A schematic diagram of the principles of the separator is given in Figure 1. In the ion source the feed material is converted into positive ions by electron bombardment. The separator therefore operates with a vacuum in the sub-micron range. Ion sources have been developed for both gaseous and solid materials. The ion beam is collimated and extracted from the source region by a series of slits and an accelerating potential. The beam is then mass separated by a magnetic field perpendicular to the plane of the paper and collection of the separated isotopes is done in the focal plane of the separator. The equations of motion are

$$1/2 \, Mv^2 = Eze \tag{1}$$

$$\frac{Mv^2}{r} = Hzev \tag{2}$$

Equation 1 equates the kinetic energy of an ion of charge ze to the change in its electrostatic potential. The ion traverses a circular orbit, whose radius is determined by the strength of the magnetic field and the momentum of the ion, Equation 2. Combining Equations 1 and 2 we see that the radius of curvature, r, is proportional to $\sqrt{M}$. In a 180° separator, such as is shown in Figure 1, the distance between collectors is twice the difference in the radii of curvature or

$$r_2 - r_1 = C \sqrt{E/H} \left(\sqrt{M_2} - \sqrt{M_1} \right) \tag{3}$$

The electromagnetic separator has proven to be very useful and versatile particularly for preparation of pure samples on a gram scale. Table II gives a summary of some of the operating experience during the year 1956-57 at the Oak Ridge Electromagnetic Separator Plant. Each separation process involves considerable development work on the chemistry of the source material to provide volatile feed of suitable chemical purity. The electromagnetic separator has inherent high losses, and for this reason the feed must be cheap material. Only a small fraction of the feed material is ionized and extracted from the slits; there are scattering losses in the beam; finally, collectors must be developed which will trap the separated beams and from which the separated isotopes can be easily removed. This usually involves further chemical processing. A useful guide to the potential of the separator can be obtained from the fact that a one ampere ion beam can produce 1 lb. of ^{235}U per year from material of natural abundance.

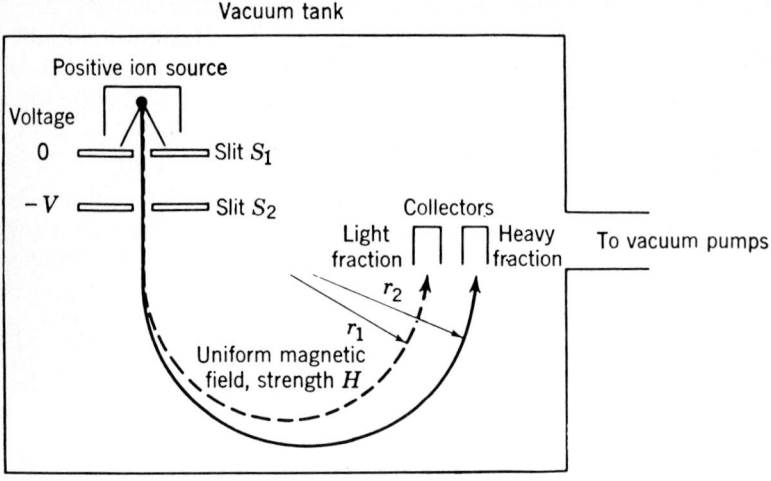

Figure 1. Principle of the electromagnetic separation of isotopes. Reproduced by permission from "Nuclear Chemical Engineering" (Ref. 3), © 1957 by McGraw-Hill Book Co.

Table II. Separated Isotope Production at Oak Ridge Electromagnetic Separator, February 1956–February 1957

Isotope	Initial Concentration of Feed (%)	Estimated Collected Weight (grams)	Purity Attained (%)
^{6}Li	99	1.5	99.999
^{7}Li	97	15.9	99.998
^{153}Eu	52	0.7	99.44
^{28}Si	92	18.3	99.98
^{40}Ca	97	12.34	99.995
^{10}B	96	3.79	99.6
^{11}B	89	6.57	99.6

Thermal Diffusion. The existence of a concentration gradient in a gas mixture subject to a temperature gradient, thermal diffusion, was predicted by Enskog and by Chapman in the development of the kinetic theory of non-uniform gases. The phenomenon was demonstrated experimentally by Chapman and Dootson. The transport equation relates the separation, q, to the temperature gradient by the equation

$$\ln q = \alpha \ln T_1/T_2 \qquad (4)$$

The thermal diffusion factor α is proportional to the mass difference, $(m_1 - m_2)/(m_1 + m_2)$. The thermal diffusion process depends on the transport of momentum in collisions between unlike molecules. The momentum transport vanishes for Maxwellian molecules, particles which repel one another with a force which falls off as the inverse fifth power of the distance between them. If the repulsive force between the molecules falls off more rapidly than the fifth power of the distance, then the light molecule will concentrate in the high temperature region of the space, while the heavy molecule concentrates in the cold temperature region. When the force law falls off less rapidly than the fifth power of the distance, then the thermal diffusion separation occurs in the opposite sense. The theory of the thermal diffusion factor α is as yet incomplete even for classical molecules. A summary of the theory has been given by Jones and Furry (15) and by Hirschfelder, Curtiss, and Bird (14). Since the thermal diffusion factor α for isotope mixtures is small, of the order of 10^{-2}, it remained for Clusius and Dickel (8) to develop an elegant countercurrent system which could multiply the elementary effect.

The Clusius-Dickel column is shown schematically in Figure 2. A wire is mounted at the axis of a cylinder. The wire is heated electrically and the outer wall is cooled. This sets up a radial thermal gradient which leads to a thermal diffusion separation in the x direction. As a result of the radial temperature gradient, a convection current is established in the gas, which causes the gas adjacent to the hot wire to move up the tube with respect to the gas near the cold wall. The countercurrent flow leads to a multiplication of the elementary separation factor. For gas consisting of elastic spheres, the light molecules will then concentrate at the top of the column, while the heavy molecules concentrate at the bottom. The transport theory of the column has been developed in detail (3, 15, 18) and will not be presented here. In a later section we shall discuss the general aspects of the multiplication of elementary separation processes by countercurrent flow.

To avoid columns of unduly large height, it has been found practical to use columns of approximately 10 feet in height and transfer material from the bottom of one column to the top of the succeeding column. The transport between columns is conveniently done by means of a thermal wave at the top and bottom of the cascade. An example of a working system of this type is shown in Figure 3 (9). The cascade is operated both as an enricher and a stripper. Natural neon is fed from the storage bulbs V_4, V_2, and V_3 into the cascade at the bottom of column T_3. Enriched ^{20}Ne is removed at the top of column T_0 and ^{22}Ne at the bottom of column T_9. The distribution of the neon isotopes in column T_4 through T_8 is shown in Figure 4. The behavior of the middle isotope ^{21}Ne is of particular interest. It concentrates in the center of the cascade since it is a heavy molecule compared with ^{20}Ne, but a light molecule compared with ^{22}Ne. A further concentration of such an intermediate isotope can be effected through the use of an auxiliary carrier gas.

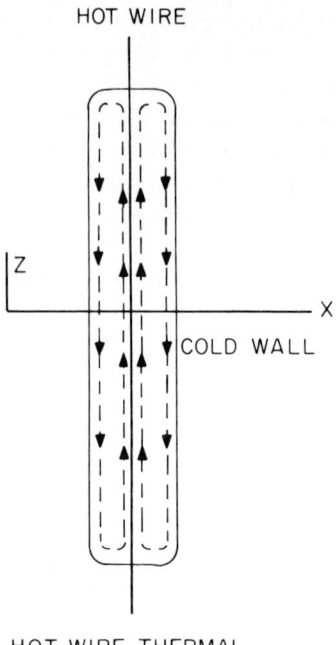

HOT WIRE THERMAL
DIFFUSION COLUMN

Figure 2. Hot wire thermal diffusion column

The thermal diffusion method requires large quantities of power and is therefore primarily of interest for preparation of laboratory scale samples. As such, it has been developed by Clusius among others, and is a very effective separation process. Overall separations as high as 10,000,000 have been achieved by the Clusius group. A summary of the evolution of the thermal diffusion column in Clusius' laboratory is given in Table III (10). Of particular note is the enrichment of ^{38}Ar, a middle isotope, from a natural abundance of 0.064% to a final isotopic purity of 99.984%.

Large Scale Processes

The most important isotope separation processes developed to date for tonnage production have been multi-stage processes. There are a significant number of design and operating variables which affect the

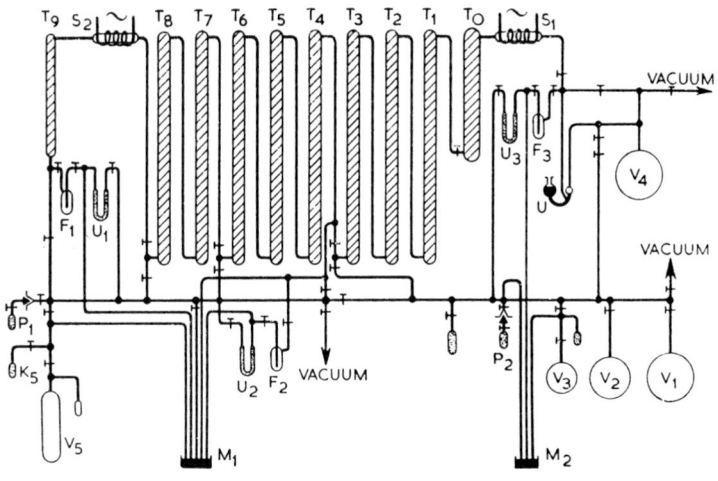

Z. Naturforsch.

Figure 3.   Column assembly used by Clusius et al. *(9) for the separation of the neon isotopes*

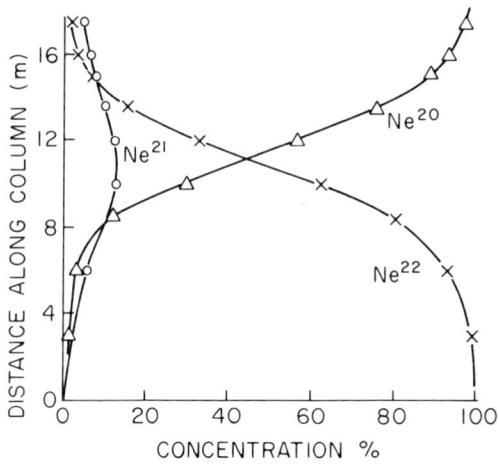

Z. Naturforsch.

Figure 4.   Distribution of the 3 neon isotopes along the columns T_1 to T_8 (9)

performance of a multi-stage cascade. Many of these are related through the cascade theory, whose development is principally attributed to K. Cohen (*11*). A very practical presentation of the theory, together with useful illustrative examples, has been given by Benedict and Pigford (*3*).

Table III.   Isotopes Separated by K. Clusius by Thermal Diffusion

Year	Isotopes	Natural Abundance	Separation Factor	Final Purity
1939	^{35}Cl	75.7	53	99.4
1939	^{37}Cl	24.3	775	99.6
1942	^{84}Kr	57.1	45	98.3
1942	^{86}Kr	17.5	940	99.5
1950	^{20}Ne	90.5	210	99.95
1950	^{15}N	0.37	135,000	99.8
1953	^{13}C	1.09	45,000	99.8
1955	^{136}Xe	8.9	810	99.0
1956	^{21}Ne	0.275	96,500	99.6
1959	^{18}O	0.204	200,000	99.75
1959	^{38}Ar	0.064	9,750,000	99.984
1960	^{22}Ne	9.21	12,500	99.92
1962	^{36}Ar	0.37	3,300,000	99.991

In any separating unit, whether a single element, a stage, or an entire cascade, a feed stream F of a two component mixture with composition $x_F, 1 - x_F$ is divided into a product stream P of composition $x_P, 1 - x_P$ and a waste stream W of a composition $x_W, 1 - x_W$

$$F \xrightarrow{\ \ \ } \boxed{\text{BLACK BOX}} \begin{array}{l} P \uparrow \quad x_P, 1 - x_P \\ \\ W \downarrow x_W, (1 - x_W) \end{array}$$
$$x_F, (1 - x_F)$$

In any separating element, stage, or cascade two material balance equations apply

$$F = P + W \tag{5}$$

$$Fx_F = Px_P + Wx_W \tag{6}$$

The elementary single stage separation factor α for a two component system is defined as

$$\alpha = \frac{x_i'/1 - x_i'}{x_i''/1 - x_i''} \tag{7}$$

where x_i' and x_i'' are mole fractions of the component of interest in the product and waste streams at the i-th elementary separating unit. The separation factor is determined by the nature of the separating process and the process material. An actual operating unit performs with an efficiency factor Z which is less than unity. Three simple examples are

(1) Distillation
$$H_2O(l) = H_2O(g)$$
$$HDO(l) = HDO(g)$$
$$P = \text{liquid}$$

$$W = \text{gas}$$

$$\alpha = \frac{(D/H)l}{(D/H)g} = \frac{P_{H_2O}}{P_{HDO}} = 1.07 \text{ at } 25°C.$$

(2) Chemical exchange reaction

$$HD(g) + H_2O(l) = HDO(l) + H_2(g)$$

If we neglect the vapor pressure of water and the solubility of hydrogen gas

$$\alpha = \frac{(HDO/H_2O)l}{(HD/H_2)g} = 3.70 \text{ at } 25°C.$$

(3) gaseous diffusion

A schematic diagram for the enrichment of ^{235}U by gaseous diffusion of UF_6 through an effusion barrier is shown in Figure 5, which also illustrates the counter-current flow and cascade principles. The limiting separation factor α is given by the kinetic theory of gases

$$\alpha = \frac{(^{235}U/^{238}U)\text{upstream}}{(^{235}U/^{238}U)\text{downstream}} = \sqrt{\frac{352}{349}} = 1.0043$$

The multiplicative process combines the waste of the i + 1 th stage with the product of the 1 − 1 th stage to form the feed of stage i. The overall separation achieved in the cascade S is defined similarly to the single stage factor

$$S = \frac{x_P/1 - x_P}{x_W/1 - x_W} \tag{8}$$

The overall separation depends on the single stage separation factor, the number of separating elements, and design and operating characteristics of the cascade. Equations 5–8 are insufficient to determine all the variables. It is instructive to consider three types of cascades: the minimum stage cascade, the minimum reflux cascade, and the ideal cascade. The material balance equations from the i + 1 th stage to the product of the cascade lead to

$$x''_{i+1} - x'_i = \frac{x'_i + x_P}{F''_{i+1}/P} \tag{9}$$

Equation 9 shows how the enrichment at the i + 1 th stage depends on the total amount of enriched product withdrawn from the separation plant. If the cascade is one which enriches the component labelled x, then we can see from Equation 9 that the waste of the i + 1 th stage always has a lower concentration of the component being enriched than the heads of the preceding stage. When the production rate, P, goes to zero or the reflux ratio at the i − 1 th stage, F''_{i+1}/P, goes to infinity, the maximum concentration gradient is established between stages. The maximum concentration gradient cascade is the one which requires the minimum number of stages. At infinite reflux ratio

$$x''_{i+1} = x'_i \tag{10}$$

and

$$\left(\frac{x''}{1-x''}\right)_{i+1} = \left(\frac{x'}{1-x'}\right)_i \tag{11}$$

The definition of the separation factor, Equation 7, when combined with infinite reflux condition, Equation 11, gives

$$\left(\frac{x'}{1-x'}\right)_{i+1} = \alpha \left(\frac{x'}{1-x'}\right)_i \tag{12}$$

$$\left(\frac{x'}{1-x'}\right)_{i+j} = \alpha^j \left(\frac{x'}{1-x'}\right)_i \tag{13}$$

The minimum number of stages required to effect a separation S is

$$n_{\text{min.}} = \ln S / \ln \alpha \tag{14}$$

For most isotope separation processes

$$\alpha - 1 \simeq \ln \alpha \equiv \epsilon \tag{15}$$

The number of separation stages or height of the plant varies inversely with the deviation of the separation factor from unity.

The single stage separation factor determines the concentration change across each stage

$$x'_i - x''_i = \frac{(\alpha - 1)x'_i(1 - x'_i)}{x'_i + \alpha(1 - x'_i)} \tag{16}$$

The material balance Equation 9 relates the waste and heads of succeeding stages. Combining Equations 9 and 16 one obtains the concentration gradient between the heads of succeeding stages

$$x'_i - x'_{i-1} = \frac{(\alpha - 1)x'_i(1 - x'_i)}{x'_i + \alpha(1 - x'_i)} - \frac{(x_P - x'_{i-1})}{F''_i/P} \tag{17}$$

The minimum reflux ratio to establish a positive concentration gradient in the cascade follows from Equation 17

$$(F''_i/P)_{\text{min}} = \frac{(x_P - x'_{i-1})\left[x'_i + \alpha(1 - x'_i)\right]}{(\alpha - 1)x'_i(1 - x'_i)} \tag{18}$$

At minimum reflux a finite enrichment is attained by an infinite number of stages. If we neglect terms of the order ϵ in the numerator of Equation 18, we get

$$(F''_i/P)_{\text{min}} = \frac{(x_P - x'_{i-1})}{(\alpha - 1)x'_i(1 - x'_i)} \tag{19}$$

If the i-th stage is the feed point

$$(F/P)_{\min} \cong \frac{(x_P - x_F)}{(\alpha - 1)x_F(1 - x_F)} \tag{20}$$

The size of a separating element or the number of parallel elements necessary is proportional to the flow. The minimum reflux condition, Equations 18–20, shows that the area of the separation cascade or the amount of material to be processed at any point varies inversely with ϵ. The minimum total size of the plant varies as ϵ^{-2} or $(\alpha - 1)^{-2}$! There is a big premium on high separation factors.

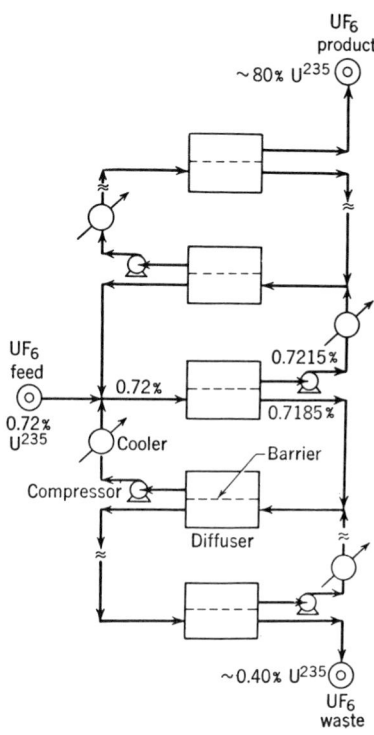

Figure 5. Gaseous-diffusion cascade for separation of $^{235}UF_6$ and $^{238}UF_6$. Reproduced by permission from "Nuclear Chemical Engineering" (Ref. 3), © 1957 by McGraw-Hill Book Co.

The two limiting cascades we have discussed are of little practical value. The minimum stage cascade produces zero amount of the maximum concentration material; the minimum reflux cascade produces the maximum amount of material with no enrichment. Both of these cascades produce an entropy of remixing at each stage. In the minimum stage cascade $x''_{i+1} > x'_{i-1}$ while in the minimum reflux cascade $x''_{i+1} < x'_{i-1}$. The entropy of remixing at the i-th stage is eliminated by the condition

$$x''_{i+1} = x'_{i-1} = x_i \qquad (21)$$

The no remixing cascade is termed the ideal cascade. The ideal cascade retains the most desirable features of each of the two minimum cascades discussed and leads to a finite concentration in a finite number of stages at a finite production rate. For a cascade with a large number of stages

$$n_{ideal} = \frac{2 \ln S}{\ln \alpha} \qquad (22)$$

When the mole fraction of desired isotope is small at the feed point, the reflux ratio at the feed point is

$$(F/P)_{ideal} = \frac{2(x_P - x_F)}{x_F(\alpha - 1)} \qquad (23)$$

The ideal cascade requires twice the number of stages as the minimum stage cascade; similarly the reflux ratio in the ideal cacade is twice that in the minimum reflux cascade.

The total flow, J, which is the sum of the flows of the two counter-current streams, in an ideal cascade is $(3, 11)$

$$J = \frac{2(1 + \sqrt{\alpha})}{\sqrt{(\alpha - 1)} \ln \alpha} \left[P (2x_P - 1) \ln \frac{x_P}{1 - x_P} + W (2x_W - 1) \ln \frac{x_W}{1 - x_W} - \right.$$
$$\left. F (2x_F - 1) \ln \frac{x_F}{1 - x_F} \right] \qquad (24)$$

The approximation $\alpha - 1 = \epsilon$ then gives

$$J = \frac{8}{\epsilon^2} \left[P (2x_P - 1) \ln \frac{x_P}{1 - x_P} + W (2x_W - 1) \ln \frac{x_W}{1 - x_W} \right.$$
$$\left. - F (2x_F - 1) \ln \frac{x_F}{1 - x_F} \right] \qquad (25)$$

The quantity in the square brackets is called the separative duty. The separative duty is a function only of the product, waste, and feed concentrations and amounts. It is a quantitative measure of the separative work done by the cascade. The function $(2x - 1) \ln x/1 - x$ is termed the separation potential. It has a minimum at $x = 1/2$, where it is equal to zero. At all other values of x the separation potential ϕ is positive. The separative duty is always positive. This statement is consistent with the fact that the entropy of isotope mixing is positive.

Our brief discussion of cascade principles serves to demonstrate the critical dependence of the size and operating costs of isotope separation plants on the elementary separation factor ϵ. The size and initial cost are proportional to ϵ^{-2}. The operating cost is less sensitive to ϵ, but varies at least as ϵ^{-1}. The economic importance of these factors is readily seen in context with the separation of ^{235}U. In 1960 the USAEC had three gaseous diffusion plants in operation. The cost of each plant was approximately 1 billion dollars; the power consumption in each plant was 1,800,000 kw. If the plants were to be built with processes or equipment giving separation factors one half the one used, the additional construction cost to the U.S. taxpayers would be nine billion dollars. The increase in the annual operating costs of the plants can be conservatively estimated from the increase in the reflux ratio or power consumption to be \$100,000,000/yr. This is a realistic demonstration of the economic benefits and importance of fundamental research and development to society.

Now that we have developed from cascade principles the importance of the elementary separation factor to the construction and operating costs of isotope separation plants, it is of interest to inquire into the magnitude of the separation factors which can be realized for isotopes of different elements by different processes. An upper limit to the gaseous diffusion separation factor is given by the Knudsen theory of molecular flow. The theory of the centrifuge (12) has now been confirmed experimentally (1). The reduced partition function ratio of a pair of isotopic molecules establishes an absolute free energy scale for isotopes and the maximum separation factors that can be realized by chemical exchange (4). The statistical mechanical theory of isotope effects in condensed media (6) serves a similar purpose for distillation processes. A comparison of separation factors for isotopes of hydrogen, carbon, and uranium by chemical exchange, distillation, gaseous diffusion, and centrifuges is given in Table IV. The correlation of the separation factors with properties of matter is given in London's book on isotope separation (18).

Table IV.   Comparison of Separation Factors

Separation Method	H-D	^{12}C-^{13}C	^{235}U-^{238}U
Chemical Exchange	3	1.02	1.001
Distillation	1.05–1.7	1.01	1.0000
Gaseous Diffusion	1.2	1.03	1.004
Centrifuge 250 m/sec.	1.01	1.01	1.026

The separation factors in Table IV together with Equation 23 lead to reflux ratios of the order of 10^4 at the feed point in plants to enrich deuterium, ^{13}C and ^{235}U from natural abundance to greater than 90% purity. It is obvious that the nature of the reflux operation is very impor-

tant to isotope separation processes. In gaseous diffusion a reflux operation, compressive work, must be carried out at each separating element.
In an ideal cascade with $\epsilon < 0.1$, the cacade theory leads to the result
that the cut, $\theta = P/F$, is 1/2. The minimum reflux energy is RT ln 2 or
400 cal. for each mole of material processed at each stage. In a distillation
process the reflux need only be carried out at the condenser and boiler
of each column. A number of separating elements, plates, can be included
within each reflux operation. The reflux is cheap and utilizes heating and
cooling. The energy quantities are typically 10,000 cal. mol^{-1} at room
temperature. The chemical exchange reaction shown in the hydrogen-
water example we have given requires conversion of hydrogen to water
at the top of each column and the conversion of water to hydrogen at
the bottom of each column. It becomes necessary to erect chemical
factories to carry out the reflux. The energy quantities are typical of those
involved in chemical reactions, usually of the order of 50,000 cal. mol^{-1}.
The utilization of the chemical exchange method, which has very favorable separation factors, particularly for the light elements, necessitates
the development of cheap reflux processes which can be carried out without material losses. For laboratory scale operation, reliable maintenance
becomes an overriding consideration and too great emphasis need not be
placed on the cost of reflux operations. Loss problems during reflux
remain an important consideration.

The utility and simplicity of a laboratory scale chemical exchange
process with chemical reflux is illustrated by the Nitrox process for
the production of ^{15}N (23). The exchange reaction is

$$^{15}NO + H^{14}NO_3 = {}^{14}NO + H^{15}NO_3$$

The separation factor achieved in practice is 1.06. The reflux reactions
developed by Spindel and Taylor (21) are

$$2NO + 3/2\,O_2 + H_2O = 2HNO_3 \qquad \text{waste reflux}$$

$$2H_2O + 3SO_2 + 2HNO_3 = 3H_2SO_4 + 2NO \quad \text{product reflux}$$

The two stage cascade employed to give 99.8% ^{15}N is shown schematically
in Figure 6. The first stage column is 2.5 cm. diameter and 5.2 meters
long. It produces 6.8% ^{15}N from natural abundance material (0.4%).
The second stage is 0.9 cm. diameter by 5.5 meters long. It produced
99.8% ^{15}N product at the rate of 0.5 gram/day. A mass spectrometric
analysis of the ^{15}N product reproduced in Figure 7 shows it to have less
^{14}N than the natural abundance of ^{15}N in ordinary nitrogen.

The only chemical exchange processes which have been developed
for large scale production are either parasitic processes or ones for which
thermal reflux has been adapted to the chemical exchange process. Two

thermal reflux concepts have been developed for chemical exchange reactions: the dual temperature system and the exchange distillation.

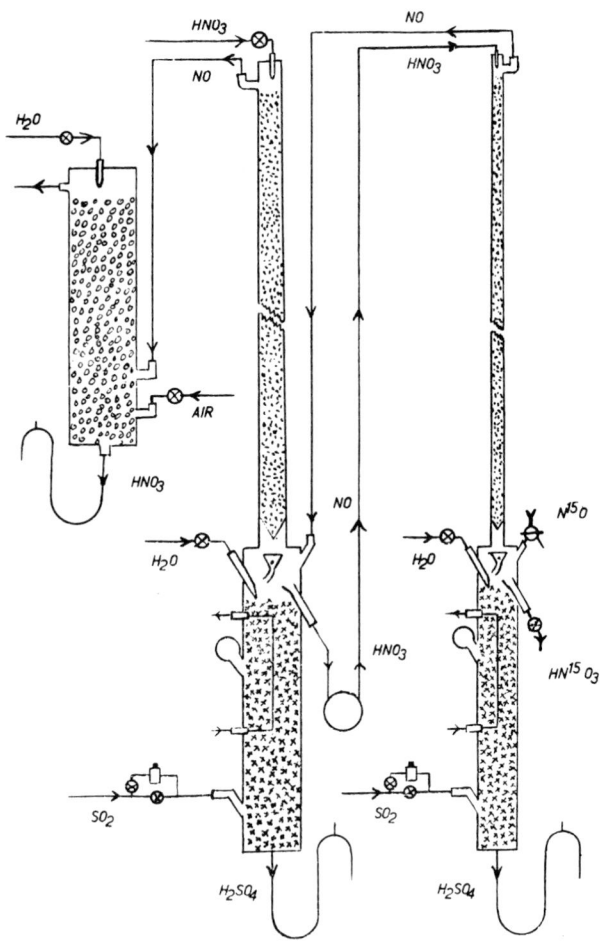

Figure 6.   Schematic diagram of a two section cascade for preparation of highly enriched nitrogen-15. "Proceedings of the International Symposium on Isotope Separation" (Ref. 17) North Holland Publishing Co.

Dual Temperature Process. A unit of a dual temperature cascade is shown schematically in Figure 8. The dual temperature system operates on the principle that isotope exchange reactions, like all chemical reactions, change their equilibrium constants with temperature. The general, but far from universal (22), rule is that in systems with large isotopic

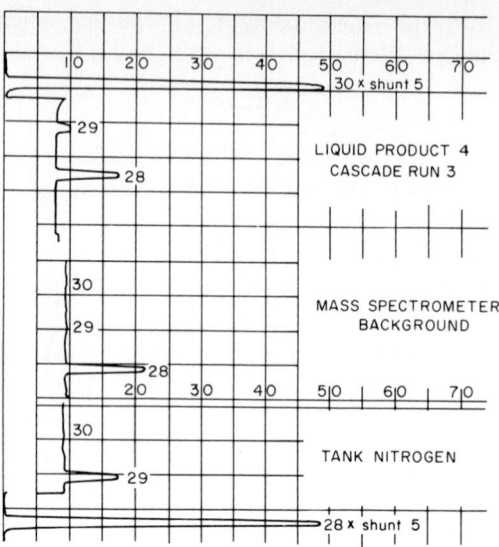

Figure 7.   Mass spectrometric comparison of N_2 obtained from HNO_3 enriched by Taylor and Spindel with tank N_2. "Proceedings of the International Symposium on Isotope Separation" (Ref. 17) North Holland Publishing Co.

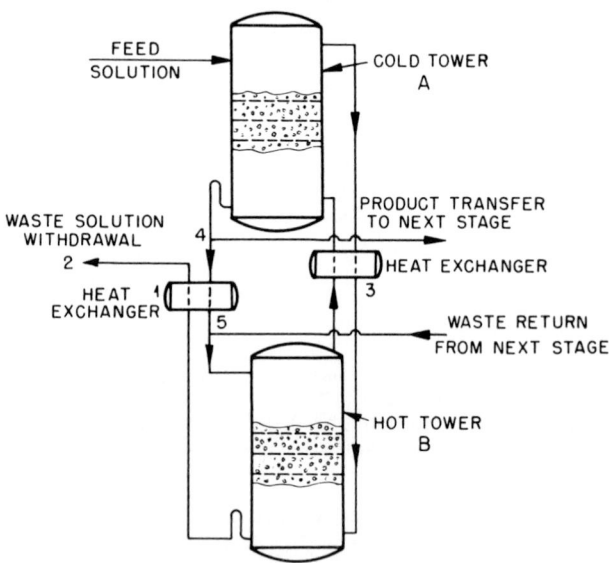

Figure 8.   Schematic stage of a dual temperature chemical exchange system

fractionation factors, the fractionation factor decreases with increasing temperature. In such systems

$$\alpha \simeq Ae^{B/T} \tag{26}$$

In the example illustrated in Figure 8 the isotope of interest is concentrated in the liquid phase. A feed solution is introduced at the top of a cold tower where it equilibrates in a multiplate column against a gas stream with which it undergoes an isotopic exchange reaction. The isotope concentration builds up to a maximum at the bottom of the cold tower. The hot tower serves as a refluxer for the cold tower. Its performance and function can be seen by focusing attention on the gas stream which is in a closed loop. At the top of the cold tower the gas stream composition is determined by equilibration against the cold feed liquid

$$\frac{x_g}{1 - x_g} = \frac{1}{\alpha_C} \frac{x_F}{1 - x_F} \tag{27}$$

This same gas is then introduced at the bottom of the hot tower. The waste liquid composition is then

$$\frac{x_W}{1 - x_W} = \alpha_H \frac{x_g}{1 - x_g} \tag{28}$$

The overall separation performed in the hot-cold stage is

$$S = \frac{\dfrac{x_F}{1 - x_F}}{\dfrac{x_W}{1 - x_W}} = \frac{\alpha_C}{\alpha_H} \tag{29}$$

The hot tower maintains a reversible concentration gradient between the product, x_P, and waste, x_W, streams.

Chemical reflux of a chemical exchange reaction accomplishes reflux by chemical inter-conversion of the two species. The conversion process supplies a countercurrent stream of enriched or depleted isotope of the appropriate isotopic composition. The use of a hot tower leads to a back transfer of enriched isotope from the enriching phase to the phase being depleted in the cold tower. The hot tower requires a number of plates comparable with that in the cold tower. The effective separation factor is, therefore,

$$\alpha_{\text{effective}} = \frac{\alpha_C}{\alpha_H} \tag{30}$$

If the feed isotopic abundance is small, Equations 27 and 28 give the fraction of the isotope fed into the plant that can be extracted

$$\frac{Px_P}{Fx_F} = \text{Fraction Extracted} \simeq 1 - \frac{\alpha_H}{\alpha_C} \qquad (31)$$

The dual temperature system requires a high temperature coefficient of the separation factor. Figure 9 shows that Equation 26 is, in fact, obeyed for many exchange reactions involving the isotopes of hydrogen. Those reactions with the largest separation factors also have the highest temperature coefficients. Of the multitude of potential hydrogen exchange reactions involving water, the one which is utilized in the largest heavy water plants built to date (the dual temperature plants at Dana, Savannah River, and Glace Bay),

$$HDS + H_2O = H_2S + HDO$$

has one of the smallest separation factors. The separation factors are 2.30 and 1.69 at 25° and 130°C. respectively (5). Yet the process is more economical than the electrolytic separation of deuterium with an α of 7. The key is the use of thermal reflux with countercurrent heat exchangers in the dual temperature process as compared with electrical work in the decomposition of water. A comparison of a number of heavy water production processes is given in Table V.

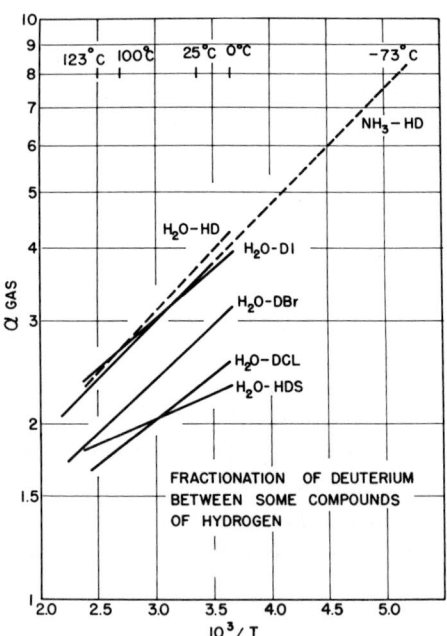

Figure 9. Semi-log plot of α vs. $1/T$. "Proceedings of the International Symposium on Isotope Separation" (Ref. 17) North Holland Publishing Co.

The first plant to produce tonnage amounts of heavy water was the Trail, B.C., plant constructed and operated according to designs of the Manhattan District of the U.S. It combined good features of the

$$HD + H_2O = HDO + H_2$$

exchange reaction with the electrolytic separation. Isotope enrichment was effected by the hydrogen-steam exchange reaction at 70°C. as well as by the reflux system. A large electrolytic hydrogen plant, which existed at Trail was utilized to supply chemical reflux. The schematic arrangement in the plant is shown in Figure 10. The reflux is achieved by electrolytic cells which are producing hydrogen for synthetic ammonia. Apportionment of reflux costs depends on how the heavy water production complicates the electrolytic hydrogen production. The Trail plant had an annual production of about 5 tons of heavy water. The limitation in such a plant is the size of the electrolytic plant.

Table V. Process Variables for Heavy Water Production Processes

Variable	Water Electrolysis	Water Distillation	Trail Plant	H_2 Distillation	H_3S-H_2O Exchange	NH_3-H_2 Exchange
Effective α	(7)	1.05	2.9	1.6	1.22	2
Minimum No. of Stages	15	300	16	35	75	20
Minimum Reflux Ratio	20,000	141,000	10,000	35,000	72,000	40,000
Percent Recovery	32	5	60	90	18	50
Operating Cost $1/lb.	500	175	27	16	13	8

Heavy water, D_2O, is of interest as a nuclear reactor moderator. A typical power reactor requires some 200 tons of heavy water. Since the natural abundance of deuterium is 1/7000, an annual production of 200 tons of D_2O requires the processing of a hydrogenous feed at a rate between 2 million ton/yr., for 100% extraction, to 20 million ton/yr., for 10% extraction. Only water, sulfuric acid, and petrochemicals are processed in this amount and can supply such quantity of feed material.

The choice of H_2S rather than H_2 as the circulating gas, in spite of the fact that the latter would give much higher effective separation factors, is based on the fact that to date no stable effective catalysts have been found which will catalyze the H_2-H_2O exchange with liquid water. The use of water vapor as in the Barr type tower makes the H_2-H_2O process unfavorable compared to the H_2S-H_2O process. Only the ammonia–hydrogen process (5) catalyzed in the liquid phase by potassium amide has emerged as competitive with the H_2S-H_2O exchange. A full

scale plant has been put in operation at Mazingarbe, France, but few
details are available.

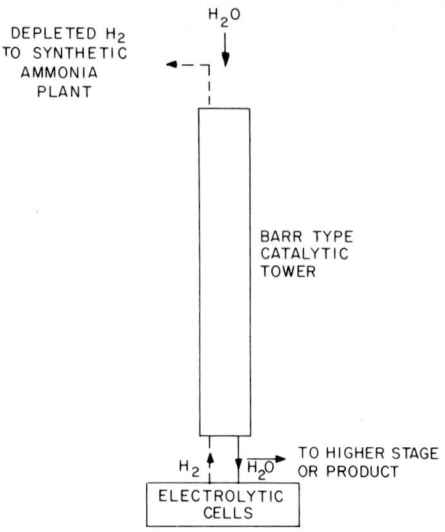

*Figure 10. Schematic arrangement of
Trail, B. C., plant for the production of
heavy water*

The history of the development of the H_2S–H_2O dual temperature
exchange process and design data of the Dana and Savannah River plants
have been given by Bebbington and Thayer (2). An economic analysis
of the operating experience at Savannah River has been given by Proctor
and Thayer (20). The Savannah River plant is a composite plant. The
first stage is an H_2S–H_2O dual temperature unit which enriches deuterium
from natural abundance, 0.015%, to 0.08%. The second stage effects a
further enrichment to 15 atom % D by the same process. At this stage
the process is switched to vacuum distillation to produce 90% D_2O.
Final concentration was made by electrolysis to give 99.75% D_2O. The
electrolytic portion of the plant was replaced by distillation some five
years ago. The major costs, both construction and operating, are expended
in producing material at about the 10% level irrespective of the process
used for enriching from 10 to 99.75%. This is a consequence of the separative work principle of the cascade. A summary of the actual Savannah
River costs are given in Table VI to VIII. If a 10 year amoritization
schedule for the plant investment is chosen and added to the operating
cost of $13.50/lb. D_2O, one arrives at the $28/lb. D_2O figure adopted
by the USAEC. The costs were calculated on the basis of the actual plant

production, which reached 500 tons/year, prior to the production curtail-
ment program.

Exchange Distillation. Experiments at Columbia University under
the Manhattan project in 1943 (*16*) as well as independent experiments
by a number of independent investigators (*17*) led to the discovery that
the logarithm of the relative volatility of the boron isotopes in addition
compounds of Lewis acids—*e.g.*, $BF_3 \cdot O(CH_3)_2$—is an order of magnitude greater than in the Lewis acid itself. This observation was explained
by the hypothesis that the fractionation in the addition compound resulted
principally from an exchange reaction. It is well known that addition
compounds of the Lewis acid BF_3 are partially dissociated in the vapor
phase but not in the liquid phase (*7*). This leads to an exchange reaction
of the type

$$^{11}BF_3 \cdot O(CH_3)_2(l) + {}^{10}BF_3(g) = {}^{10}BF_3 \cdot O(CH_3)_2(l) + {}^{11}BF_3(g)$$

Table VI.   Dual Temperature Portion of the Savannah River D_2O Plant

Stage	Column				
First	Parallel	Series	Diameter	Height	Trays
Cold 33°C.	24	1	11 feet	120 feet	70
Hot 133°C.	24	1	12 feet	120 feet	60
Second					
Cold 33°C.	24	2	6.5 feet	120 feet	85
Hot 133°C.	24	2	6.5 feet	120 feet	70

**Table VII.   Construction Cost of the Savannah River D_2O Plant
(1951-52 dollars)**

	Millions of Dollars	
Chemical exchange separation (direct)	110	
Vacuum distillation	2.5	
Electrolytic plant	1.5	114
Steam and electric power	15	
Water treatment	7	
H_2S manufacture	1	
Site facilities	6	29
		143

**Table VIII.   Distribution of Operating Costs at
Savannah River D_2O Plant ($13.50/lb.)**

Chemical Exchange	93.2%
Water Distillation	4.2
Electrolytic Separation	2.6

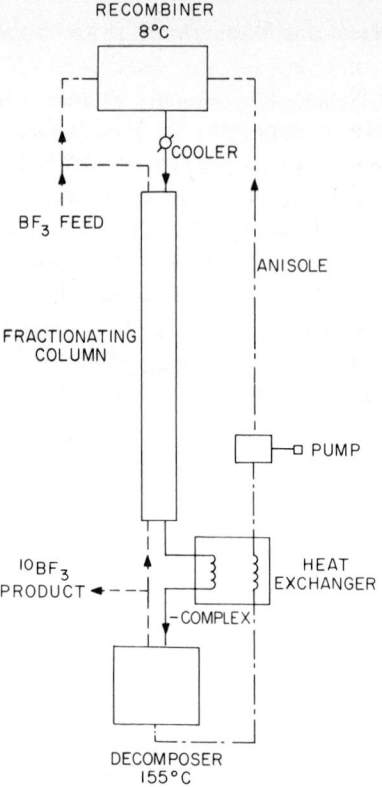

*Figure 11. Use of chemical asso-
ciation and dissociation for thermal
reflux in a chemical exchange separation (BF$_3$ · anisole process)*

The overall separation factor, $\alpha = (^{11}B/^{10}B)g/(^{11}B/^{10}B)l$, observed was
1.016 at 100°C. If one assumes that the vapor pressures of $^{10}BF_3 \cdot O(CH_3)_2$
and $^{11}BF_3 \cdot O(CH_3)_2$ are nearly identical, which one predicts from theory
and semi-quantitative experiments indicate, then the observed separation
factor, after correction for incomplete dissociation of the complex in the
vapor, leads to a value of 1.027 for the exchange equilibrium constant.
Direct measurements of the latter gave 1.025 ± 0.002, confirming the
nature of the separation process between the gas and the liquid. The
distillation of a dissociable complex, such as $BF_3 \cdot O(CH_3)_2$ provides automatic reflux for the chemical exchange reaction. Several plants of this
type have been built for the separation of the boron isotopes.

The presence of undissociated addition complex in the gas phase,
which vaporizes without fractionation with respect to the liquid, reduces
the separation factors which could be attained by exchange distillation.

Further, this nonfractionating component in the vapor phase increases the cross-sectional requirement for the distillation column. Independent groups at Oak Ridge National Laboratory under G. H. Clewett and at the University of Moscow under G. M. Panchenkov have investigated the fractionation factors for a wide variety of addition compounds of BF_3. The anisole complex, $\phi COCH_3 \cdot BF_3$, has nearly ideal properties. Its vapor pressure is small near its freezing point, 2°C. At this temperature the separation factor is 1.039. At 160°C. the complex decomposes quantitatively and the anisole formed contains about 50 p.p.m. of BF_3. These physico-chemical characteristics of the complex permit one to design a chemical exchange separation with complete thermal reflux. Such a system is shown schematically in Figure 11. Laboratory scale plants utilizing the anisole process have been built (*13, 19*). Problems associated with irreversible decomposition of the complex at high temperature make the process less than ideal for large scale production.

The exchange distillation combines the best features of the chemical exchange and distillation processes. Only the phase rule of Gibbs provides a conceptual and in some cases practical distinction between exchange distillation and distillation. The statistical mechanical theory of isotope exchange equilibria and phase equilibria predicts that exchange distillation processes will usually have larger separation factors than simple distillation at the same temperature. To find a suitable working substance for each isotope to be separated is indeed a challenge for the chemist.

Acknowledgment

This manuscript is based on my lecture "Isotope Separation," one in the Distinguished Visiting Professorship series held in the fall of 1966 at the State University of New York at Buffalo. I wish to thank the New York State Science and Technology Foundation for sponsoring the lectures and C. C. Furnas and G. M. Harris for their hospitality.

Literature Cited

(1) Beams, J. W., Snoddy, L. B., Kuhlthau, A. R., *Proc. Second United Nations Intern. Conf. Peaceful Uses Atomic Energy, Geneva* **4**, 428 (1958).
(2) Bebbington, W. P., Thayer, V. R., *Chem. Eng. Progr.* **55**, 70 (1959).
(3) Benedict, M., Pigford, T. H., "Nuclear Chemical Engineering," McGraw-Hill Book Co., Inc., New York, 1957.
(4) Bigeleisen, J., Mayer, M. G., *J. Chem. Phys.* **15**, 261 (1947).
(5) Bigeleisen, J., "Proceedings of the International Symposium on Isotope Separation," pp. 121-157, J. Kistemaker, J. Bigeleisen, A. O. C. Nier, eds., North-Holland Publishing Co., Amsterdam, 1958.
(6) Bigeleisen, J., *J. Chem. Phys.* **34**, 1485 (1961).
(7) Brown, H. C., Adams, R. M., *J. Am. Chem. Soc.* **64**, 2557 (1942).
(8) Clusius, K., Dickel, G., *Naturwiss.* **26**, 546 (1938).

(9) Clusius, K., Huber, M., Hürzeler, H., Schumacher, E., *Z. Naturf.* **11a**, 709 (1956).
(10) Clusius, K., *J. Chim. Physique* **60**, 163 (1963).
(11) Cohen, K., "The Theory of Isotope Separation," McGraw-Hill Book Co., Inc., New York, 1951.
(12) *Ibid.*, Chapter 6.
(13) Healy, R. M., Joseph E. F., Palko, A. A., *ORNL* **2069**, May 1956.
(14) Hirschfelder, J. O., Curtiss, C. F., Bird, R. B., "Molecular Theory of Gases and Liquids," Chapters 7 and 8, John Wiley and Sons, Inc., New York, 1954.
(15) Jones, R. C., Furry, W. H., *Reviews of Modern Physics* **18**, 151 (1946).
(16) Kilpatrick, M., Hutchison, C. A., Taylor, E. H., Judson, C. M., "Separation of the Boron Isotopes," USAEC Technical Information Service, Oak Ridge, Tenn., 1952.
(17) Kistemaker, J., Bigeleisen, J., Nier, A. O. C., Eds., "Proceedings of the International Symposium on Isotope Separation," Part III, North-Holland Publishing Co., Amsterdam, 1958.
(18) London, H., "Separation of Isotopes," George Newnes, Ltd., London, 1961.
(19) Panchenkov, G. M., Moiseev, V. D., Makarov, A. V., *Dokl. Akad. Nauk SSR* **112**, 659 (1957).
(20) Proctor, J. F., Thayer, V. R., *Chem. Eng. Progr.* **58**, 53 (1962).
(21) Spindel, W., Taylor, T. I., *J. Chem. Phys.* **23**, 1318 (1955).
(22) Stern, M. J., Spindel, W., Monse, E. V., *J. Chem. Phys.* **48**, 2908 (1968).
(23) Taylor, T. I., Spindel, W., "Proceedings of the International Symposium on Isotope Separation," pp. 158-177, J. Kistemaker, J. Bigeleisen, A. O. C. Nier, eds., North-Holland Publishing Co., Amsterdam, 1958.
(24) Urey, H. C., *Repts. Progr. Phys.* **VI**, 48 (1939).

RECEIVED February 29, 1968. Research carried out under the auspices of the U. S. Atomic Energy Commission.

2

Isotopic Exchange between Hydrogen and Liquid Ammonia Catalyzed by Alkali Amides

ROBERT DELMAS, PIERRE COURVOISIER, and JEAN RAVOIRE

Section de Chimie des Isotopes—DPC/SIS, C.E.N. Saclay—B.P. n° 2, 91—GIF-sur-YVETTE—France

The catalytic action of alkali amides on the isotopic exchange between hydrogen and liquid ammonia has been reinvestigated. It was clear before this work that the rate of exchange is first order with respect to the concentration of dissolved hydrogen, but the nature of the catalytic species was still under discussion. A kinetic study and a careful calculation of the dissociation coefficients of the amides of sodium, potassium, and cesium have been made. If the results are interpreted according to the theory of the acid-base catalysis given by Bell, the conclusion is that only the free amide ion acts as a catalytic species. The kinetic data are in agreement with an associative mechanism.

Claeys, Dayton, and Wilmarth (4) have shown that potassium amide dissolved in liquid ammonia is a catalyst for the ortho-para conversion of hydrogen and for the isotopic exchange between molecular hydrogen and liquid ammonia. This last reaction may be written in the range of low deuterium concentration:

$$NH_3 + HD \rightleftarrows NH_2D + H_2 \tag{1}$$

Wilmarth and Dayton (18) established that this reaction is homogeneous and that the rate of exchange is first order with respect to the concentration of dissolved hydrogen. In order to establish the catalytic action of potassium amide, they took into consideration its dissociation according to

$$KNH_2 \rightleftarrows K^+ + NH_2^- \tag{2}$$

25

and they used the equilibrium constant of this reaction given by Hawes
(11) ($K_D = 0.73 \times 10^{-4}$) to evaluate the concentration of the amide ion.
Assuming that the activity coefficients are equal to unity, which is a good
approximation in the range of concentrations used (0.4×10^{-3} to $26 \times 10^{-3}M$), they established that the rate of exchange is first order with
respect to the concentration of the amide ion.

A few years later, Bar-Eli and Klein (1), studying the same reaction,
expanded the range of concentrations of potassium amide to $200 \times 10^{-3}M$.
Using the same dissociation constant as Wilmarth and Dayton and assuming also that the activity coefficients are equal to unity, they concluded
that two catalytic species are present: the free amide ion NH_2^- and the
ion pair $K^+NH_2^-$.

Also, it has been shown in our laboratory by Dirian, Botter, Ravoire,
and Grandcollot (7) that the law proposed by Wilmarth and Dayton is
not valid when the concentration of potassium amide is higher than $20 \times 10^{-3}M$. A second term involving the cation was also added to the kinetic
equation and the activities were used instead of the concentrations.

In summary, the following equations were proposed:

$k = k_o[NH_2^-]$ Wilmarth and Dayton,
$k = k_1[NH_2^-] + k_2[KNH_2]$ Bar-Eli and Klein,
$k = k_1 \, a_{NH_2^-} + k_2 \, a_{NH_2^-} \, a_{K^+}$ Dirian, Botter, Ravoire, and
                                   Grandcollot.

In the similar cases of the exchanges between hydrogen and water
catalyzed by potassium hydroxide, and between hydrogen and methanol
catalyzed by methoxy ions, hydroxide ions, and methoxy ions have been
shown to be the only catalytic species (16).

The discrepancy remaining in the case of ammonia has led us to
continue the study of this system (6).

Kinetic Study

A kinetic study has been made with the amides of sodium, potassium,
rubidium, and cesium at the temperatures $-45.3°C.$, $-59.2°C.$, and
$-70.0°C.$, and in a range of concentrations of alkali amide between 1×10^{-3} and $200 \times 10^{-3}M$.

The reaction occurs between liquid ammonia and dissolved hydrogen,
however gaseous hydrogen is present above the liquid phase. In order to
reach the actual chemical rate of the reaction, dissolved and gaseous
hydrogen must be in isotopic equilibrium at all times. To satisfy this
condition, the reaction cell used ensures a very efficient mixing of the
liquid and the gas (see Figure 1). Four capillary tubes connected to a
hollow axle are immersed in the liquid. Because of rotation, the gas
bubbles into the liquid and re-enters the axle through a hole. The rota-

tion is performed using magnets. The maximum speed of rotation is about 3,000 r.p.m. It has been verified that for the fastest reaction conditions the observed rate is independent of the speed of rotation. The volume of the reaction cell is about 200 cc. and the amount of liquid ammonia is between 20 and 40 ml. Hydrogen and ammonia are both of natural isotopic composition—*i.e.*, about 130 parts per million (p.p.m.) in deuterium. The deuterium content of ammonia is practically constant during a set of measurements due to the large excess of this reactant. The deuterium content of hydrogen decreases during a measurement from 130 to about 20 p.p.m. depending upon the separation factor of deuterium between liquid ammonia and hydrogen which varies from 6.21 at −45.3°C. to 8.29 at −70.0°C. (*13*). The analyses are performed by mass spectrometry (*12*).

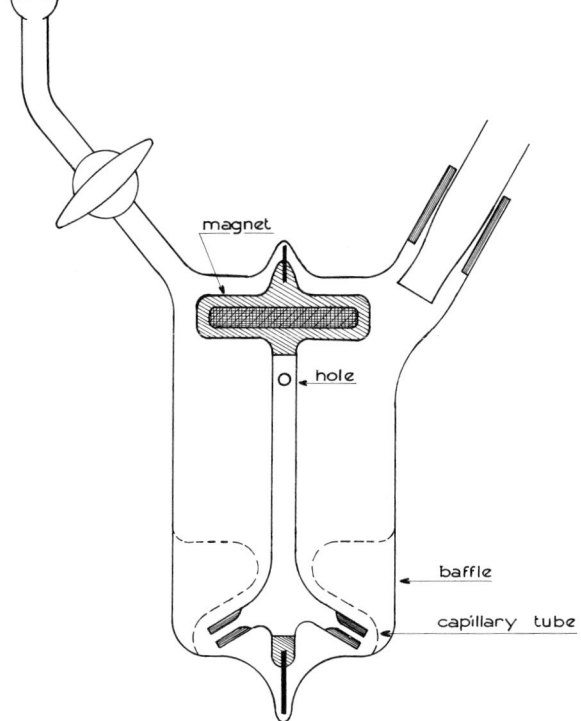

Figure 1.   Reaction cell

New measurements of the solubility of hydrogen in liquid ammonia have been made. The values are close to those used in our previous work (*7*) and those used by Bar-Eli and Klein (*1*).

The experimental procedure for performing the kinetic measurements is the following: a known amount of alkali metal is introduced into the reaction cell in the presence of argon. The cell is attached to the vacuum line, cooled below the boiling point of ammonia ($-33.5°C.$) and dry ammonia is introduced. Alkali amide is prepared *in situ*. Beforehand traces of a ferrous salt have been allowed to be absorbed on the cell walls and serve as a catalyst for the reaction

$$M + NH_3 \rightarrow MNH_2 + \tfrac{1}{2}H_2 \qquad (3)$$

where $M = Na, K, Rb,$ or Cs.

The solution being at the desired temperature, hydrogen is introduced, stirring is started and samples are drawn off at different times.

By adding ammonia, various concentrations can be studied without having to prepare a fresh catalyst.

At the end of a set of measurements, ammonia is removed and the remaining alkali amide is hydrolyzed. The overall alkalinity is determined first. Then the ammonia is displaced and determined separately. The overall alkalinity serves only as a check. It should be twice the alkalinity of ammonia but owing to a small formation of potassium hydroxide during the kinetics experiments, it is always slightly higher.

The kinetic treatment summarized in the appendix is similar to the one used in previous work ($1, 7, 18$). If y_o, y, and y_e are the deuterium concentrations in hydrogen at time $t = 0$, $t = t$ and $t = \infty$, respectively, we first calculate

$$k' = \frac{1}{t} \ln \frac{y_o - y_e}{y - y_e}. \qquad (4)$$

Then k, which is the pseudo-rate constant of the homogeneous reaction, is calculated from the relationship

$$k = k' \; \frac{\text{total amount of hydrogen}}{\text{amount of dissolved hydrogen}}. \qquad (5)$$

Figure 2 shows the curves obtained at $-59.3°C.$ when k is plotted as a function of c, c being the overall catalyst concentration. A linear relationship exists when c is greater than about $25 \times 10^{-3}M$. At same concentration and temperature, k for sodium, potassium, rubidium, and cesium are roughly in the ratios $0.3 : 1 : 1.3 : 1.5$.

These results are in good agreement with the results previously published, and in particular, with the very precise ones given by Bar-Eli and Klein concerning the reaction between D_2 and NH_3 catalyzed by potassium amide.

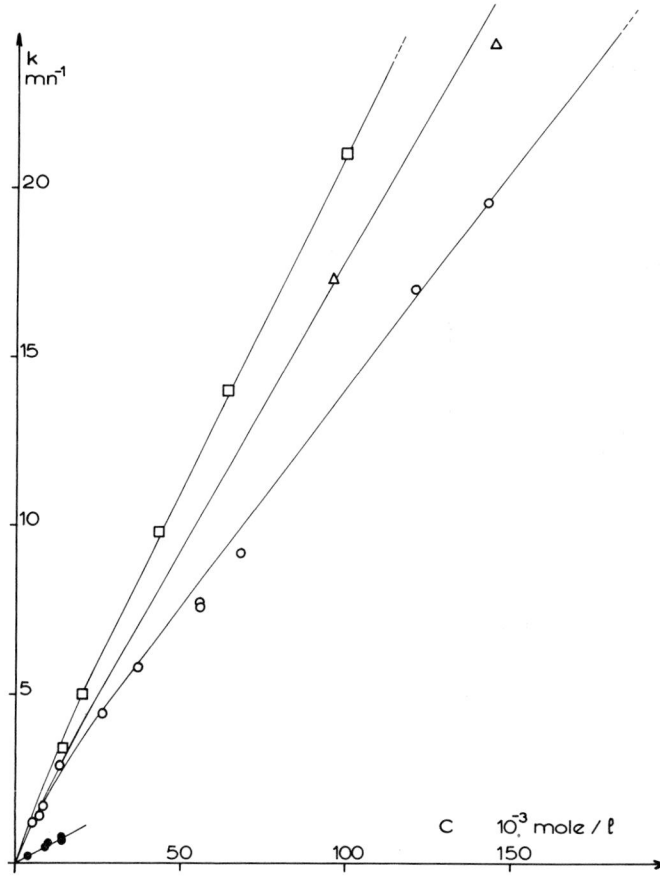

Figure 2. k *as a function of alkali amide at* −59.3°C.
● *sodium,* ○ *potassium,* △ *rubidium,* □ *cesium*

Dissociation of Alkali Amides

The main reason for the discrepancy remaining in the nature of the catalytic species is the lack of knowledge of the dissociation of the alkali amides. The main contribution of this work is a careful analysis of this dissociation, made with the help of the existing data and of a few new experimental results.

The most elaborate treatment of the dissociation of electrolytes in solutions is the one given by Fuoss and Onsager (9, 10). The so-called F.O. equation, applied to I-I associated electrolytes is

$$\Lambda = \Lambda_0 - S(c\gamma)^{1/2} + Ec\gamma \log c\gamma + Jc\gamma - K_A c\gamma f \Lambda \tag{6}$$

where

    Λ is the equivalent conductance,

    Λ_0 is the limiting value of Λ when $c \to 0$,

    γ is the fraction of electrolyte dissociated,

    f is the mean activity coefficient of the two ions,

    K_A is the association constant, $K_A = \dfrac{[KNH_2]}{[K^+][NH_2]} \dfrac{1}{f^2} \; (=1/K_D),$ (7)

    S, E, and J are coefficients independent of the concentration and dependent upon the three parameters, Λ_0, K_A and a, a being the ionic diameter.

A computer program has been written to solve the F.O. equation.

Precise results of the conductivity of alkali amides have been given by Franklin (8) and Hawes (11) in the case of potassium and by Hawes (11) in the case of sodium. No data are available for rubidium and cesium amide. Measurements have been made on cesium amide and potassium amide.

The capacity of the cell is 450 cc. It is constructed of silica, the adsorption of water on borosilicate glass being too troublesome. The electrodes are made of platinized platinum and have been calibrated with an aqueous solution of potassium chloride 0.01N at 0°C. Introduction of alkali metal and ammonia is made in a similar way to that used in kinetic studies. The formation reaction of the alkali amides is catalyzed by the electrodes. Various concentrations are studied with the same preparation of alkali amide. After ammonia has been removed, the alkali amide is hydrolyzed in the cell. The amounts of alkali ammonium hydroxides are determined by conductimetric titration.

Data and results for the equivalent conductance are shown in Figure 3. The solid line is the experimental curve taken from Hawes' results with potassium amide above $1.5 \times 10^{-3}M$ (lower concentrations also have been investigated). Two of our experimental points for potassium amide are shown. They correspond to $c = 1.93 \times 10^{-3}M$ and $c = 2.04 \times 10^{-3}M$. A third one at a lower concentration ($c = 0.99 \times 10^{-3}M$) is also in good agreement.

Calculations have been made for potassium amide using Hawes' results obtained below $2 \times 10^{-3}M$. Since the precision obtained for a by the F.O. equation is very poor, it is better to take a as the sum of the radii of the two ions (3 A.). The value found for Λ_0 is 308 Ω^{-1} cm.^{2} and for K_A is 9.820 liter/mole. They are both known with reasonably high precision since a large error on a results in small errors on Λ_0 and K_A.

The dotted line in Figure 3 is the equivalent conductance calculated using the values of the parameters thus obtained. It appears that the range of validity of the F.O. equation is 0-5 × 10⁻³M. No difference between cesium amide and potassium amide can be detected in the range of validity of the F.O. equation. It can be shown (6) that Λ_0 and a are almost the same for potassium amide and cesium amide, which is why the value of K_A for cesium amide has been assumed to be the same as that for potassium amide (9.820 liter/mole).

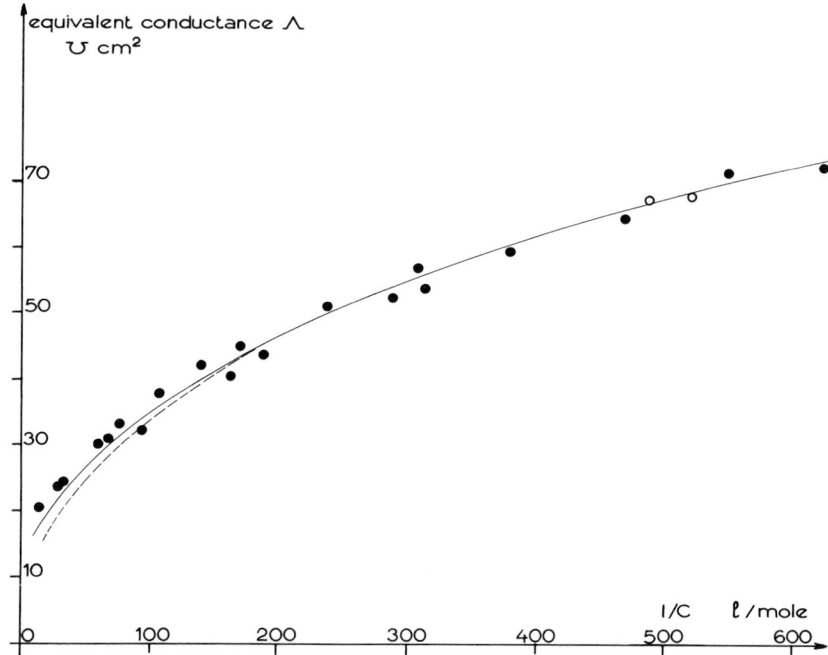

Figure 3.   *Conductance of potassium and cesium amide at −33.5°C. Experimental equivalent conductance: —KNH₂ Hawes, ○ KNH₂ this work, ● CsNH₂ this work, ... calculated equivalent conductance*

A treatment similar to the one used for potassium amide leads, in the case of sodium amide, to: $a = 2{,}7$ A., $\Lambda_0 = 277\ \Omega^{-1}$ cm.² and $K_A = 44.730$ liter/mole.

By solving the set of equations:

$$- \ln f = \frac{A\sqrt{\gamma c}}{1 + Ba\sqrt{\gamma c}} \quad \text{(Debye-Hückel equation)} \qquad (8)$$

in which A and B are known constants characteristic of the medium,

$$1 - \gamma = K_A f^2 \gamma^2 c \quad \text{(derived from Equation 7)} \qquad (9)$$

γ can be known in the range of validity of the Debye-Hückel equation. This range is assumed to be limited to an upper value of 10 × 10⁻³M.

Figure 4 shows $[NH_2^-]_o$ as a function of c assuming Equation 8 to be still valid above this limit, $[NH_2^-]_o$ being equal to γc.

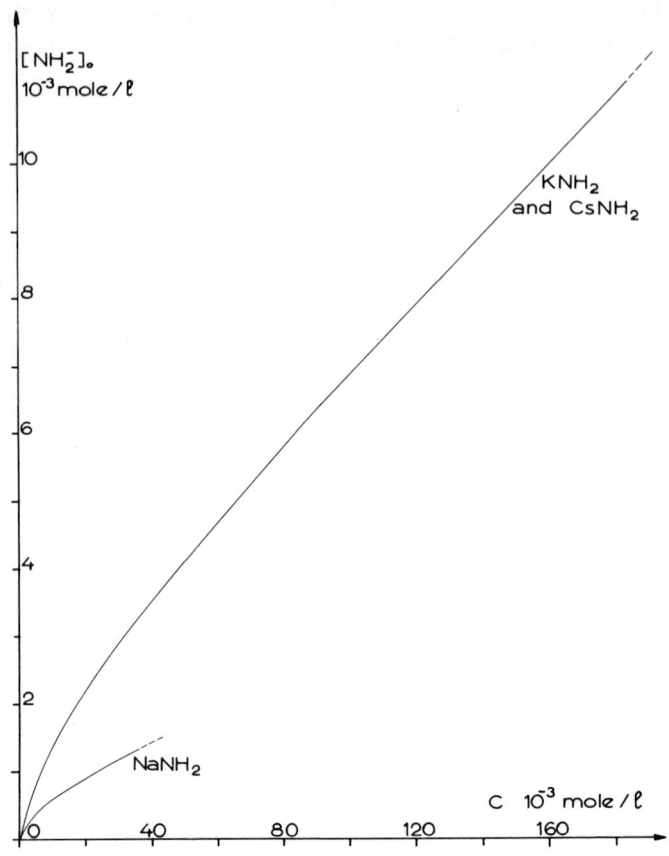

Figure 4.   Concentration of the amide ion as a function of the
overall alkali amide concentration

As soon as the concentration is higher than about $5 \times 10^{-3}M$ another phenomenon first mentioned by Hawes (11), has to be considered. The nonvalidity of the F.O. equation above the limit of $5 \times 10^{-3}M$ should give a deviation in the opposite direction from the one observed. The explanation is that triple ions are responsible for this higher conductivity. The triple ions may be formed in the case of potassium according to

$$K^+ + KNH_2 \leftrightarrows (K_2NH_2)^+ \qquad (10)$$

$$NH_2^- + KNH_2 \leftrightarrows (K[NH_2]_2)^- \qquad (11)$$

The triple ions of the first type, $K_2NH_2^+$, appear to have a structure close to NH_4^+ and appear to be more stable than the triple ions of the second type, the latter being very unlikely. The consequence is that K^+ is in weaker concentration and NH_2^- in higher concentration than expected from extrapolation of the range of validity of the F.O. equation as given in Figure 4. Calculation of K_I, the equilibrium constant of Equation 10, is, however, not possible. Triple ions are also present in the solutions of other alkali amides. Since the mobility of the free electronic pair in the ion pair MNH_2 is greater the larger the radius of the cation, we can expect the inequalities:

$$K_1(CsNH_2) > K_1(RbNH_2) > K_1(KHN_2) > K_1(NaNH_2).$$

Another interesting remark related to conductivities concerns the mobility of NH_2^-. NH_2^- is smaller than the halide ions. We then should expect a higher mobility for NH_2^- in solution. The lower mobility observed indicates that NH_2^- is solvated.

All data presented in this chapter have been drawn from results obtained at $-33.5°C$. It can be shown (6) that between $-33.5°C$. and $-70.0°C$. the dissociation of alkali amides does not vary significantly with temperature.

Order with Respect to the Catalyst

According to the theory of the acid-base catalysis given by Bell (3) the rate of a reaction in which the determining step is the interaction between a catalyst C and a substrate S, both being ionic, is given by the equation:

$$\log v = \log v_o + \frac{2\,A\,Z_sZ_c\sqrt{\mu}}{1 + Ba\sqrt{\mu}} + B'\mu \tag{12}$$

where:

$$v_o = k'_o [S][C] \tag{13}$$

μ is the ionic strength,

B' is a constant characteristic of the medium, and

Z_s and Z_c are the electric charges of S and C.

The equation is still valid when C or S is a neutral molecule if the electrical interactions between an ion and a neutral molecule are neglected. In our particular case the substrate, H_2, is a neutral molecule and the term $\dfrac{2\,AZ_sZ_c\sqrt{\mu}}{1 + Ba\sqrt{\mu}}$ vanishes. Since the ionic strength always remains small (below 0.01), it is reasonable to consider the term $B'\mu$ as negligible.

Figure 5 shows a plot of k as a function of $[NH_2^-]_o$ at $-45.2°C$. $[NH_2^-]_o$ is the concentration of amide ions calculated without taking into account the presence of triple ions, as explained previously. k is independent of the cation and proportional to $[NH_2^-]_o$. The linear relationship is valid in the whole range of solubility in the case of sodium and up to about $1.5 \times 10^{-3}M$ and $5 \times 10^{-3}M$ in the case of cesium and potassium respectively. The deviation arising above these concentrations is attributed to the presence of the triple ions, $M_2NH_2^+$, which, as this has been shown, lead to an increase in the concentration of the amide ion. Then, the kinetic law may be written:

$$k = k_o[NH_2^-]. \tag{14}$$

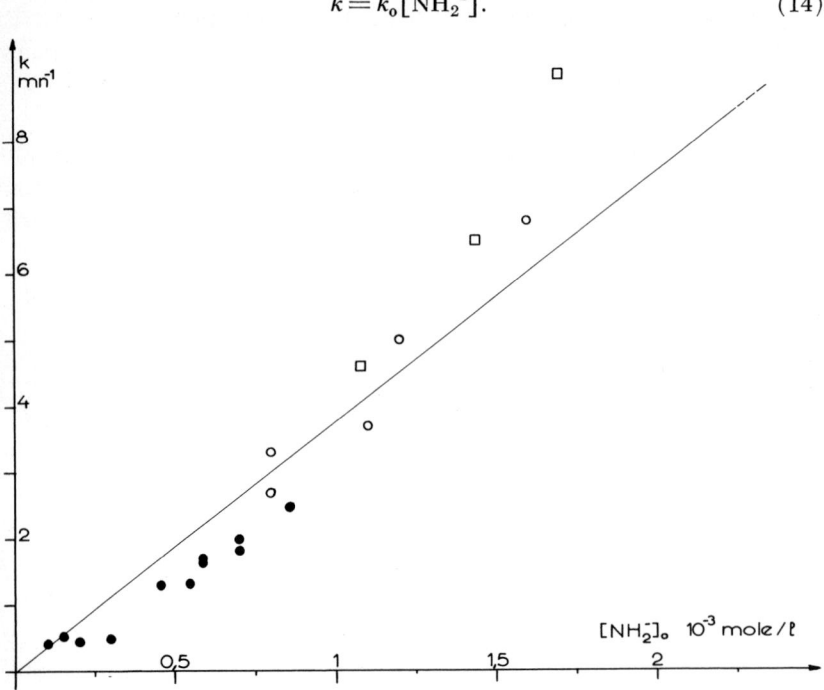

Figure 5.   k as a function of the concentration of the amide ion at $-45.2°C$.
● from sodium amide, ○ from potassium amide, □ from cesium amide

This law already has been reported in brief by the authors (5).

A confirmation of the fact that the catalytic action is caused by NH_2^- alone has been found by experiments on common ion effects and secondary salt effects. If potassium bromide is added to a solution of potassium amide, the concentration of amide ions changes for two reasons. By secondary salt effect, the ionic strength increases and f decreases according to the Debye-Hückel equation (Equation 8). In Equation 7 of the association constant of potassium amide, $[NH_2^-]$, increases. But by common ion effects, the addition of potassium ions from potassium bromide leads to a decrease in the concentration of amide ions. The association constant of potassium bromide being known, calculations are possible. The precision is not very good because the calculations have been made above the range of validity of the Debye-Hückel equation and, moreover, the presence of triple ions has been ignored. But it may be satisfactorily estimated for this purpose. Calculations show a slight decrease in the concentration of amide ions. A slight decrease of k is also observed. The same kind of calculations and measurements have been made with sodium amide, the salt being sodium chloride. In this case, the common ion effect is more important than the secondary salt effect and k decreases markedly. Table I shows the results obtained at $-45.2°C$.

Table I.

Catalyst	Salt	Decrease of $[NH_2^-]_o$ after addition of salt	Decrease of k
KNH_2 0.019M	KBr 0.13M	ratio 1.4 ± 0.2	ratio 1.16
$NaNH_2$ 0.010M	NaCl 0.15M	ratio 2,5	ratio 2,2
$NaNH_2$ 0.015M	NaCl 0.075M	ratio 1,3	ratio 1,6

Energy and Entropy of Activation

According to the transition state theory, k_o may be written:

$$k_o = \frac{eRT}{Nh} \exp \frac{\Delta S^*}{R} \exp - \frac{E_a}{RT} \tag{15}$$

where

R is the gas constant,

T is the absolute temperature,

N is Avogadro's number,

ΔS^* is the entropy of activation,

and

E_a is the energy of activation.

The energy of activation, calculated between $-45.2°C$. and $-70.0°C$. is $5.5 ± 0.2$ kcal./mole. The difference with the value given by Bar-Eli and Klein (*1*), 7.4 ± 0.3 kcal./mole, is owing to the different values used for the solubility of hydrogen. The temperature coefficient we have used is higher, and therefore the temperature coefficient of k is smaller.

The entropy of activation calculated at −45.2°C. is −18 ± 1 e.u. The difference between our value and the value given by Bar-Eli and Klein (*1*), −9.2 e.u., is mainly because of the difference in the values of the energy of activation.

Mechanism

Wilmarth and Dayton (*18*), Dirian, Botter, Ravoire and Grandcollot (*7*) have proposed a dissociative mechanism

$$\text{NH}_2^- + \text{HD} \overset{\text{slow}}{\leftrightarrows} \text{NH}_2\text{D} + \text{H}^- \tag{16}$$

$$\text{H}^- + \text{NH}_3 \overset{\text{fast}}{\rightarrow} \text{NH}_2^- + \text{H}_2 \tag{17}$$

with the intermediate formation of a hydride ion.

Many arguments are against this mechanism. As shown by Bar-Eli and Klein (*1*), the hydride ion from LiH is not a catalyst for this reaction. In the similar case of water, Schindewolf (*16*) has shown that the hydride ion does not appear in a solution of potassium hydroxide in water. The kinetic isotopic effect observed is also in contradiction to a dissociative mechanism (*1*). The largely negative value of the entropy of activation is an argument for a highly organized activated complex.

We then proposed, first, a mechanism close to the one already given by Bar-Eli and Klein (*1*). As shown by conductimetric data, NH_2^- is solvated. A N–H bond of the solvation ammonia molecule is polarized by NH_2^- and then weakened. The exchange occurs between a HD molecule and the solvated NH_2^- ion, through a four center mechanism, in the following way:

$$\tag{18}$$

Another mechanism is also possible. The slow step is an associative exchange between NH_2^- and HD, and it is followed by the exchange between NHD^- and NH_3, which is known to be very fast from nuclear magnetic resonance (15):

$$
\begin{array}{c}
H^- \\
| \\
H\!-\!N\,|_{(solv.)} \\
+ \\
H\!-\!D
\end{array}
\;\rightleftharpoons\;
\left[
\begin{array}{c}
H^- \\
| \\
H\ldots N_{(solv.)} \\
\vdots\quad\vdots \\
H\ldots D
\end{array}
\right]^*
\;\rightarrow\;
H +
\begin{array}{c}
H^- \\
| \\
|N\,|_{(solv.)} \\
|\quad| \\
H\quad D
\end{array}
\tag{19}
$$

$$
NHD^- + NH_3 \rightarrow NH_2^- + NH_2D \tag{20}
$$

This mechanism is impossible in the case of the exchange between, for instance, hydrogen and dimethylamine, exchange which is much faster than the exchange between hydrogen (2, 14). In contradiction with Bar-Eli and Klein, the opinion of the authors is that with ammonia and primary amines this mechanism may contribute to the exchange to some extent. An argument which supports the occurrence of this mechanism is that an isotopic exchange does occur between hydrogen and solid non-solvated potassium amide (17).

Appendix

Kinetic Treatment

Let us consider a homogeneous system composed of liquid ammonia, dissolved hydrogen and dissolved catalyst. Because of an important isotopic effect, R, the rate of exchange of the H^1 atoms between hydrogen and ammonia (expressed in atg. cm.$^{-3}$ mn.$^{-1}$), cannot be calculated. However, since only traces of deuterium are present, it is possible to calculate Rp_1, where p_1, takes into account the isotopic effect and is constant at constant temperature. Then, the following equation is valid:

$$
\ln \frac{y_o - y_e}{y - y_e} = \left[\frac{1}{[H_2]} + \frac{1}{\alpha[NH_3]} \right] Rp_1 t \tag{21}
$$

where

y_o, y, and y_e are deuterium concentrations in hydrogen at time $t = 0$, $t = t$ and $t = \infty$,

$[H_2]$ is the concentration of the H atoms belonging to the H_2 molecules, in atg. cm.$^{-3}$,

[NH$_3$] is the concentration of the H atoms belonging to the NH$_3$ molecules, in atg. cm.$^{-3}$,

α is the separation factor between ammonia and hydrogen and is equal to $\dfrac{(D/H)_{NH_3(l)}}{(D/H)_{H_2}}$ at equilibrium,

and

t is the time in minutes.

Since NH$_3$ is in much larger amount than H$_2$, Equation 21 becomes

$$\ln \frac{y_0 - y_e}{y - y_e} = \frac{Rp_1}{[H_2]} t \tag{22}$$

The actual kinetic law is of the form:

$$Rp_1 = k_o [H_2] [\text{catalyst}]^n \tag{23}$$

Because of the well-established first order relation with respect to the concentration of hydrogen, [H$_2$] no longer appears in the kinetic equations and k is defined as

$$k = \frac{Rp_1}{[H_2]} = k_o [\text{catalyst}]^n \tag{24}$$

k appears as a pseudo rate constant. (Note K in Equation 24 is equivalent to k' in References 1 and 18 and K in Reference 7.)

k would be directly calculated if the system was actually homogeneous. The presence of gaseous hydrogen, at all time in isotopic equilibrium with dissolved hydrogen, results in replacing Equation 22 by

$$\ln \frac{y_0 - y_e}{y - y_e} = \frac{Rp_1}{[H_2]_g} t \tag{25}$$

in which [H$_2$]$_g$ is a pseudo-concentration of hydrogen, equal to the total amount of hydrogen divided by the volume of liquid ammonia. k' is defined as

$$k' = \frac{Rp_1}{[H_2]_g}. \tag{26}$$

k' can be directly calculated and is related to k by

$$Rp_1 = k[H_2] = k'[H_2]_g. \tag{27}$$

Practically, k' is determined first and k is calculated from

$$k = k' \frac{\text{total amount of hydrogen}}{\text{amount of dissolved hydrogen}}. \tag{5}$$

Acknowledgments

The authors wish to acknowledge the generous assistance of P. Grand-collot in writing in the computer program, F. Botter, I. Lambert, M. Magat, E. Roth, G. Dirian, and E. Rochard for many helpful discussions.

Literature Cited

(1) Bar-Eli, K., Klein, F. S., *J. Chem. Soc.* **1962,** 1378.
(2) *Ibid.*, **1962,** 3083.
(3) Bell, R. P., "Acid-Base Catalysis," Oxford University Press, London, England, 1949.
(4) Claeys, Y., Dayton, J. C., Wilmarth, W. K., *J. Chem. Phys.* **18,** 759 (1950).
(5) Delmas, R., Courvoisier, P., Ravoire, J., *J. Chim. Phys.* **62,** 1423 (1965).
(6) Delmas, R., thesis, Paris (1967).
(7) Dirian, G., Botter, F., Ravoire, J., Grandcollot, P., *J. Chim. Phys.* **60,** 138 (1963).
(8) Franklin, E. C., *Z. für Phys. Chem.* **69,** 290 (1909).
(9) Fuoss, R. M., *J. Am. Chem. Soc.* **81,** 2659 (1959).
(10) Fuoss, R. M., Accascina, F., "Electrolytic Conductance," Interscience Publishers, Inc., New York, N. Y., 1959.
(11) Hawes, W. W., *J. Am. Chem. Soc.* **55,** 4422 (1933).
(12) Nief, G., Botter, R., "Advances in Mass Spectrometry," Waldron, Pergamon Press, London, 1959.
(13) Ravoire, J., Grandcollot, P., Dirian, G., *J. Chim. Phys.* **60,** 130 (1963).
(14) Rochard, E. (private communication).
(15) Swift, T. J., Marks, S. A., Sayre, W. G., *J. Chem. Phys.* **44,** 2797 (1966).
(16) Schindewolf, U., *Ber. Bunsenges, Phys. Chem.* **67,** 219 (1963).
(17) Schindewolf, U. (private communication).
(18) Wilmarth, W. K., Dayton, J. C., *J. Am. Chem. Soc.* **75,** 4553 (1953).

RECEIVED August 28, 1967.

3

The Chemical Fractionation of Boron Isotopes

A. A. PALKO and J. S. DRURY

Chemistry Division, Oak Ridge National Laboratory, Oak Ridge, Tenn.

This review deals with studies performed at the Oak Ridge National Laboratory concerning the chemical fractionation of boron isotopes between BF_3 and its molecular addition compounds. This research resulted in the development of a new separation process which was superior to methods previously employed. The work also led to a theoretical explanation of the exchange reaction which accounted for the anomalous concentration of boron-10 in the molecular addition compound, and the observed variations of the isotopic equilibrium constants as a function of different donors. The model predicted maximum isotopic equilibrium constants for the exchange reaction which were consistent with the experimental data. It also predicted the behavior of the other boron halides.

Naturally occurring boron contains 19.8% boron-10 and 80.2% boron-11. The absorption cross section of the natural product for thermal neutrons is 752 barns; for pure boron-10 and boron-11, the corresponding values (8) are 3837 and 0.005 barns, respectively. Thus, isotopically pure boron-10 is five times more effective as a neutron shield than natural boron. In view of this difference, it is not surprising that a demand arose, very early in the nuclear era, for separated boron isotopes.

The search for a method by which boron isotopes might be separated began as a classified program of the Manhattan Project in 1943, at Columbia University. Seven separation schemes were considered: thermal diffusion of BF_3 and distillation of BF_3, $(CH_3O)_3B$, H_3BO_3, $(C_2H_5)_2O \cdot BF_3$, $(CH_3)_2O \cdot BF_3$, and $(C_2H_5O)_3B \cdot 2BF_3$. The distillation of $(CH_3)_2O \cdot BF_3$ was selected as the most promising separation method.

Although the selected isotope separation process was deemed superior to any other separation method then known, it had certain deficiencies. Under equilibrium conditions, only 60% of the $Me_2O \cdot BF_3$ complex present in the vapor phase of the distillation columns was dissociated into BF_3 and Me_2O. The presence of undissociated complex in the vapor phase substantially reduced the single-stage isotopic fractionation factor for the process, and increased both the capital investment for the plant and the unit cost of the product. Also, appreciable irreversible decomposition of the $Me_2O \cdot BF_3$ complex occurred, with an attendant loss of boron-10 as well as BF_3 and Me_2O. To minimize this decomposition, it was necessary to operate the distillation equipment at reduced pressure. This restriction reduced the capacity of the separation plant and substantially increased the cost of the product. Furthermore, in the operational procedures current in 1954, difficulties were encountered in recovering product BF_3 from the $Me_2O \cdot BF_3$ complex.

The domain of the search for an improved separation process was defined by certain criteria: (a) isotopic fractionation should be achieved by means of a two-phase, chemical exchange reaction which was amenable to countercurrent operation in a multistage contactor at ambient temperature and pressure; (b) the single-stage isotopic fractionation factor for the reaction should be appreciably larger than that for the distillation of $Me_2O \cdot BF_3$; (c) the molecular species in each process stream should be thermally refluxable—*i.e.*, convertible from one species to the other by the addition or removal of heat alone; (d) process materials should be more stable with respect to irreversible decomposition than those used in the $(CH_3)_2O$ process; and (e) the chemical form of the product should permit a ready, quantitative conversion of the separated isotopes to the elemental state.

Criteria (a) and (c) limited research largely to a class of isotopic exchange reactions represented by Equation 1:

$$D \cdot {}^{11}BX_3(l) + {}^{10}BX_3(g) = D \cdot {}^{10}BX_3(l) + {}^{11}BX_3(g) \qquad (1)$$

where $D \cdot BX_3$ was a molecular addition compound, D was a Lewis base containing F, O, S, Se, N, P, As, or C, and X was H, CH_3, or a halogen. Criteria (b) and (d) generally limited the Lewis base to those containing N, O, or S donors. The same criteria restricted X, for the most part, to the first member of the halogen family. Our research thus dealt mainly with BF_3 complexes of ethers (dimethyl, diethyl, diphenyl, and methylphenyl), thioethers (dimethyl, diethyl, di-*n*-butyl, and diphenyl), mercaptans (ethyl and butyl), amines (triethyl, *N*-methyl diphenyl, and *N,N'*-dimethylphenyl), and a small group of other molecules (tetrahydrofuran, phenol, thiophenol, nitrobenzene, methyl isocyanide, dimethyl selenide, and dimethyl telluride). In addition, brief studies were made of BCl_3 complexes of diphenyl ether, diphenyl thioether, thiophenol, and acetyl chloride.

Donors were screened first on the basis of dissolving sufficient Lewis acid. A Lewis acid:donor ratio of 1.0 was desired. If warranted, the equilibrium constant for Reaction 1 was then determined. Attractive donors were tested for reversible dissociation of the molecular addition compound. Those surviving this test were usually given complete examinations with respect to the kinetics of exchange, chemical stability, corrosion characteristics, and physical properties of engineering interest. Finally, bench-scale equipment was set up in which the selected exchange reaction was integrated with the reflux reactions and purification steps, and the entire process was operated for weeks or months to demonstrate the feasibility of the process. During the latter stages of the investigation, Raman and infrared spectroscopic studies were made of certain isotopically substituted molecular addition compounds. These studies enabled isotopic equilibrium constants to be calculated for comparison with those obtained experimentally. Consideration of all information generated by the program led to the development of a theoretical model of the exchange reaction which satisfactorily accounted for the known chemistry of Reaction 1.

Physical Properties of the Molecular Addition Compounds of BF_3

Adducts formed from very weak Lewis bases were excluded because of unattractive BF_3/donor ratios. Conversely, adducts formed from very strong donors were solids which were not amenable to counter-current processing unless dissolved in an appropriate solvent. The necessity for the solvent to be unreactive with gaseous BF_3 introduced operational complications likely to be uneconomic. In addition, the rate of exchange of BF_3 with adducts of very strong donors proved to be unacceptably slow. Thus, in general, we sought donors of intermediate basicity which formed liquid complexes at ambient temperatures. Typically, the heats of association of such adducts ranged from about 5 to 20 kilocalories per mole.

Potentially interesting donors were first screened on the basis of the saturation pressure of the adduct. (The term "saturation pressure" refers to the total pressure of vapor in equilibrium with a sample of molecular addition compound. The vapor may consist of free acid, base, undissociated complex, or a combination of all of these constituents.) Measured quantities of BF_3 and the donor were equilibrated at a given temperature in the apparatus shown in Reference 14. Manometric observations (corrected for the free volume of the equipment) were made over that part of the liquid range which lay between room temperature and the freezing point of the complex. Estimates of the heat of association of the complexes were obtained from the temperature dependence of the saturation pressures, or, in a few instances, from liquid- or gas-phase calorimetric measurements. The freezing point of each complex was determined from recorded cooling curves, and from direct observations of the temperature at which crystallization occurred. The results of these studies are summarized in Table I and Table II.

Table I.   Saturation Pressures of Some 1:1 Molecular Addition Compounds from the Freezing Point to Room Temperature

$$Log\ P = a - (b/T)$$

Adduct	Freezing Point °C.	a ± std. error	b ± std. error	$-\Delta H_{association}$ (kcal./mole)	Ref.
$Et_3N \cdot BF_3$	19.6	—	—	35.7	(1)
$MeNC \cdot BF_3$	Donor decomposed by BF_3			—	(18)
$C_6H_5NMe_2 \cdot BF_3$	92	Adduct dissociates irreversibly			(18)
		upon melting			
$(C_6H_5)_2NMe \cdot BF_3$	100	Adduct dissociates irreversibly			(18)
		upon melting			
$Me_2O \cdot BF_3$	−12	9.806	2775	13.6[b]	(14)
$Et_2O \cdot BF_3$	−59	10.082	2879	11.9[b]	(14)
$Bu_2O \cdot BF_3$	~ −30	5.65 ± 0.05	1010 ± 15	5[a]	(19)
$HCOOEt \cdot BF_3$	~ −8	5.70 ± 0.05	1330 ± 20	6[a]	(19)
$MeCOOEt \cdot BF_3$		7.20	1870	8.5[a]	(9)
$EtCOOEt \cdot BF_3$		9.83	2726	12.6[a]	(9)
$(CH_2)_4O \cdot BF_3$	12	9.734	3126	16.8[b]	(15)
$C_6H_5OH \cdot 0.8BF_3$	−15	9.94 ± 0.008	1900 ± 16	8.7[a]	(20)
$C_6H_5OMe \cdot 0.9BF_3$	~ 2	10.1 ± 0.1	2140 ± 33	12.4	(21)
$C_6H_5OEt \cdot BF_3$		10.9	2575	11.8[a]	(11)
$(C_6H_5)_2O \cdot BF_3$	Does not form at −40°C.				
$C_6H_5NO_2 \cdot BF_3$	~ 0	—	—	9.2[c]	(4)
$C_6H_5OBu \cdot BF_3$		12.04	2650	12.1[a]	(10)
$Me_2S \cdot BF_3$	−20	10.164 ± 0.001	2209 ± 70	10.2[a]	(19, 22)
$Et_2S \cdot BF_3$	−62	10.030 ± 0.004	2111 ± 21	9.6[a]	(23)
$Bu_2S \cdot BF_3$	< −60	10.39 ± 0.06	2174 ± 19	12.8[a]	(24)
$C_6H_5SH \cdot BF_3$	Does not form at −40°C.				(18)
$(C_6H_5)_2S \cdot BF_3$	Does not form at −40°C.				(18)
$Me_2Se \cdot BF_3$	−43	9.945 ± 0.005	1824 ± 25	8.3[a]	(19)
$Me_2Te \cdot BF_3$	Does not form at −30°C.				(19)
$MeCOCl \cdot BCl_3$	~ −60	—	—		(6)
$(C_6H_5)_2O \cdot BCl_3$	~ 4	—	—	5.3[a]	(6, 13)
$C_6H_5SH \cdot BCl_3$	Adduct completely dissociated at 25°C.				(18)
$(C_6H_5)_2S \cdot BCl_3$	42	—	—	8.8[a]	(18)

[a] Estimate was based on the relationship, $\Delta H_{association} = 2.303\ Rb$, where R is the gas constant and b is the coefficient of the temperature term in the equation, log $P = a - (b/T)$.
[b] This value was obtained from gas-phase dissociation measurements.
[c] Datum is from measurements made in nitrobenzene solutions.

Table II. Solubility of BF$_3$ in Donor (moles BF$_3$/mole Donor)

Donor	Temp. (°C.)	Pressure 400 Torr	Pressure 760 Torr
Me$_2$O	−19.0		1.201
	−16.5	1.103	—
	−9.0	1.082	—
	−8.1	—	1.133
	5.5	—	1.085
	6.0	1.051	—
	22.0	1.034	1.050
	30.0	—	1.038
	31.0	1.027	—
Et$_2$O	−20.0	—	1.276
	−19.0	1.161	1.271
		1.159	—
	−10.0	1.111	—
	−9.5	—	1.185
	−8.5	1.106	1.182
	5.5	1.069	1.116
	22.0	1.043	1.070
		1.043	
(CH$_2$)$_4$O	8.0	1.021	1.062
	14.0	1.011	1.048
	22	1.005	1.032
Et$_2$S	−25.0	1.116	—
	−17.0	1.085	—
	−16.0	—	1.138
	−8.0	1.052	—
	−6.0	—	1.092
	10.5	0.997	1.032
	22.5	0.936	0.996
	31.0	—	0.950
	31.5	0.857	—
EtSH	−78	—	3.425
	−50	—	2.402
	0	—	0.0324
	25	—	0.000
C$_6$H$_5$NO$_2$	−4.0	0.2134	0.765
	1.1	0.0792	—
	7.0	—	0.1146
	11.0	0.0538	0.0948
	14.0	0.0458	0.0838
	21.0	0.0318	0.0597
	25.0	0.0253	0.0506

The index of stability obtained by directly comparing the saturation pressures of two complexes was biased by the volatility of the free donor

(2) if the boiling point of the latter was relatively low. Better estimates of stability were obtained by comparing the thermal dependence of the saturation pressures. This procedure was equivalent to a comparison of the enthalpies of formation of the adducts from their constituent molecules. Such comparisons were usually consistent with the order of stability determined by other criteria. However, for structurally diverse complexes, these comparisons were not always dependable since, in some cases, entropy effects strongly influenced the thermal dependence of the saturation pressures.

In general, we found that the stability of similar BF_3 adducts varied with different donor atoms, decreasing in the order $N > O > S > Se >$ Te. Thus, $Me_2O \cdot BF_3$ was more stable than $Me_2S \cdot BF_3$ or $Me_2Se \cdot BF_3$. The stability of BF_3 adducts containing the same donor atom, but different substituents in the donor molecule, also varied. The presence of an electrophilic group in the donor molecule decreased the basicity of the donor and weakened the adduct. Thus, $(C_6H_5)_2O \cdot BF_3$ did not form, and $C_6H_5OMe \cdot BF_3$ was less stable than $Me_2O \cdot BF_3$. Conversely, the presence of a small nucleophilic substituent in the donor molecule tended to stabilize the resulting adduct. However, if the nucleophilic substituent were sufficiently large a weakened adduct could result, owing to steric interference between the substituent and the boron trihalide (3). Thus, $Me_2S \cdot BF_3$ was somewhat more stable than $Et_2S \cdot BF_3$. Here, the β-carbon atoms in the ethyl groups of the latter compound interfere with the normal positioning of the fluorine atoms in the adduct. A similar degree of steric interference existed between the β-carbon atoms and the fluorine atoms of the Bu_2S adduct, but this complex was somewhat more stable than the ethyl compound, presumably because the butyl groups contribute a greater inductive effect than the ethyl groups. This dominance of inductive effect over steric interference in the Bu_2S adduct would not be expected in the $Bu_2O \cdot BF_3$ molecule. Here, the smaller size of the donor atom led to severe steric interference between the alkyl groups and the fluorine atoms (3).

A further example of the influence of steric interference in ether adducts of BF_3 was provided by a comparison of the stabilities of $(C_2H_5)_2O \cdot BF_3$ and $(CH_2)_4O \cdot BF_3$. Although the atomic compositions of these molecules differed only by two protons, the enthalpy of association of the latter molecule exceeded that of the former by more than 40%. It seems clear that the increase in stability of the tetrahydrofuran complex must be attributed to the ring structure of the donor which locks the interfering ethyl groups out of the way of the fluorine atoms, thus eliminating, or at least reducing, steric interference (3, 17).

Table III. Equilibrium Constants and Related

$$^{10}BF_3(g) + Donor \cdot {}^{11}BF_3(l) = {}^{11}BF_3(g) +$$

Donor	a ± std. error	b ± std. error	$-\Delta H°$ (cal. mole^{-1})
Me$_2$O	0.018 ± 0.005	8.8 ± 1.5	40
Et$_2$O	0.010 ± 0.005	7.1 ± 1.3	33
Bu$_2$O	(0.006)	(1.6)	(7)
HCOOEt			
MeCOOEt	0.094	32.5	148.5
EtCOOEt			
(CH$_2$)$_4$O	0.0089 ± 0.006	6.0 ± 1.8	28
C$_6$H$_5$OH	0.023 ± 0.001	10.1 ± 0.3	46
C$_6$H$_5$OMe	0.022 ± 0.006	10.5 ± 1.8	48
C$_6$H$_5$OEt	0.026	12.9	59
C$_6$H$_5$OBu			
Me$_2$S	0.020 ± 0.004	10.7 ± 1.1	49
Et$_2$S	0.012 ± 0.002	8.5 ± 0.6	39
Bu$_2$S	0.018 ± 0.005	9.6 ± 1.2	44
Me$_2$Se	0.013 ± 0.001	8.1 ± 0.4	37
Et$_3$N	0.012 ± 0.002	6.4 ± 0.5	30

The Isotopic Exchange Reaction

After preliminary screening on the basis of vapor pressure measurements, attractive donors were screened further on the basis of their equilibrium constants for the isotopic exchange reaction:

$$\text{Donor} \cdot {}^{11}BF_3(l) + {}^{10}BF_3(g) = \text{Donor} \cdot {}^{10}BF_3(l) + {}^{11}BF_3(g). \quad (2)$$

The equilibrium constants for a particular donor were determined by stirring appropriate quantities of the donor and BF$_3$ for several hours in a suitable reaction vessel (24). Replicate aliquots of BF$_3$ before and after equilibration were analyzed for boron-10 by means of a 6-inch, 60°-sector ratio mass spectrometer. In our experiments the amount of boron trifluoride in the gas phase was deliberately kept small, compared with the amount of boron trifluoride in the liquid phase. For this condition, the ratio of boron-10 to boron-11 in the gas before and after equilibration approximated the true single-stage fractionation factor, $^{10}B/^{11}B(\text{liquid})/$ $^{10}B/^{11}B(\text{gas})$. When corrected for the BF$_3$ present in the liquid phase in excess of the 1:1 mole ratio required by the molecular addition compound (Table II), these single-stage fractionation factors represented the isotopic equilibrium constants for Reaction 2. Equilibrium constants for the exchange of boron between BF$_3$ gas and fifteen addition compounds of BF$_3$ are shown in Table III. Curves of the form, log K_{eq} = $(b/T) - a$, were fitted to the data by means of the least squares technique. From the slopes of these curves and the values of the isotopic

Thermodynamic Functions for the Isotopic Exchange Reaction

Donor · $^{10}BF_3(l)$; Log $K_{eq} = (b/T) - a$

$-\Delta F°$ (cal. mole^{-1})	$-\Delta S°$ (e.u.)	K_{eq} 30°C.	0°C.	Ref.
15	0.08	1.026	1.033	(19)
19	0.05	1.031	1.037	(23)
				(19)
		1.029 (20°C.)		(29)
		1.033 (28°C.)		(9)
		1.019 (45°C.)		(9)
15	0.04	1.026	1.031	(18)
14	0.11	1.024	1.040	(20)
18	0.10	1.030	1.039	(21)
26	0.10	1.042 (25°C.)		(11)
		1.026 (25°C.)		(10)
22	0.09	1.037	1.046	(19)
22	0.06	1.037	1.043	(23)
19	0.08	1.032	1.040	(24)
19	0.06	1.032	1.039	(19)
13	0.05	1.022	1.028	(23)

equilibrium constants, the thermodynamic quantities, $\Delta F°$, $\Delta H°$, and $\Delta S°$, were computed for the isotopic exchange reaction. It may be seen from Figure 1 that the equilibrium constants for Reaction 2 varied with donor, donor substituents, and with temperature. At 30°C. the following donor order was observed: diethyl sulfide > dimethyl sulfide > dimethyl selenide > dibutyl sulfide > diethyl ether > methyl phenyl ether > dimethyl ether > tetrahydrofuran > phenol > triethyl amine. In general, the isotopic equilibrium constants for donors containing sulfur were greater than those for similar donors containing oxygen. Equilibrium constants for donors containing oxygen were greater than those for corresponding bases containing nitrogen. For molecular addition compounds in which the donor atom was sulfur, the value of the isotopic equilibrium constant at 30°C. varied with substituents in the following order: ethyl > methyl > butyl. At lower temperatures this order was methyl > ethyl > butyl, owing to differences in enthalpy of the respective exchange reactions. For oxygen donors, the order at 30°C. was ethyl > methyl ⩾ tetrahydrofuran > butyl > OH. With esters, the order at 30°C. was acetate > formate > propionate. In general, it was observed that weaker molecular addition compounds resulted in larger isotopic equilibrium constants. A detailed discussion of the theory of isotopic fractionation by means of Reaction 1 will be presented later in this paper.

The rate of exchange of boron between the molecules participating in Reaction 1 is important in practical applications. If the reaction is to be used in packed columns, the half-time of the exchange reaction should be of the order of seconds, otherwise the effective stage length will be excessive. Qualitative observations made during equilibrium constant determinations indicated that the rate of exchange of boron between BF_3 and the molecular addition compound was probably rapid for adducts which were highly dissociated in the vapor phase, such as the anisole complex, but was considerably slower for stronger molecular addition compounds such as the triethylamine complex. The rates of exchange of these two complexes with BF_3 were determined quantitatively by contacting the normal BF_3 complex with boron-10 enriched gas. Analysis of the gas before and after equilibration showed how much exchange occurred. For the anisole system, the half-time of exchange was less than four seconds. A half-time of about fifty minutes was estimated for the triethylamine system (Table IV).

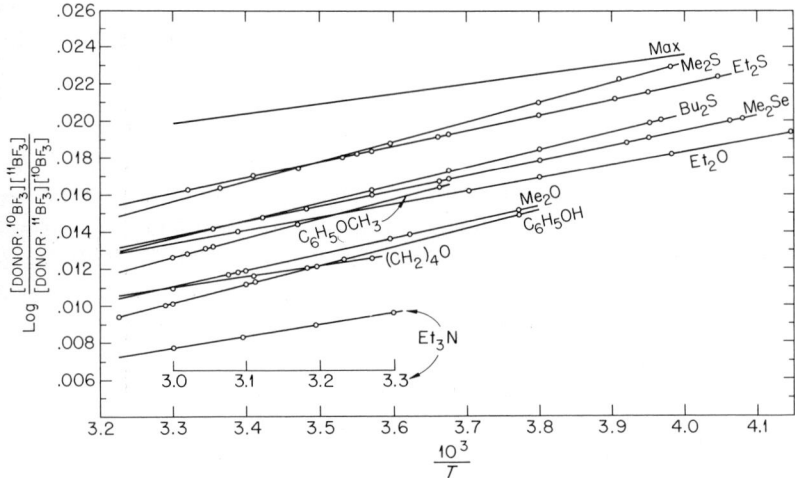

Figure 1. Variations of the isotopic equilibrium constants of the reaction

$$Donor \cdot {}^{11}BF_3(l) + {}^{10}BF_3(g) = Donor \cdot {}^{10}BF_3(l) + {}^{11}BF_3(g)$$
With donor and temperature

From Table III it is apparent that a number of different donors could be used to obtain very attractive fractionation factors. Indeed, at 30°C., the isotopic equilibrium constant was 1.03, or more, for phenetole, anisole, diethyl ether, ethyl formate, dimethyl selenide, dimethyl sulfide, and diethyl sulfide. However, all of these donors were not equally satisfactory for our purpose. The boron trifluoride complexes of the thioethers, the selenide, and the ester had a pronounced tendency toward irreversible decomposition and were too unstable to be seriously considered for an industrial process. Diethyl ether, which had been rejected earlier for the exchange-distillation method in the Manhattan Project studies, was rejected by our criteria also, though on different grounds. Since the BF_3 adduct of this ether was partially associated in the vapor phase, it was not amenable to thermal refluxing. Thus, of all the donors listed in Table III, only anisole and phenetole remained for consideration. The former compound was an inexpensive, commercially-available solvent; the latter compound was expensive, and was available only in research quantities. We chose anisole as the donor to be further investigated. If, at some future date, phenetole becomes commercially available and economically competitive with anisole, it will be an attractive substitute for anisole since its BF_3 adduct yields a somewhat larger separation factor than does the BF_3 adduct of anisole.

Reflux Studies

In chemical exchange systems, reflux consists of converting the chemical forms of the isotopic species from that of one reactant to that of the other. In the systems under consideration in this paper, these reactions are:

$$\text{Donor} \cdot BF_3(l) \xrightarrow{\text{heat}} \text{Donor}(l) + BF_3(g) \tag{3}$$

$$\text{Donor}(l) + BF_3(g) \xrightarrow{\text{cool}} \text{Donor} \cdot BF_3. \tag{4}$$

Reactions 3 and 4 are termed the product-end reflux and the waste-end reflux, respectively. In practical applications, the donor resulting from Reaction 3 is used as the reactant in Reaction 4. The BF_3 associated with the donor in Reaction 3 is enriched in boron-10. The BF_3 associated with the donor in Reaction 4 is depleted in boron-10. It is obvious that, if remixing of separated isotopes is to be avoided, the donor from the product-end reflux reaction must be free of BF_3 or any other boron-containing species. The crucial nature of Reaction 3 becomes even more apparent when it is realized that, for systems of interest in this paper, each mole of product must undergo Reaction 3 approximately 200 times. It is also obvious that, for reflux ratios of this magnitude, very little irreversible decomposition of the adduct, or the donor, can be tolerated.

The reversible dissociation of the anisole adduct was first examined under laboratory conditions. A quantity of the 1:1 complex was placed in a round-bottom flask which was attached to a vacuum train. The flask was equipped with a refluxing condenser, a pressure regulator and a port for sampling the liquid phase. The flask was heated electrically at a predetermined pressure until BF_3 no longer escaped from the flask.

	Wt. Adduct (g)	Vol. BF_3 (STP ml.)	Elapsed Time (sec.)
Table IV. Rate of (Donor · $^{11}BF_3(l) + {}^{10}BF_3(g) =$			
Adduct			
$C_6H_5OCH_3 \cdot 0.87\ BF_3$	10.523	224.5	15
	10.207	164.0	7
$Et_3N \cdot 1.0\ BF_3$	10.480	128.6	15
	11.296	160.3	30
	12.737	147.8	300
	12.083	126.3	1800
			3600

^{a} Without isotope effect.

Samples of the liquid were then obtained for analysis, and the experiment was repeated at a higher pressure. From Table V it may be seen that only 50-60 parts per million of BF_3 remained in the anisole when the complex was heated to 160°C. This degree of recovery of BF_3 from the complex was satisfactory even for the production of very high purity boron-10.

Table V. Reversible Dissociation of the Anisole · BF_3 Complex

Temperature (°C.)	Pressure of BF_3 (torr)	Moles BF_3 Remaining per 10^6 Moles of Anisole
157.0	800	69
159.8	875	60
163.2	937	42
165.0	999	54
166.2	1060	59

Integrated Operation of the Anisole System

To confirm the favorable results obtained for the anisole system under laboratory conditions, a bench-scale, integrated pilot plant was constructed. This unit consisted of a packed exchange column, 1 inch o.d. × 36 inches long; a packed column, 1 inch o.d. × 22 inches long, in which the adduct was formed (waste-end refluxer); a packed column, 2 inch o.d. × 30 inches long, to which a reservoir was attached (product-end refluxer); and a solvent purification still. Pumps, valves, and instrumentation were supplied as needed to ensure automatic operation of the equipment. Continuous runs, one as long as 78 days, were made in this equipment. Appropriate samples were taken to measure the isotopic

Exchange for the Reaction
Donor · $^{10}BF_3(l)$ + $^{11}BF_3(g)$)

| % ^{10}B | | Cal'd. % ^{10}B | |
Before	After	at Equilibrium[a]	Cal'd. % Exchange
40.71	23.05	23.2	100
40.82	23.96	21.45	90
47.19	44.41	21.70	10.9
47.19	44.12	22.03	12.2
25.26	23.55	20.10	33.1
25.26	23.14	20.05	40.7
25.26	22.46	20.05	53.6

fractionation, the solvent decomposition rate, the boron content of the product-end refluxer, as well as the corrosion rates of various materials of construction. Tables VI and VII summarize the results. The data of Table VI show that irreversible decomposition of the donor solvent is acceptably low under realistic operating conditions. It may also be seen that corrosion, as measured by the presence of Fe, Cr, and Ni in the liquid, is acceptably low. The data in Table VII illustrate the effectiveness of the recombiner in converting BF_3 gas to the 1:1 molecular addition compound.

Table VI.   Data Relating to Donor and Adduct Stability
During Operation of the Bench-Scale Pilot Plant

Run No.	Length of Run (days)	Donor Recovered, %	Decomp. Rate, %/Day[a]	Metal in Donor, p.p.m.				
				B	Fe	Cr	Ni	Cu
23[b]	20			128			3	26
29[b]	19	93.4	0.35					
30[c]	50	80	0.40	470	6	2	38	59
31[d]	20	92	0.40	169	119	3	5	54
32[e]	37	95	0.35	566	2		1	2.4
33[f]	78	78	0.28	315	2.5		1.2	3.5

[a] % Working inventory/day.
[b] Nickel packing in exchange column, decomposer, and recombiner.
[c] Stainless steel packing.
[d] Same as Run 30 plus addition of copper.
[e] Same as Run 30 plus addition of black iron.
[f] Apparatus contained stainless steel packing, transfer lines, and pumps. Valves were Monel, hence copper is in effluent.

The results of the foregoing laboratory investigations of the anisole donor were sufficiently attractive to warrant an engineering evaluation of the technical feasibility of using this method to separate large quantities

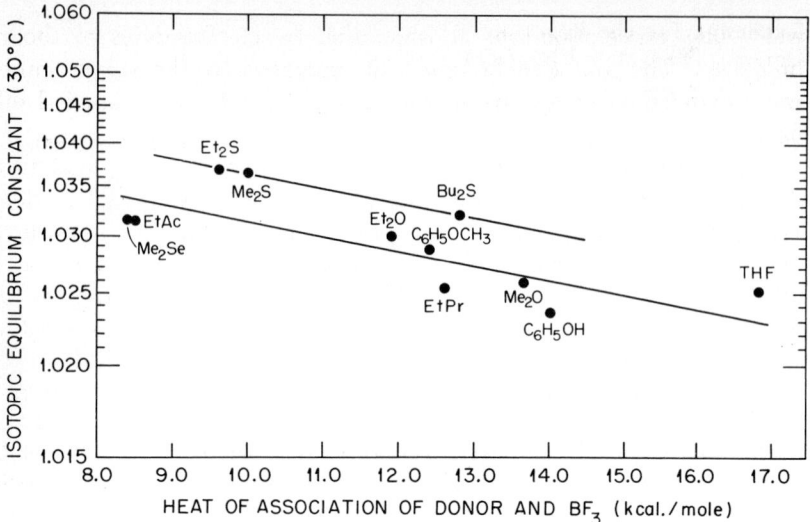

Figure 2. Isotopic equilibrium constants for the reaction

Donor · $^{11}BF_3(l)$ + $^{10}BF_3(g)$ = Donor · $^{10}BF_3(l)$ + $^{11}BF_3(g)$
As a function of the enthalpy of association of the adduct

of boron isotopes. This work was performed at another U. S. Atomic Energy Commission installation by an engineering research group who reported their findings in detail elsewhere (*16*). After thoroughly studying the system from the standpoint of HTU in a 6-inch i.d. column, flooding rate for 5/8-inch Pall packing, solvent degradation, reversible dissociation of the complex, recombination of the complex, solvent-drying procedures, materials of construction, and corrosion, they concluded that the large-scale anisole process was technically feasible.

Table VII.   Operation of the Waste-End Refluxer in the Bench-Scale Pilot Plant

Run No.	Mole Ratio BF_3/Anisole Leaving Recombiner	Temp. (°C.)	Pressure (torr)
16	1.07	6	850
17	1.06	7	950
20	0.92	20	875

Since the anisole process was superior to the dimethyl ether process with respect to separation factor, throughput, irreversible decomposition, and ease of product recovery, it was expected to be more economical as well. This expectation was substantiated by cost analyses of the two processes. The unit cost of boron-10 separated by the anisole process was estimated to be approximately one-half that for the dimethyl ether process (*12*).

The second objective of the present investigation was to understand the mechanism by which boron isotopes are fractionated in Reaction 1. We wished to explain why boron-10 concentrated preferentially in the molecular addition compound, contrary to the usual expectation that the heavy isotope should be preferred by the complexed species. We also wished to explain the variations of the isotopic equilibrium constants for Reaction 1 for various donor molecules. Further, it was desirable to compute theoretical maxima for the isotopic equilibrium constants of Reaction 1 to serve as guides for the practical work. Finally, we wished to evaluate the potential usefulness of other boron trihalides in the fractionation of boron isotopes by Reaction 1.

Theory of Isotopic Fractionation in the Exchange of Boron Between BF₃ and Its Molecular Addition Compounds (25)

The unusual isotopic chemistry of Reaction 2 may be understood in terms of the electronic configurations and structural details of BF_3 and its constituent atoms. Thus, the three valence electrons of boron have a nominal $2s^2 2p^1$ configuration. When BF_3 is formed, the valence electrons of boron hybridize to sp^2 orbitals which form normal sigma bonds with the unpaired p electron of each fluorine atom. This results in a planar BF_3 molecule having the usual 120° central valence bond angle, and a left-over empty boron orbital, which projects from the plane of the molecule at an angle of 90°. The seven valence electrons of fluorine have a nominal $2s^2 2p^5$ configuration. Three pairs of these electrons are non-bonding. Because of the small size of the fluorine atom, these non-bonding electron pairs are closer in fluorine than in any other element. The repulsive forces between them, consequently, are greater than in other elements. The repulsive forces are so great that when BF_3 is formed, one pair of these electrons occupies the empty p boron orbital. Thus, one of the three fluorine atoms in BF_3 is effectively double-bonded to boron while the other two have conventional sigma bonds. Three such configurations are possible, and resonance occurs between them (*27*). Cotton and Leto (*5*) estimated this resonance energy to be 48 kcal./mole. It is this surprisingly large energy associated with the π-bonding which is directly responsible for the unexpected enrichment of the heavy boron isotope in the gas phase.

When a molecular addition compound is formed from BF_3 and a Lewis base, energy associated with the π-bond in the BF_3 molecule is absorbed, and energy associated with the coordinate covalent bond in the adduct is released. It is convenient to view these changes as separate, discrete steps, and to regard the exchange as preceding through a hypothetical, intermediate molecule $\overline{BF}_3$, in which no π-bonding occurs—*i.e.*, a molecule in which each fluorine atom is attached to the boron with a normal sigma bond. We may now regard Reaction 2 as a composite of two separate reactions and rewrite it as shown by Equations 5 and 6.

$$^{10}BF_3 + {}^{11}\overline{BF}_3 = {}^{11}BF_3 + {}^{10}\overline{BF}_3 \tag{5}$$

$$D \cdot {}^{10}BF_3 + {}^{11}\overline{BF}_3 = D \cdot {}^{11}BF_3 + {}^{10}\overline{BF}_3 \tag{6}$$

It will be seen that when the reactions are written in this manner, the isotopes concentrate in the so-called "correct" direction; that is, the heavy isotope is associated in each case with what is obviously the more strongly bonded species. The expressions for the isotopic equilibrium constants for these reactions are given by Equations 7 and 8,

$$K_{eq} (5) = \frac{\dfrac{Q(^{11}BF_3)}{Q(^{10}BF_3)}}{\dfrac{Q(^{11}\overline{BF}_3)}{Q(^{10}\overline{BF}_3)}} \tag{7}$$

$$K_{eq} (6) = \frac{\dfrac{Q(D \cdot {}^{11}BF_3)}{Q(D \cdot {}^{10}BF_3)}}{\dfrac{Q(^{11}\overline{BF}_3)}{Q(^{10}\overline{BF}_3)}} \tag{8}$$

where Q represents the vibrational partition function for the indexed isotopic species. The ratio of these equilibrium constants is the equilibrium constant for the exchange reaction written in the composite form:

$$K_{eq} (2) = \frac{K_{eq} (5)}{K_{eq} (6)} = \frac{\dfrac{Q(^{11}BF_3)}{Q(^{10}BF_3)}}{\dfrac{Q(D \cdot {}^{11}BF_3)}{Q(D \cdot {}^{10}BF_3)}} \tag{9}$$

At a given temperature, the isotopic equilibrium constant for Reaction 5 is, of course, fixed. The equilibrium constant for Reaction 6 will depend on the value of the vibrational partition function ratio for the isotopic species of the molecular addition compound. The numerical value of the numerator in Equation 8 will vary from donor to donor and will be smallest for weakly bound molecular addition compounds. As the equilibrium constant for Reaction 6 approaches unity as a limit, the equilibrium constant for Reaction 2 approaches the equilibrium constant for Reaction 5. The equilibrium constant for Reaction 5 thus represents the maximum value which the equilibrium constant for Reaction 2 may assume. Computed values (25) of this equilibrium constant are shown in Figure 1.

If other boron trihalides are substituted for BF_3 in Reaction 1, the degree of π-bonding decreases as the principal quantum number of the valence shell electrons increases. Further, the equilibrium constant for Reaction 5 tends to unity as the B-X stretching force constant decreases. On the other hand, the Lewis acid is becoming stronger, the molecular addition compound is becoming more stable, and the equilibrium constant for Reaction 6 is becoming larger. When the equilibrium constant for Reaction 5 equals that for Reaction 6, isotopic fractionation will not occur in Reaction 1. When the equilibrium constant for Reaction 5 is less than that for Reaction 6, the equilibrium constant for Reaction 1 will be less than unity; that is, the heavy isotope of boron will then concentrate in the molecular addition compound. One may, therefore, expect the isotopic equilibrium constant for Reaction 1 to decrease progressively on substituting BCl_3, BBr_3, and BI_3 for BF_3. At some point in this process, one also expects the heavy isotope to concentrate in the molecular addition compound. It is clear that this effect will be greater for stronger Lewis acids. These effects were observed by Healy and Palko (21) who measured the fractionation of boron between BCl_3 and its complexes with diphenyl ether and acetyl chloride.

Thus, the fractionation of boron isotopes between boron trifluoride and its molecular addition compounds may be explained in terms of unique characteristics of the boron and fluorine atoms. The model presented here adequately describes the direction of enrichment as well as the magnitude of the equilibrium constant. It accounts for observed variations in the size of fractionation factor for different donors as well as for different substituents on the same donor. The model correctly predicts the isotopic behavior of other boron halides when these are substituted for BF_3 in the exchange reaction. Finally, the proposed model provides insight into the design of a practical chemical exchange system for the separation of boron isotopes.

Literature Cited

(1) Boyd, A. C., Ph.D. Thesis, Purdue Univ., 1957 (DDS pb. 22,248).
(2) Brown, H. C., Pearsall, H., *J. Am. Chem. Soc.* **67**, 1765 (1945).
(3) Brown, H. C., Adams, R. M., *J. Am. Chem. Soc.* **64**, 2557 (1942).
(4) Brown, H. C., Holmes, R. R., *J. Am. Chem. Soc.* **78**, 2174 (1956).
(5) Cotton, F. A., Leto, J. R., *J. Chem. Phys.* **30**, 993 (1959).
(6) Healy, R. M., Palko, A. A., *J. Chem. Phys.* **28**, 211 (1958).
(7) Hoard, J. L., Blair, V. J., *J. Am. Chem. Soc.* **57**, 1985 (1935).
(8) Hughes, Donald A., Harvey, John A., *U. S. At. Energy Comm. Rpt.* **BNL-325** (2nd edition), 1964.
(9) Katal'nikov, S. G., Chih-ch'in, Jung, *Zh. Fiz. Khim.* **39**, 1393 (1965).

(10) Katal'nikov, S. G., Vasenin, G. H., *Zh. Fiz. Khim.* **41,** 1174 (1967).
(11) Katal'nikov, S. G., Paramonov, R. M., *Zh. Fiz. Khim.* **40,** 401 (1966).
(12) Larson, C. E., *U. S. At. Energy Rpt.* **KA-720,** November 1966.
(13) Martin, D. R., *Chem. Rev.* **34,** 469 (1944).
(14) McLaughlin, D. E., Tamres, M., Searles, S., *J. Am. Chem. Soc.* **82,** 5621 (1960).
(15) McLaughlin, D. E., Tamres, M., *J. Am. Chem. Soc.* **82,** 5618 (1960).
(16) Merriman, J. R., Pashley, J. H., Snow, N. W., *U. S. At. Energy Rpt.* **K-1653,** April 15, 1966, Federal Scientific Tech. Information, National Bureau of Standards, U. S. Dept. of Commerce, Springfield, Va.
(17) Morris, H., Kulevsky, N., Tamres, M., Searles, S., *Inorg. Chem.* **5,** 124 (1966).
(18) Palko, A. A., *J. Inorg. Nucl. Chem.* **27,** 287 (1965).
(19) Palko, A. A., Drury, J. S., *J. Chem. Phys.* **46,** 2297 (1967).
(20) *Ibid.,* **35,** 103 (1961).
(21) Palko, A. A., Healy, R. M., Landau, L., *J. Chem. Phys.* **28,** 214 (1958).
(22) Palko, A. A., Drury, J. S., *J. Chem. Phys.* **33,** 779 (1960).
(23) *Ibid.,* **40,** 278 (1964).
(24) Palko, A. A., *J. Chem. Phys.* **30,** 1187 (1959).
(25) Palko, A. A., Drury, J. S., *J. Chem. Phys.* **47,** 2561 (1967).
(26) Panchenkov, G. M., Moiseev, C. D., Markarov, A. V., *Doklady Akad. Nauk. U.S.S.R.* **112,** 659 (Feb. 1957).
(27) Pauling, L., "The Nature of the Chemical Bond," p. 318, Cornell University Press, Ithaca, New York, 1960.
(28) Pendred, D., Richards, R. E., *Trans. Faraday Soc.* **51,** 468 (1955).
(29) Ribnikar, S., "Proceedings of the International Symposium on Isotope Separation," p. 204, Amsterdam, North-Holland Publishing Co., 1958.
(30) Ribnikar, S. V., Bootsma, G. A., *Bull. Inst. Nucl. Sci. Boris Kidrich (Belgrade)* **1,** 91 (1957).

RECEIVED August 28, 1967. Research sponsored by the U. S. Atomic Energy Commission under contract with the Union Carbide Corporation.

4

The Enrichment of Lithium Isotopes by Extraction Chromatography

D. A. LEE

Chemistry Division, Oak Ridge National Laboratory, Oak Ridge, Tenn.

Lithium isotopes were fractionated by extraction chroma-tography. The chemical exchange reaction used was aque-ous lithium hydroxide equilibrated with lithium dibenzoyl-methane-trioctylphosphine oxide in dodecane. Granulated Teflon supported a dodecane solution of dibenzoylmethane-trioctylphosphine oxide in dodecane as the stationary phase. The mobile phase was an aqueous solution of lithium hydroxide. The single stage separation factor was 1.003, as determined by frontal analysis at "breakthrough." ⁶Li concentrated in the aqueous phase. Separation of lithium isotopes by extraction chromatography was compared with separations made by ion exchange resin chromatography. The nature of the isotopic species involved determined the magnitude of the separation factor.

There are two isotopes of lithium, ^6Li and ^7Li, which occur in nature with a $^6Li/^7Li$ abundance ratio of 0.080. Several methods have been employed for the fractionation of these isotopes. At the Oak Ridge National Laboratory, ^6Li has been enriched to 99.999% purity in an electromagnetic separator (Calutron) (18). Trauger, et al. (27) have described the separation of lithium isotopes by molecular distillation. Electromigration (8) has also been used to fractionate these isotopes. Okamoto and Kakihana (20) have enriched lithium isotopes by electro-migration in a cation exchange membrane. Several reversible chemical processes have been investigated. Lewis and MacDonald (17) studied the exchange of lithium between lithium amalgam and lithium chloride in absolute ethyl alcohol. Later, L. Perret, L. Rozand, and E. Saito (22) equilibrated lithium amalgam with lithium bromide in dimethyl forma-mide and measured a separation factor of 1.05. Extensive investigations have been made of ion exchange techniques (4, 10, 19, 23, 25, 26). In these systems the measured separation factors were generally very small (1.000-1.005).

The influence of various physico-chemical parameters upon the separation factor for lithium isotopes in ion exchange systems has been studied. Increasing the crosslinking of the resin from 2x to 24x increased the separation factor (11) from 1.0006 to 1.0038. The change in the separation factor was attributed to changes in hydration of the lithium species in the resin phase. Glueckauf (3) used the solution molalities of the resin phase and the difference in the crystallographic radii of ^6Li and ^7Li to calculate the separation factors. His calculated values agree very well with these observed separation factors.

The effect of temperature upon the separation factor was studied (12). The separation factor decreased as the temperature increased. The exothermic enthalpy of exchange ($-\Delta H°$) for the isotopic reaction $^6Li(aq.) + \, ^7Li(res.) \rightleftharpoons \, ^7Li(aq.) + \, ^6Li(res.)$ was 2.26 cal./mole, and the entropy change was -1.81×10^{-3} cal./mole degree at 25°C.

The influence of the hydrating tendency of cations co-sorbed with lithium isotopes on an ion exchange column was investigated in a series of experiments summarized in Table I. As the heat of hydration of the co-sorbed cation increased, the isotopic separation factor increased (13). The nature of the anion in the solution phase had very little effect upon the separation factor. However, for systems involving complexes of lithium with ethylenediaminetetraacetic acid, there was a reversal of the isotope effect. That is, ^7Li concentrated in the resin phase instead of the aqueous phase as it usually did in ion exchange resin systems.

Table I.   Variation of the Separation Factor with the Nature of the Co-sorbed and Eluting Cation (13)

Cation	Separation Factor[a]
NH_4^+	1.0023
K^+	1.0029
NH_3OH^+	1.0033
H^+	1.0037
Ca^{2+}	1.0037
Cu^{2+}	1.0045
Cr^{3+}	1.0053
Al^{3+}	1.0049

[a] ($^6Li/^7Li$) resin/($^6Li/^7Li$) aqueous.

Knyazev and Sklenskaya (9) calculated the isotopic separation factors for exchange reactions between lithium complexes of nitrilotriacetic acid, ethylenediaminetetraacetic acid and aminobarbituric-N,N'-diacetic acid, and aqueous lithium ions. These reactions were postulated for a single phase system; therefore, the separations cannot be observed experimentally. As the pK of the lithium complex increased, the calculated separation factor increased.

The influence of eluent concentration in ion exchange systems on the separation factor for lithium isotopes was examined by several workers (*2, 6, 21*). Lee and Drury (*14*) found that the separation factors decreased with increasing eluent concentration when Dowex-50 and Zeo Karb resins were used. Comparable results were obtained with either chloride or acetate eluents.

The separation factors for lithium isotopes in ion exchange systems were too small to be practical. To increase the separation factor significantly, lithium species involving other types of lithium compounds would have to be considered for equilibration. The separation of isotopes by chemical exchange depends upon the fact that the isotopic species in the two phases are dissimilar with respect to chemical bonding. That is, in one phase the isotopic species should be strongly bonded, and in the other phase the species should be weakly bonded. The chemistry of lithium limits the variety of chemical species available for isotope separation by chemical exchange. In aqueous solution, lithium exists almost exclusively as a hydrated ion. The concentration of lithium in the resin phase of an ion exchange system is somewhat greater than the concentration of lithium ions in the exterior solution. Although there is association between the lithium ions and the functional groups of the resin matrix, still the lithium species involved is a hydrated lithium ion. This similarity of bonding of the lithium species in each phase accounts for the small separation factors in ion exchange resin systems. Organolithium compounds, which are used extensively in certain organic syntheses, are bonded differently. However, they are very reactive compounds which are unstable toward air and moisture, and any use of organolithium compounds in isotope separation systems appears to be impractical.

Recently, it was found that lithium formed extractable complexes with mixtures of dibenzoylmethane (HDBM) and tri-*n*-octylphosphine oxide (TOPO) or tributyl phosphate (TBP). The β-diketone and the phosphine oxide or phosphate in a hydrocarbon diluent worked synergistically to extract lithium from basic aqueous solutions (*15*). From alkaline solutions of lithium salts, or from mixtures of lithium and sodium, or lithium and ammonium salts, the extracted lithium complex was LiDBM · 2TOPO. From alkaline solutions of lithium salt mixed with potassium, rubidium, or cesium salts, the extractable lithium species was a dimer, $Li_2(DBM)_2$ · 2HDBM · 4TOPO (*16*). The enolic form of dibenzoylmethane is a very weak acid which, when neutralized, will form a chelate with lithium ion. TBP and TOPO are neutral adduct-forming donors which displace the water molecules around the lithium in the chelate, thus making the complex more soluble in the water-immiscible organic phase. In the case of the dimer, excess HDBM molecules also participate in adduct formation.

Although both the lithium atom in this new complex and the lithium atom in the hydrated lithium ion are probably tetrahedrally coordinated to oxygen atoms, still the force constants of the lithium-oxygen bonds are undoubtedly influenced differently in the two species because of the structure of the ligands and the environment of the particular solvent. Therefore, it was of interest to investigate the possibility of separating lithium isotopes by an exchange reaction in which LiDBM · 2TOPO in a water-immiscible organic solvent was equilibrated with hydrated lithium ions in a basic aqueous solution. From the standpoint of dissimilar species in the two phases, this system appears to have advantages over the aqueous ion exchange resin system for lithium isotope separation, and a larger separation factor should be expected. To determine whether or not this solvent extraction process was feasible with respect to exchange rates and magnitude of the single stage separation factor, the process was evaluated by a technique new to isotope separation, extraction chromatography.

Extraction chromatography (reversed phase partition chromatography) has been used in analytical and biochemistry to effect chemical separations. It is a method which combines the simplicity of ion exchange and the selectivity of solvent extraction. Ion exchange theory may be used to calculate the number of theoretical plates in the column and the enrichment coefficient. Extraction chromatography as a separation method has been recently reviewed by Cerrai (1) and Katykhin (7).

The procedure for the enrichment of lithium isotopes by extraction chromatography was as follows. A dodecane or p-xylene solution of HDBM-2TOPO was absorbed onto an inert support of granulated Teflon. This was the stationary phase in a column 120 cm. long × 2.5 cm. I.D. An aqueous lithium hydroxide solution containing the mixture of isotopes to be separated was passed through the column. At each plate in the column, isotopic equilibrium was established between the lithium species in the two phases. Multiplication of the enrichment occurred as lithium proceeded down the column. At the "breakthrough" the isotopes were partially fractionated along the profile of the elution curve. The concentration of lithium in the elutriant samples was determined by flame spectrophotometry. The number of theoretical plates in the column was then calculated from a plot of the elution curve. The reverse situation was also examined. That is, a column loaded with lithium dibenzoyl-methane-trioctylphosphine oxide complex was stripped from the column with dilute hydrochloric acid and the isotopic separation factor was determined. In this case, the isotopes were eluted in reverse order.

The calculation of the number of plates in the column was accomplished by using the theoretical treatment of Glueckauf for "breakthrough" chromatography (5). The number of theoretical plates in the column (N) was given by $N = \overline{V}V'/(\overline{V} - V')^2$, where V is the elution volume at the point of inflection and V' is the elution volume at the concentration c', defined by $c'/c^\circ = 0.1587$. Glueckauf gave an alternative equation for the number of plates in the column (Figure 1):

$$N = 2\pi(\overline{V}/\Delta V)^2$$

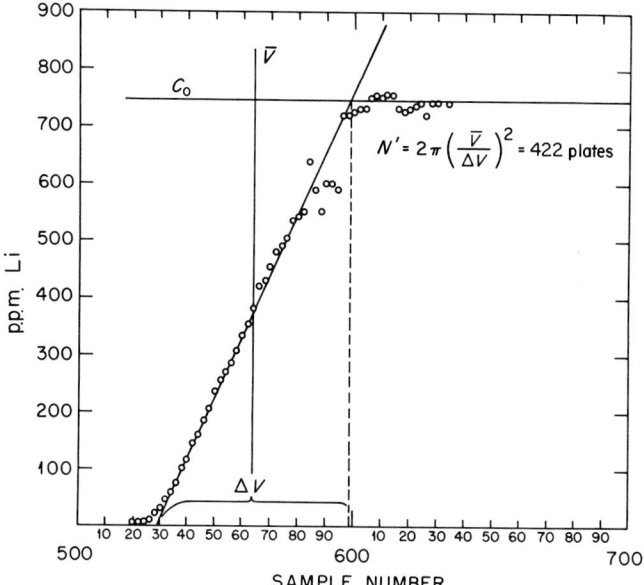

Figure 1.   Breakthrough elution curve of LiOH on DBM-TOPO column

Along the gradient of the "breakthrough" curve, the lithium samples were isotopically assayed by mass spectrometry. The single stage enrichment factor was determined as follows (24):

$$\epsilon = \alpha - 1 = \sum_{i=1}^{m} \frac{V_i C_i (R_o - R_i)}{QR_o}$$

where

α = the ^{6}Li-^{7}Li separation factor

V_i = the volume of the i-th fraction collected (ml.)

C_i = the molar concentration of Li in the i-th fraction

R_i = the ratio of ^6Li to ^7Li in the i-th fraction

R_o = the ratio of ^6Li to ^7Li in the original lithium compound

Q = the total capacity of the exchange bed in milliequivalents.

It was found that ^6Li concentrated in the aqueous phase, as shown in Figure 2. This was a reversal from the usual results obtained in ion

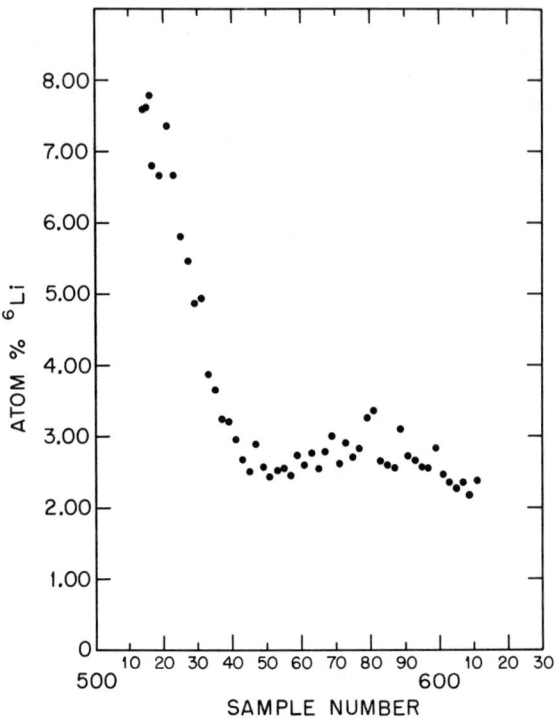

Figure 2.   *Lithium isotope enrichment by extraction chromatography. Li DBM · 2 TOPO vs. LiOH*

exchange systems. In the latter systems, ^6Li usually concentrated in the resin phase. The single stage separation factor was 1.003, a value comparable to the separation factor typically found for ion exchange resin systems. It was unfortunate that the significant change in the isotope effect resulted in an isotope reversal instead of an addition to the effect found for aqueous ion exchange systems. If complexes of lithium could be found in which lithium was coordinated to atoms other than oxygen in one phase, a larger isotope effect might be expected.

Conclusion

The present work has been the first application of extraction chromatography to isotope separation. This technique proved to be a simple and convenient laboratory-scale method for studying lithium isotope separation by liquid-liquid extraction. The method may have even more interesting possibilities for isotopes of elements which form a variety of complexes which are soluble in organic solvents.

The prospect of separating lithium isotopes on a large scale by the extraction of lithium from aqueous solutions is not very promising. In the system we have studied, reflux could be accomplished by an acid-base mechanism; however, because of the small separation factor, an extremely large reflux ratio would be required. This would necessitate a very large plant using enormous quantities of acid and base, and the cost would be excessive.

From an academic standpoint, the separation of isotopes by extraction chromatography presents a useful tool for studying isotopic species in solution. The nature of the species may sometimes be elucidated by determining small variations in the single stage separation factor if isotope separation is promoted by certain physico-chemical parameters. These parameters may include the pK of the complex, pH of the aqueous solution, temperature, concentration, nature of the organic solvent, anion complexing in the aqueous phase, and other factors depending on the chemistry of the particular isotope.

Literature Cited

(1) Cerrai, E., *Chromatog. Rev.* **6**, 129 (1964).
(2) Ciric, M. M., Pupezin, J. D., *Bull. Boris Kidrich Inst. Sci.* **13**, 29 (1962).
(3) Glueckauf, E., *J. Am. Chem. Soc.* **81**, 5262 (1959).
(4) Glueckauf, E., Barker, K. H., Kitt, G. P., *Disc. Faraday Soc.* **7**, 199 (1949).
(5) Glueckauf, E., "Isotope Separation by Chromatographic Methods," AERE-R2896, Atomic Energy Res. Estab., Harwell, Berkshire, 1959.
(6) Katal'nikov, S. G., Revin, V. A., Andreev, B. M., Minev, V. A., *Atomnaya Energiya* **11**, 528 (1961).
(7) Katykhin, G. S., *Zh. Analit. Khim.* **20**, 615 (1965).
(8) Klemm, A., *J. Naturforsch* **6a**, 512 (1951).
(9) Knyazev, D. A., Sklenskaya, E. V., *Russ. J. Phys. Chem.* **37**, 1134 (1963).
(10) Lee, D. A., *J. Chem. Eng.* **6**, 565 (1961).
(11) Lee, D. A., Begun, G. M., *J. Am. Chem. Soc.* **81**, 2332 (1959).
(12) Lee, D. A., *J. Phys. Chem.* **64**, 187 (1960).
(13) Lee, D. A., *J. Am. Chem. Soc.* **83**, 180 (1961).
(14) Lee, D. A., Drury, J. S., *J. Inorg. Nucl. Chem.* **27**, 1405 (1965).
(15) Lee, D. A., *J. Chromatog.* **26**, 342 (1967).
(16) Lee, D. A., Taylor, W. L. (unpublished data, 1966).
(17) Lewis, G. N., MacDonald, R. T., *J. Am. Chem. Soc.* **58**, 2519 (1936).

(18) Love, L. O., Bell, W. A., Jr., Prater, W. K., Banic, G. M., Cameron, A. E., "Proceedings of the International Symposium on Isotope Separation," J. Kistemaker, J. Bigeleisen, A. O. C. Nier, Eds., North-Holland Publishing Co., Amsterdam, 1958.
(19) Menes, F., Saito, E., Roth, E., "Proceedings of the International Symposium on Isotope Separation," J. Kistemaker, J. Bigeleisen, A. O. C. Nier, Eds., North-Holland Publishing Co., Amsterdam, 1958.
(20) Okamoto, M., Kakihana, H., *Nippon Kagaku Zasshi* **88**, 313 (1967).
(21) Panchenkov, G. M., Kuznetsova, E. M., Kaznadzei, O. N., *Atomnaya Energiya* **7**, 556 (1959).
(22) Perret, L., Rozand, L., Saito, E., "Second International Conference on the Peaceful Uses of Atomic Energy," Vol. **4**, 595, United Nations, New York, 1958.
(23) Powell, J. E., *J. Inorg. Nucl. Chem.* **24**, 183 (1962).
(24) Spedding, F. H., Powell, J. E., Svec, H. J., *J. Am. Chem. Soc.* **77**, 6125 (1955).
(25) Taylor, T. I., Urey, H. C., *J. Chem. Phys.* **5**, 597 (1937).
(26) *Ibid.*, **6**, 429 (1938).
(27) Trauger, D. B., Keyes, J. J., Jr., Kuipers, G. A., Lang, D. M., "Proceedings of the International Symposium on Isotope Separation," J. Kistemaker, J. Bigeleisen, A. O. C. Nier, Eds., North-Holland Publishing Co., Amsterdam, 1958.

RECEIVED August 28, 1967. Research sponsored by the U. S. Atomic Energy Commission under contract with the Union Carbide Corporation.

The Photochemical Separation of the Carbon Isotopes

G. LIUTI,[1] S. DONDES, and P. HARTECK

Rensselaer Polytechnic Institute, Troy, N. Y.

The photolysis of CO using the 2062.4 A. line of iodine produces a ^{13}C enrichment in the reaction product, C_3O_2 and an ^{18}O enrichment in the reaction product CO_2. The reaction mechanism is as follows:

$$^{13}CO^* + CO \rightarrow CO_2 + {}^{13}C \tag{Ia}$$

$$^{13}CO^* + {}^{12}CO \rightarrow {}^{13}CO_2 + {}^{12}C \tag{Ib}$$

$$^{12}C\,{}^{18}O^* + CO \rightarrow {}^{12}C\,{}^{16}O\,{}^{18}O + {}^{12}C \tag{Ic}$$

$$^{13}C + {}^{12}CO + M \rightarrow {}^{13}C = {}^{12}C = O \tag{II}$$

$$^{13}C = {}^{12}C = O + CO + M \rightarrow$$
$$O = {}^{12}C = {}^{13}C = {}^{12}C = O + M \tag{III}$$

The distribution of the ^{13}C in C_3O_2 and CO_2 shows that the reaction between $^{13}CO^*$ and CO forms ^{13}C and CO_2, Reaction Ia.

The possibility of separating isotopes photochemically has been considered for a long time (*11*). Kuhn and Martin (*3, 7, 16*) obtained a very small separation of the chlorine isotopes in the photolysis of phosgene using the 2816-A. line. However, up to the present time, the only successful photochemical separation of isotopes was performed by Billings *et al.* (*2, 4*) (a special situation), where the resonance lines of mercury isotopes preferably excite the same isotopic species, which then, under the conditions of the experiment, undergo a chemical reaction which leads to the separation of the isotopes. The conditions which are favorable to make the photochemical separation of isotopes possible, similar to those proposed by Billings *et al.* (*2, 4*), are:

[1] Present address: Goddard Space Flight Center, Greenbelt, Md.

(1) A difference in the absorption spectrum

(2) A light source emitting a sufficiently narrow line

(3) A chemical reaction involving the excited species

(4) No energy exchange of the excited species prior to chemical reaction

(5) No atom or radical reactions which follows and quenches the initial step

We have been able to enrich the ^{13}C isotopes from its natural abundance of 1.13% substantially by exciting the Cameron level of carbon monoxide (see Figure 1 for energy levels of CO) with the 2062.4 iodine line (see Figure 2 for energy levels of iodine).

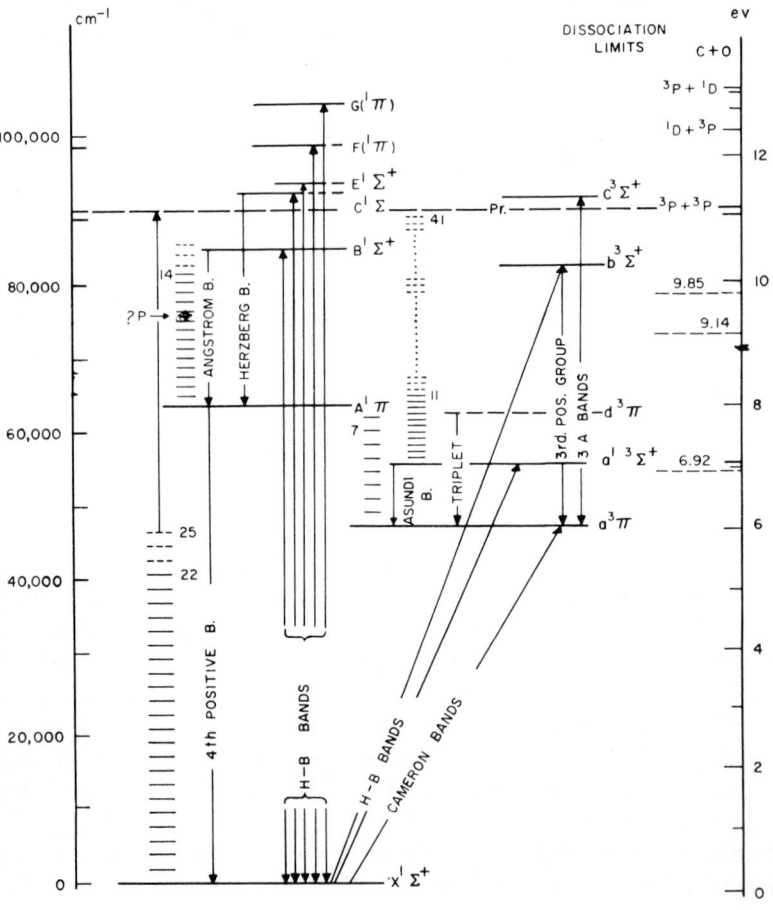

Figure 1. Energy levels of CO (10)

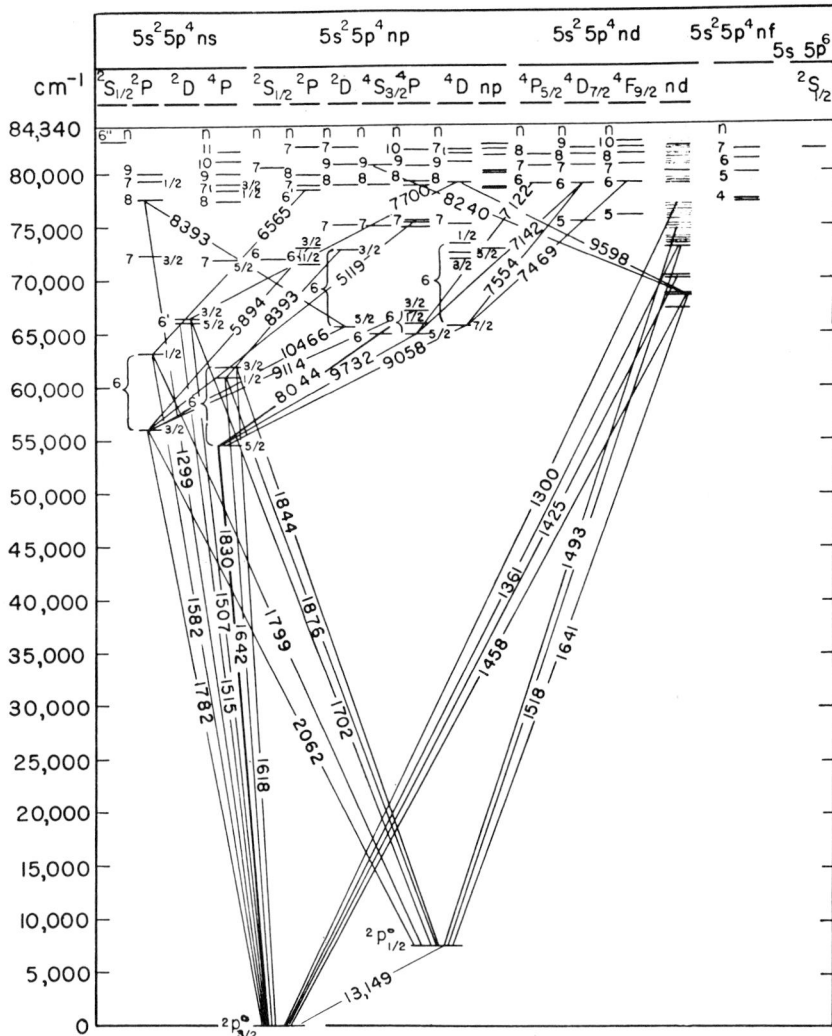

Figure 2.   Energy level diagram for iodine (8)

From Condition 1 above, an isotopic shift for the 0,0 level of the Cameron band system exists for both $^{13}C^{16}O$ and $^{12}C^{18}O$, being equal to 4.7 cm.$^{-1}$ for $^{13}C^{16}O$ and 5.2 cm.$^{-1}$ for $^{12}C^{18}O$ (6). These shifts correspond to a difference of -0.20 and -0.22 A. between the 0,0 levels of the isotopic molecules at 2060 A. Tanaka *et al.* (12) showed that the band-head corresponding to the R_3 branch of the 0,0 level of the Cameron band system lies at 2062.6 A. The corresponding bandheads of the $^{13}C^{16}O$ and $^{12}C^{18}O$ lie at 2062.4 A. of the iodine line.

From Condition 2, iodine is a monoisotopic element giving a very sharp line at 2062.4 A. (*15*). (Using the 1849 A. line of normal Hg in Hg sensitized CO produced C_3O_2 but no enrichment of the ^{13}C isotope.)

From Condition 3, we (*8*) have shown that when CO is excited to the $A^3\Pi$ state, it reacts with another CO molecule to produce CO_2 and C, which, with the addition of two other CO molecules produces C_3O_2 in the gas phase (*see* below).

In addition to the isotopic enrichment that was observed, the mechanism for the formation of carbon suboxide *via* excited CO molecules in the chemical behavior of the important intermediate C_2O could be elucidated (*8*).

Experimental

The photochemical lamp used in this study was developed by Harteck, Reeves, and Thompson (*5*). This lamp is shown in Figure 3. The lamp consisted of concentric cylinders, the inner made of commercial quartz (Amersil Corporation) and the outer of 96% silica glass. Both condensed (d.c.) and "glow" (a.c.) discharges of about 8,000 volts could be applied to the electrodes. To provide the iodine vapor, a side-arm was attached which contained resublimed iodine. To provide a stable discharge and to prevent a chemical attack of the aluminum electrodes by the iodine vapor, argon was flowed through the inner tube continuously at about 1 mm. pressure.

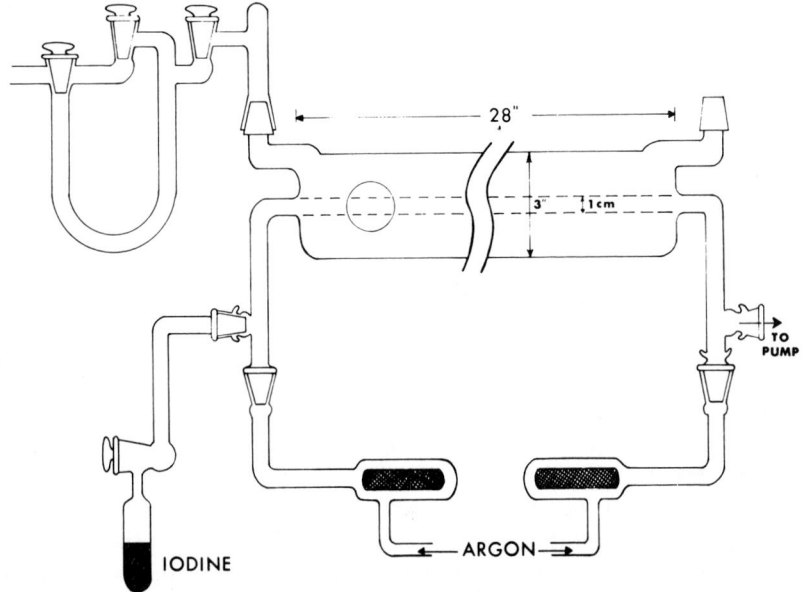

Figure 3.   Schematic diagram of the photochemical lamp used in enriching the ^{13}C isotope

The carbon monoxide used was fractionally distilled at low temperatures between liquid oxygen and liquid nitrogen baths. (No changes in the natural abundance of ^{13}C was noted.) After a series of distillations the carbon monoxide was inserted into the outer jacket of the photochemical lamp to a pressure of about 700 mm. (Note: The yield of carbon suboxide was radically reduced by the presence of impurities, especially oxygen.) The lamp was operated for a period of about two hours. Longer irradiations caused some polymerization on the quartz by the carbon suboxide. When the irradiation of the pure CO was completed, the unreacted CO, together with the products of the irradiation, was pumped slowly through a U-tube immersed in a liquid oxygen bath to collect all the products formed. The products were then analyzed with a CEC 21-130 mass spectrometer.

To determine the effects of a magnetic field, an adjustable magnet with about 6 cm. diameter pole pieces, was set in the center of the photochemical lamp. Magnetic fields of about 800 and 1000 gauss were used.

Results and Discussion

A typical set of results for the products of the reaction, *i.e.*, CO_2 and C_3O_2 is shown in Table I, and for isotopic enrichment in Table II. A separation between ^{13}C and ^{12}C occurs with a substantial enrichment factor. A separation between ^{18}O and ^{16}O occurs. The amount of heavy isotopes produced is small owing to the very low absorption coefficient (0.0076) (*13*) of CO at 2062.4 A. (*See* Figure 4).

Table I. The Mass Spectra of the Products of Reaction, of Pure CO_2 and of Pure C_3O_2 (70 Volts Ionizing Electrons)

		Intensity	
M./e.	Products	Pure CO_2	Pure C_3O_2
28	132.7	103.0	27.0
34	9.0		9.1
36	1.54		1.2
40	100.0		100.0
41	2.4		2.2
44	1197.	1197.	
45	14.7	15.0	
46	5.4	5.25	
52	2.55		2.4
68	92.0		94.5
69	3.17		3.0
70	.45		0.41

With the isotopic enrichment as a labeling technique, we could determine the processes involving CO* and its subsequent reactions. These are:

Table II. A Listing of a Typical Set of Experiments

		Exp. 1		Exp. 2	
M./e.		Intensity	% ^{13}C	Intensity	% ^{13}C
69	($^{16}O^{12}C^{13}C^{12}C^{16}O$)	9	8.9	16.5	8.4
68	($^{16}O^{12}C^{12}C^{12}C^{16}O$)	92		180	
46	($^{16}O^{12}C^{18}O$)	59	0.74 [a]	128.5	0.74 [a]
45	($^{16}O^{13}C^{16}O$)	154	1.90	333	1.90
44	($^{16}O^{12}C^{16}O$)	7920		17180	
41	($^{13}C^{12}C^{16}O$)	8	7.6	15	7.0
40	($^{12}C^{12}C^{16}O$)	97		201	

[a] % ^{18}O.

(a) The primarily excited CO molecule, upon collision with another CO molecule, does not tend to transfer the energy, but rather reacts with the molecule.

(b) If ^{13}C were statistically distributed in the C_3O_2, the percentage of ^{13}C in the fragment ion C_2O^+ would be 2/3 of that in C_3O_2. If, however, all of the ^{13}C (except the statistical abundance in the end CO groups) were located in the central position of C_3O_2, the mass ratio $\dfrac{41}{40}\Big/\dfrac{69}{68}$ should equal 0.87.

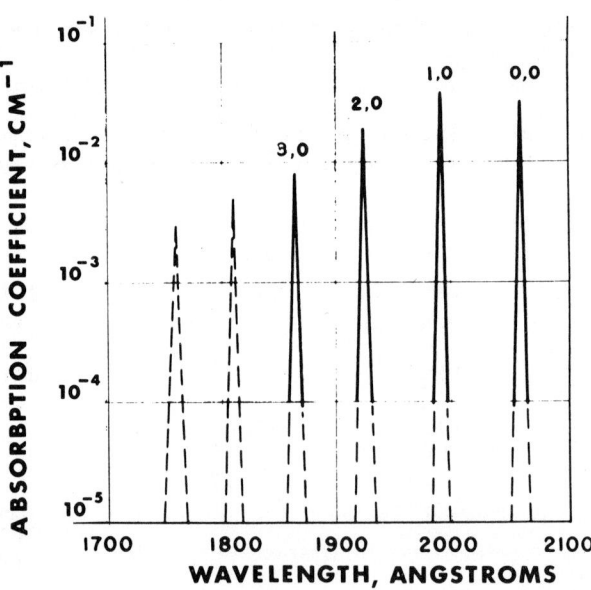

Figure 4.   Absorption spectrum of CO (9)

The data in Table II show that the average ratio of masses $\dfrac{41}{40}\Big/\dfrac{69}{68}$ is 0.85. This result provides strong support for the following mechanism

Showing the Isotopic Enrichment of ^{13}C

Exp. 3		Averages	Normal C_3O_2	
Intensity	*% ^{13}C*	*Av. % ^{13}C*	*Intensity*	*% ^{13}C*
13	9	8.73 ± 0.2	3.0	3.1
131			94.5	
131	0.75	0.74^a ± 0.01		
336	1.90	1.90 ± 0.01		
17300				
12.5	8.0	7.55 ± 0.3	2.2	2.18
142.5			100	

which requires that ^{13}C introduced into C_3O_2 by reaction of $^{13}C^*$ appear in the central position.

$$^{13}CO^* + CO \rightarrow CO_2 + {}^{13}C \tag{Ia}$$

$$^{13}CO^* + {}^{12}CO \rightarrow {}^{13}CO_2 + {}^{12}C \tag{Ib}$$

$$^{12}C\ {}^{18}O^* + CO \rightarrow {}^{12}C\ {}^{16}O\ {}^{18}O + {}^{12}C \tag{Ic}$$

$$^{13}C + {}^{12}CO + M \rightarrow {}^{13}C = {}^{12}C = O \tag{II}$$

$$^{13}C = {}^{12}C = O + CO + M \rightarrow O = {}^{12}C = {}^{13}C = {}^{12}C = O + M \tag{III}$$

(c) The distribution of the ^{13}C in C_3O_2 and CO_2 shows that, in the reaction between $^{13}CO^*$ and CO, ^{13}C and CO_2 are formed (Reaction Ia).

Considering that C_3O_2 contains only one atom of enriched ^{13}C and taking into account the ^{13}C enrichment in CO_2, it can be calculated that, of the reacting excited CO molecules, 7.1% are ^{13}CO. From the average ^{13}C content in C_3O_2 in three typical experiments, an enrichment factor of 2.68 was obtained.

Further experiments are planned with enriched $^{13}C^{16}O$ and $^{12}C^{18}O$ for finer details. In addition, the oxidation of C_3O_2 with O-atoms to form predominantly CO (about 90%) and CO_2 (*1, 9, 14*) which has been conducted by us with normal carbon suboxide will be applied here. The carbon monoxide obtained from the enriched suboxide, will then be further photolyzed for further enrichment.

Acknowledgment

We would like to thank the U. S. Atomic Energy Commission for financial support. This work was performed under Contract AT(30-3)-321.

Literature Cited

(1) Becker, K. H., Bayes, K. D., *J. Chem. Phys.* **45**, 396 (1966).
(2) Billings, B. H., Hitchcock, W. J., Zelikoff, M., *J. Chem. Phys.* **21**, 1762 (1953).

(3) Evans, R. D., "The Atomic Nucleus," p. 268, McGraw-Hill, New York, 1955.
(4) Gunning, H. E., Strausz, P. O., *Advan. Photochem.* 1, 209 (1963).
(5) Harteck, P., Reeves, R. R., Thompson, B. A., Z. *Naturforsch.* 19, 2 (1964).
(6) Herzberg, G., "Spectra of Diatomic Molecules," p. 520, D. Van Nostrand, Inc., New York, 1950.
(7) Kuhn, W., Martin, H., *Naturwiss.* 20, 722 (1932).
(8) Liuti, G., Harteck, P., Dondes, S., *J. Chem. Phys.* 44, 4051 (1966).
(9) Liuti, G., Kunz, C., Dondes, S., *J. Am. Chem. Soc.* 89, 5542 (1967).
(10) McNesby, J. R., Okabe, H., *Advan. Photochem.* 3, 177 (1964).
(11) Rozenberg, J., "Photochemical Isotope Separation," Bibliography #56, Commissariat a l'Énergie Atomique-France, 1965.
(12) Tanaka, Y., Jursa, A. S., LeBlanc, F., *J. Chem. Phys.* 26, 862 (1957).
(13) Thompson, B. A., Reeves, R. R., Harteck, P., *J. Geophys. Res.* 68, 6431 (1963).
(14) Von Weyssenhoff, H., Dondes, S., Harteck, P., *J. Am. Chem. Soc.* 84, 1526 (1962).
(15) Zaidel, A. N., Prokof', V. K. ev, Raiskii, S. M., "Tables of Spectrum Lines," p. 386, Pergamon Press, New York, 1961.
(16) Zuber, K., *Helv. Phys. Acta.* 9, 285 (1936).

RECEIVED July 27, 1967.

Isotope and Ortho-Para Separations of the Molecular Hydrogens by Adsorption at Low Temperatures

W. J. HAUBACH,[1] P. RADHAKRISHNA,[2] A. KATORSKI,[3] R. WANG, and DAVID WHITE

University of Pennsylvania, Philadelphia, Pa.

The theory of isotope and ortho-para separation of diatomic molecules, by preferential adsorption at low temperatures, is reviewed, and a comparison between theory and experiment is made for the isotopic molecular hydrogens. In the plane surface approximation for a molecule-surface interaction coupling the angular motions with the center of mass vibrations normal to the surface, good agreement is found between the measured and calculated separation factors. It is, however, not possible (solely on the basis of the experimental separation factors) to establish the exact form of the potential of interaction. The influence of surface heterogeneity on the separations is discussed and in both cases (spin and isotopic) reasonable agreement between theory and experiment is obtained for monolayers on a heterogeneous surface.

The separation of the ortho-para nuclear spin species of the homonuclear hydrogens (4, 5, 18, 21) by adsorption at low temperatures has generated a considerable interest in the angular dependent molecule-surface interactions (7, 22). These anisotropic interactions, responsible for the ortho-para separations play an important role in the total binding energy of a diatomic or polyatomic molecule to the surface (13) and therefore are important in isotopic separations by preferential adsorption. Whereas, in the case of adsorbed isotopic atomic species the surface field constrains only the mass dependent translational motions, in the case of

---

[1] Present address: Mound Laboratory, Monsanto Research Corp., Miamisburg, Ohio.
[2] Present address: Atomic Energy Commission, Roskilde, Denmark.
[3] Deceased.

diatomic molecules the same surface field also influences the angular motions. This latter effect whose magnitude is in part dependent on the rotational constant (16, 22) has also been shown to be important in accounting for differences in vapor pressures of isotopic heteronuclear diatomics. The model (1, 8) used to account for these differences is very similar, in many respects, to that used in the description of surface phenomena (16, 22).

In this paper a brief review of the theory of ortho-para and isotopic separations of diatomic molecules, by adsorption on surfaces at low temperatures is presented together with a comparison between theory and experiment. Although the model used to represent the surface-molecule interactions is an over-simplification of the physical situation, it will nevertheless be seen that all of the predictions of the theory have, indeed, been verified by experiment. The good agreement between theory and the available experimental results, the latter being entirely thermo-dynamic in nature, is more a result of the insensitivity of the data to appreciable changes in the parameters describing the surface-molecule interactions, than the verification of the particular analytical form used in the approximation. It is, however, clear that regardless of the exact form of the potential of interaction, both the angular anisotropy of the surface field and the strong coupling of the constrained rotational and vibrational motion of an adsorbed molecule are the important factors in accounting for the observations.

Model for Adsorbed Diatomic Molecules

The model described below is that previously given by White and Lassettre (22). The adsorbent is regarded as a plane-surfaced semi-infinite solid. The forces between the solid adsorbent and the adsorbed diatomic molecules are assumed to be centered at the positions of the component atoms of the molecule. The total interaction between the molecule and the surface is simply the sum of the atom-surface inter-actions (16, 22). The interaction potential for each atom of the adsorbed molecule is given by $f(z_i)$ where z_i is the distance of the i-th atom measured normal to the surface. Let the distance from the center of mass to the atoms of mass m_1 and m_2, respectively be b_1 and b_2, as shown in Figure 1. The potential energy, V, of the adsorbed diatomic molecule is then

$$V(z,\theta) = f(z_1) + f(z_2) = f(z + b_1\cos\theta) + f(z - b_2\cos\theta) \qquad (1)$$

where z is the distance of the center of mass of the molecule from the surface and θ the angle the axis of the molecule makes with the z axis.

An important feature of Equation 1, regardless of the form of $f(z_i)$ is that the response of heteronuclear diatomic molecules to this surface field cannot be the same as for homonuclears. This can readily be seen by expanding (*1*) in a power series in $\eta = \cos\theta$,

$$V(z,\theta) = 2f(z) + (b_1 - b_2)f'(z)\eta + \frac{b^2_1 + b^2_2}{2} f''(z)\eta^2 + \dots \quad (2)$$

Defining the internuclear distance $b = b_1 + b_2$ and Δ the distance (along the bond joining the two atoms) between the center of mass of the molecule and the midpoint between the two atoms (*see* Figure 1),

$$V(z,\theta) = 2f(z) + 2\Delta f'(z)\eta + \frac{b^2}{4} f''(z)\eta^2 + \Delta^2 f''(z)\eta^2 + \dots \quad (3)$$

For homonuclear diatomics, $b_1 = b_2$, $\Delta = 0$, the potential is represented by even powers in η and all terms containing Δ vanish. On the other hand, for heteronuclears the potential consists of both even and odd powers of η multiplied by coefficients containing Δ. This Δ has been referred to as the displacement of the center of interaction (*1, 8*) of the molecule from the center of gravity.

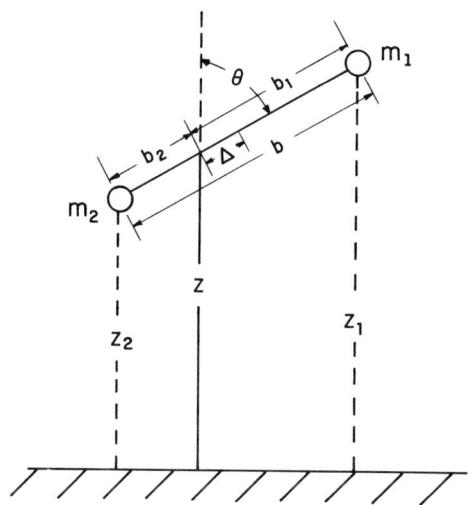

Figure 1. *Diatomic molecule adsorbed on plane surface*

In order to obtain the energy levels of the adsorbed diatomic molecule, it is necessary to solve the Schroedinger equation for the Hamiltonion (*13*).

$$H = \frac{p_x^2}{2M} + \frac{p_y^2}{2M} + \frac{p_z^2}{2M} + \frac{p_\theta^2}{2I} + \frac{p_\phi^2}{2I\sin^2\theta} + V(z,\theta) \quad (4)$$

where M is the mass of the molecule, I the moment of inertia, and $V(z,\theta)$ the potential energy of interaction of the molecule with the surface. Representing the eigenfunction by the product

$$\psi = F(x,y)G(\phi)R(z,\theta) \tag{5}$$

the Schroedinger equation becomes separable in the variables x, y, and ϕ. From the F equation one obtains the energy levels of a particle in a two-dimensional box, from the G equation

$$G(\phi) = [(2\pi)^{1/2}]^{-1} \exp(im\phi), m = 0, \pm 1, \pm 2$$

and the R equation is

$$-\left(\frac{h^2}{8\pi^2 M}\right)\frac{\partial^2 R}{\partial z^2} - \left(\frac{h^2}{8\pi^2 I}\right)\left\{\left(\frac{1}{\sin\theta}\right)\frac{\partial}{\partial\theta}\left[\sin\theta\frac{\partial R}{\partial\theta}\right] - \left(\frac{m^2}{\sin^2\theta}\right)R\right\} \tag{6}$$
$$+ V(z,\theta)R = ER.$$

To obtain the rotation-vibration eigenvalues, E, of Equation 6 it is necessary to specify a particular form for $V(z,\theta)$. Substituting a Morse type function

$$f(z) = \frac{D}{2}\{e^{-2az} - 2e^{-az}\} \tag{7}$$

where D and a are constants, in Equation 1 gives the molecule-surface potential energy of interaction

$$V(z,\theta) = \frac{D}{2}e^{-2az}\left[\exp\left(\frac{-2y\rho\eta}{\rho+1}\right) + \exp\left(\frac{2y\eta}{\rho+1}\right)\right]$$
$$-De^{-az}\left[\exp\left(\frac{-y\rho\eta}{\rho+1}\right) + \exp\left(\frac{y\eta}{\rho+1}\right)\right] \tag{8}$$

where $\rho = b_1/b_2 = m_2/m_1 \geqslant 1$ and $y = ab$. (The definition $y = ab$ used here is that of Katorski and White (16). In an earlier paper White and Lassettre (22) defined $y = (ab/2)^2$). Thus

Thus

$$y(\text{Reference } 16) = 2\sqrt{y(\text{Reference } 22)}$$

It should be noted that even though the constants, a and D, of Equation 7 can, to a good approximation, be assumed the same for a series of isotopic molecules, the molecule potential energy of interaction given by (9) differentiates between homonuclear and heteronuclear species through the constant ρ. (y is the same for isotopic molecules). This constant is, in fact, simply a function of Δ

$$\rho = \frac{1 + \dfrac{2\Delta}{b}}{1 - \dfrac{2\Delta}{b}} \tag{9}$$

the displacement of the center of interaction from the molecular center of gravity.

The form of V, Equation 8, as a function of z is dependent on the molecular orientation. Both the potential minima and the corresponding distance of the center of mass from the surface at the minimum change with molecular orientation. Thus, on a complete rotation, if the minimum energy is maintained at each angle, the center of mass is displaced from its equilibrium position which is $z = 0$ at $\pi/2$. Furthermore, the maximum displacement of the center of mass on a complete rotation increases with increasing ρ. This is illustrated in Figure 2. The potential, Equation 8, is therefore not separable in z and θ (or η), the nature of the coupling being determined by the parameter ρ.

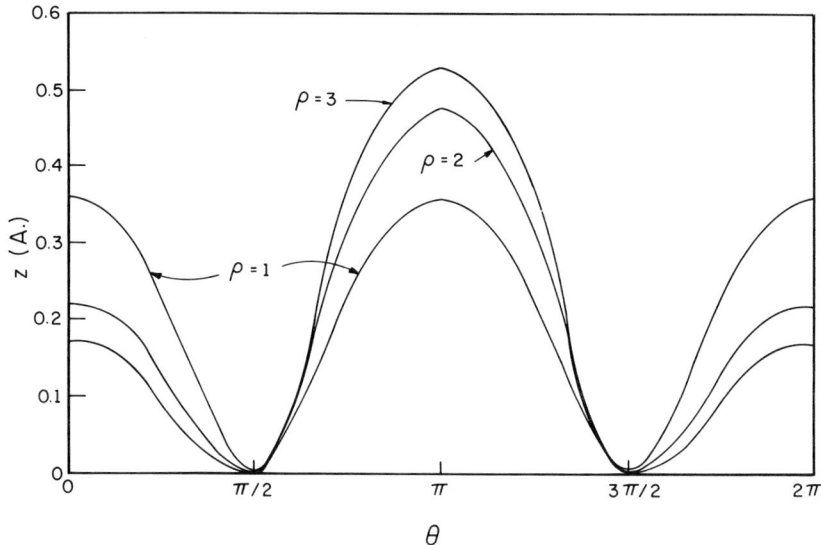

Figure 2.   *Distance of molecular center of mass from surface at potential minimum as a function of molecular orientation.* $\rho = 1$, *homonuclear molecules;* $\rho = 2$, *HD;* $\rho = 3$, *HT*

Even though the variables of the differential Equation 6 are not separable in the exact sense, a condition for separability can be imposed by application of the variation theorem

$$E_{0} = \frac{\int uQu\,d\tau}{\int u^{2}\,d\tau} \tag{10}$$

where Q designates the operator on the left hand side of Equation 6 and u is a function obeying the same boundary conditions as R. Since Q is Hermitian, the quantity E_o takes its extreme value only when u is an eigenfunction of Q. If the condition that u is a product-type function, $u = S(z)T(\eta)$, is imposed, application of the calculus of variations shows that E_o is an extreme when the functions S, T satisfy the two dependent differential equations

$$-\left(\frac{h^2}{8\pi^2 M}\right)\frac{d^2 S}{dz^2} + \{\alpha De^{-2az} - 2\gamma De^{-az}\}S = E_z S \tag{11}$$

and

$$-\frac{d}{d\eta}\left\{(1-\eta^2)\frac{dT}{d\eta}\right\} + \frac{m^2 T}{(1-\eta^2)} + \frac{\beta}{2}\left\{\exp\left(\frac{-2y\rho\eta}{\rho+1}\right) + \exp\left(\frac{2y\eta}{\rho+1}\right)\right\}T$$

$$-\delta\left[\exp\left(\frac{-y\rho\eta}{\rho+1}\right) + \exp\left(\frac{y\eta}{\rho+1}\right)\right]T = \left(\frac{8\pi^2 I E_\eta}{h^2}\right)T. \tag{12}$$

When the functions S and T are normalized to unity, then the constants α, β, γ, δ are given by

$$\alpha = \frac{1}{2}\int_{-1}^{1}\left\{\exp\left(\frac{-2y\rho\eta}{\rho+1}\right) + \exp\left(\frac{2y\eta}{\rho+1}\right)\right\}T^2 d\eta \tag{13}$$

$$\gamma = \frac{1}{2}\int_{-1}^{1}\left\{\exp\left(\frac{-y\rho\eta}{\rho+1}\right) + \exp\left(\frac{y\eta}{\rho+1}\right)\right\}T^2 d\eta \tag{14}$$

$$\beta = \frac{8\pi^2 ID}{h^2}\int_{-\infty}^{\infty} e^{-2az}S^2 dz \tag{15}$$

$$\delta = \frac{8\pi^2 ID}{h^2}\int_{-\infty}^{\infty} e^{-az}S^2 dz \tag{16}$$

and the rotational vibrational energy E is given by

$$\frac{8\pi^2 IE}{h^2} = \frac{8\pi^2 IE_z}{h^2} + \frac{8\pi^2 IE_\eta}{h^2} - \alpha\beta + 2\gamma\delta. \tag{17}$$

E_z, E_η are constants determined by imposing the boundary condition on Equation 11 that $S(z)$ vanish at $z = \pm\infty$ and the condition on Equation 12 that $T(\eta)$ be bounded and single valued at $\eta = \pm 1$.

The solution of the simultaneous differential Equations 11 and 12 has already been discussed in detail in Reference 16. Only the four lowest rotational-vibrational energies, as a function of y and D, for all of the isotopic hydrogens have been calculated and tabulated. These are the states which correlate, in the case of the free molecule, with the states

$l = 0$, $m = 0$; $l = 1$, $m = 0$, $m = \pm 1$; and $l = 2$, $m = 0$. Since the rotational constants of the isotopic hydrogens are large, these four states are, to a good approximation, adequate for the description of the thermodynamic properties of the adsorbed state over a considerable temperature range.

Thermodynamic Properties of Adsorbed Isotopic Hydrogens

The available experimental data consists essentially of heats of adsorption, ΔH, and separation factors, S, for an adsorbed phase—gas phase equilibria. For a gaseous mixture of two isotopic species, i and j, in equilibrium with an adsorbed phase, the separation factor, S_{ij}, is defined as follows

$$S_{ij} = \frac{(X_i/X_j)_a}{(X_i/X_j)_g} \qquad (18)$$

where the subscripts a and g of the mole fraction ratios, X_i/X_j, refer to the adsorbed phase and gas phase respectively.

Both ΔH, and S can be expressed in terms of the partition functions of the adsorbed and gas phases, the energy levels for the adsorbed phase being the eigenvalue of Equation 4 for the model described above. Just as in the adsorbed phase the molecules in the gas phase are assumed to be non-interacting. It is convenient in comparing the thermodynamic properties of isotopes to compute the partition functions using as the zero of energy the lowest energy state. This has been chosen as the Σ_g^+ ($l = 0$ $m = 0$) state of para-hydrogen and is designated as E_o. Since the thermodynamic properties of interest are associated with gas phase-adsorbed phase equilibria, the electronic and internal vibrational contributions to the molecular partition function have been neglected. The assumption here is that the surface does not perturb these degrees of freedom. For an i-th isotope of mass M_i, adsorbed on a surface of area A and nuclear spin degeneracy g_n, the partition function Q_i^a is

$$Q_i^a = g_n (2\pi M_i kT/h^2) A q_i^a \exp(-E_o/kT) \qquad (19)$$

$$q_i^a = \sum_j g_j \exp\left[-(E_i^j - E_o)/kT\right] \qquad (20)$$

where g_j is the degeneracy of the jth rotation-vibration level. The average energy per molecule of the adsorbed phase is

$$\bar{E}_i^a = (U_i^a/q_i^a) + E_o + kT \qquad (21)$$

where

$$U_i^a = \sum_j g_j (E_i^j - E_o) \exp -\frac{(E_i^j - E_o)}{kT}. \qquad (22)$$

For the gas of volume V, the partition function of the i-th isotope is

$$Q_i{}^g = g_n (2\pi M_i T / h^2)^{3/2} V q_i{}^g \tag{23}$$

$$q_i{}^g = \sum_j (2J + 1) \exp \left[\frac{-J(J + 1) h^2}{8\pi^2 I_i kT} \right] \tag{24}$$

where I_i is the moment of inertia. The average energy per gaseous molecule is, therefore

$$\overline{E_i}{}^g = (U_i{}^g / q_i{}^g) + \frac{3}{2} kT \tag{25}$$

where

$$U_i{}^g = \sum_j (2J + 1) \frac{J(J + 1) h^2}{8\pi^2 I_i} \exp \left[\frac{-J(J + 1) h^2}{8\pi^2 I_i kT} \right]. \tag{26}$$

The energy of adsorption per molecule is

$$\Delta E_i = \overline{E_i}{}^a - \overline{E_i}{}^g = (U_i{}^a / q_i{}^a) - (U_i{}^g / q_i{}^g) + E_o - \tfrac{1}{2} kT \tag{27}$$

and the heat of adsorption at constant pressure is

$$\Delta H_i = \Delta E_i + kT. \tag{28}$$

For a gaseous mixture of two isotopic species, 1 and 2, in equilibrium with an adsorbent, the separation factor is simply the ratio of partition functions

$$S_{2,1} = \frac{Q_2{}^a / Q_1{}^a}{Q_2{}^g / Q_1{}^g} = \left(\frac{M_1}{M_2} \right)^{1/2} \frac{q_2{}^a / q_1{}^a}{q_2{}^g / q_1{}^g} \tag{29}$$

where M_1 and M_2 are the molecular weights. For an equilibrium involving only ortho-para species, $M_1 = M_2$ and the separation factor becomes simply the ratio of the rotational-vibrational partition functions of the adsorbed phase to the rotational partition functions of the gas phase.

Typical curves illustrating the magnitudes and variation with temperature of the separation factors and heats of adsorption for all the isotopic species and nuclear spin isomers of the molecular hydrogens are shown in Figures 3 and 4. The separation factors are all relative to para-hydrogen. It should be noted that the calculation of these, as well as any other thermodynamic properties, involves only two arbitrary parameters, namely y and D. These are the parameters which determine the form of the potential energy of interaction Equation 8 and the values chosen for the illustrations are typical of physical adsorption on a variety of common adsorbents. Changing y and D does not change the general form of the temperature dependence shown in Figures 3 and 4, nor the relative magnitudes of the separation factors and heats of adsorption for the different hydrogen species at any given temperature. Increasing D, which increases the depth of the potential well, increases both the magnitude of the separation factors for all species and their heats of adsorption. In addition, the rate of increase of the separation factor with decreasing temperature is increased. The influence of y on the thermodynamic properties is more subtle. Increasing y for a given D tends to push all of the rotational-vibrational levels toward the dissociation limit thus decreasing the heats of adsorption. The relative separations of the levels for a particular isotope are, however, also affected; tending to increase, thus, in general, increasing the magnitudes of the separation factors.

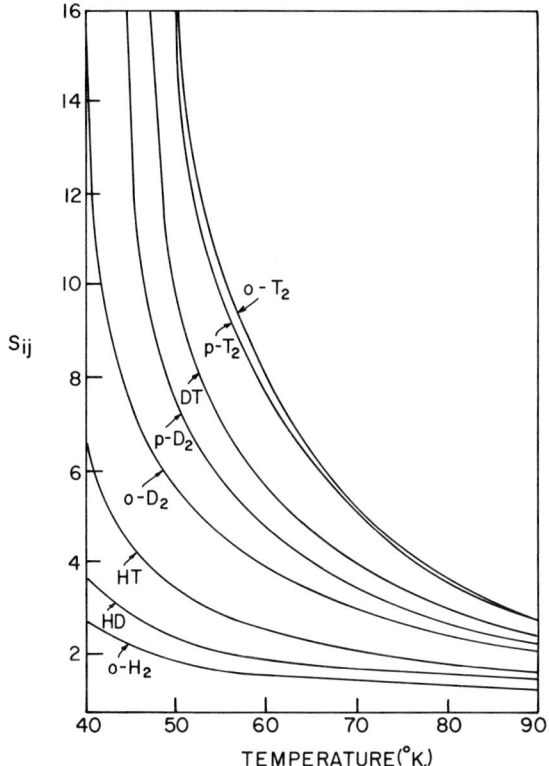

Figure 3. Separation factors (relative to parahydrogen) of all the isotopic hydrogens as a function of temperature. Potential parameters y = 1.8, D = 2.4 kcal. mole⁻¹

Unfortunately, the potential parameters y and D cannot be established with any degree of certainty solely on the basis of theoretical considerations. The existing information on molecule-surface interactions is sparse and furthermore, because of the complex nature of a surface, it is difficult to generalize. In principle, however, these parameters can be established from experimental measurements on a series of isotopic species. Given the heat of adsorption of a single isotope and either one ortho-para or isotope separation factor, the magnitude of y and D for the adsorption of all the isotopic and nuclear spin species can be specified. A test of the theory, in particular the model for the adsorbed phase, can then be made by comparison of other measured separation factors and heats of adsorption with those calculated from the theory.

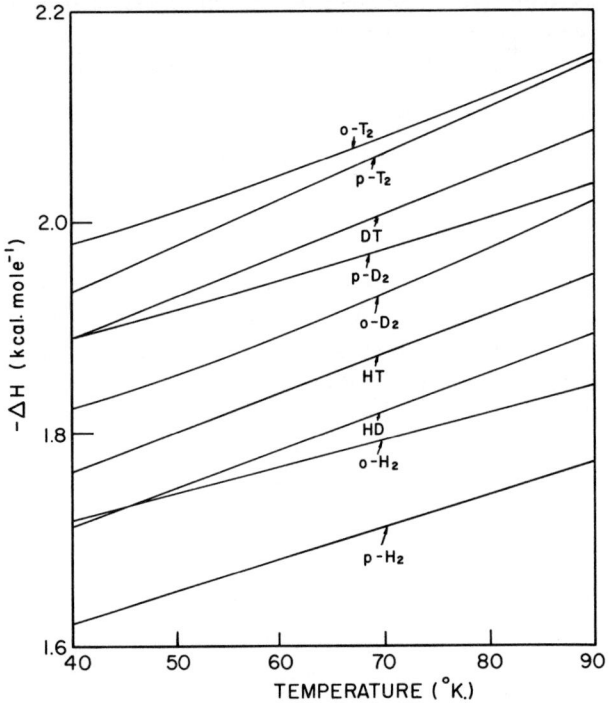

Figure 4.   Heats of adsorption of all the isotopic hydro- gens as a function of temperature. Potential parameters
$$y = 1.8, \ D = 2.4 \ kcal. \ mole^{-1}$$

Comparison of Theory with Experiment

In this section the discussion will be confined to the examination of the behavior of isotopic molecular hydrogens adsorbed on solid surfaces at low temperatures. A considerable amount of experimental data is available for these isotopes and furthermore, the approximations employed in the model and the calculation of the thermodynamic properties of the adsorbed phase from the lowest lying energy states are more applicable to this system than to diatomic molecules of larger mass and smaller rotational constants.

There are several interesting predictions of the theory which are illustrated in Figure 3. For a given surface (y and D fixed), and at a fixed temperature (at least in the range 20° to 90°K. where calculations have been performed (16, 22)) the calculated separation factors, relative to para-hydrogen exhibit the following trend

$$S_{o\text{-}H_2} < S_{HD} < S_{HT} < S_{o\text{-}D_2} < S_{p\text{-}D_2} < S_{DT} < S_{p\text{-}T_2} < S_{o\text{-}T_2}.$$

Thus, if an equimolar gaseous mixture of all the molecular hydrogen species is equilibrated with a solid adsorbent, the mole-fractions of the various species, X_i, adsorbed on the surface would in decreasing order be

$$X_{o\text{-}T_2} > X_{p\text{-}T_2} > X_{DT} > X_{p\text{-}D_2} > X_{o\text{-}D_2} > X_{HT} > X_{HD} > X_{o\text{-}H_2} > X_{p\text{-}H_2}.$$

As expected, the highest surface concentration is for the heaviest isotope, the concentration decreasing with decreasing mass. This is primarily a consequence of the change in zero point energy associated with the center of mass vibration relative to the surface. The effect of constraining the angular motions on the surface, the magnitude of the rotational barrier depending on the rotational constant of the molecule and the position of the center of gravity along the internuclear axis, can most readily be seen by comparing the relative concentrations on the surface of molecular species of the same mass. Two generalizations are possible:

(1) For a given isotope, the nuclear spin isomer (ortho-para species) consisting of rotationally excited molecules—*i.e.*, primarily $J = 1$ at low temperature—is always preferentially adsorbed on the surface. Thus, $X_{o\text{-}H_2} > X_{p\text{-}H_2}$, $X_{p\text{-}D_2} > X_{o\text{-}D_2}$, and $X_{o\text{-}T_2} > X_{p\text{-}T_2}$.

(2) A homonuclear species (D_2) is more strongly bound to the surface than the heteronuclear of the same mass (HT). Thus, X_{D_2} (ortho or para) $> X_{HT}$.

There is an interesting consequence of (1) in the separation of two or more isotopic homonuclear hydrogens by preferential adsorption—*e.g.*, H_2 and D_2. Since the equilibrium concentration of ortho-hydrogen and para-deuterium in the adsorbed phase is always greater than para-hydrogen and ortho-deuterium respectively, it is evident that the magnitude of the isotope separation factor S_{D_2,H_2}, which includes both ortho and para species, will be influenced by the ortho-para concentration of the gaseous mixture. It can readily be shown that if a surface is equilibrated with a hydrogen-deuterium gaseous mixture where the ratio of the ortho-para concentrations are given by $X_{o\text{-}H_2}/X_{p\text{-}H_2}$ and $X_{p\text{-}D_2}/X_{o\text{-}D_2}$ for hydrogen and deuterium respectively, then the isotope separation faction S_{D_2,H_2} defined as

$$S_{D2,H2} = \cfrac{\cfrac{Xa_{o-D_2} + Xa_{p-D_2}}{Xa_{o-H_2} + Xa_{p-H_2}}}{\cfrac{Xg_{o-D_2} + Xg_{p-D_2}}{Xg_{o-H_2} + Xg_{p-H_2}}} \qquad (30)$$

is given by the expression

$$S_{D2,H2} = S_{o-D_2,p-H_2} \left\{ \cfrac{\left(\cfrac{X_{o-H_2}}{X_{p-H_2}} + 1\right)\left(S_{p-D_2,\,o-D_2}\cfrac{X_{p-D_2}}{X_{o-D_2}} + 1\right)}{\left(S_{o-H_2,p-H_2}\cfrac{X_{o-H_2}}{X_{p-H_2}} + 1\right)\left(\cfrac{X_{p-D_2}}{X_{o-D_2}} + 1\right)} \right\} \qquad (31)$$

For a fixed temperature $S_{o-D_2,p-H_2}$ and the ortho-para separation factors $S_{p-D_2,o-D_2}$, $S_{o-H_2,p-H_2}$ are given by Equation 29 and are constants for a given surface. The dependence of the isotope separation factor on the gas phase ortho-para concentrations is shown in Figure 5. The maximum isotope separation factor is obtained when para-hydrogen is separated from para-deuterium. The minimum is obtained when ortho-hydrogen is separated from ortho-deuterium.

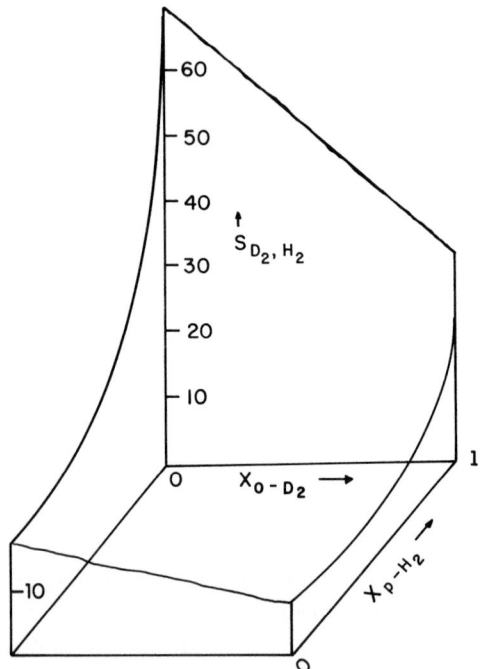

Figure 5.   The variation of $S_{D2,H2}$ with ortho-para composition at 27°K. Potential parameters $y = 1.8$, $D = 2.4$ kcal. mole^{-1}

The chromatographic separations of isotopic hydrogens have indeed verified all of the above mentioned predictions of the theory. The measured retention times, t_i, or net retention volumes V_{Ri} give directly the separation factors

$$S_{ij} = \frac{t_i}{t_j} = \frac{V_{Ri}}{V_{Rj}}. \tag{32}$$

For the isotopic hydrogens t_i or V_{Ri} exhibit the following trend,

$$p - H_2 < o - H_2 < HD < HT < o - D_2 < p - D_2 < DT < T_2$$

the same trend given by the theory for the separation factors relative to p-H_2. Furthermore, with decreasing temperature there is an increase in both the retention times and volumes.

A quantitative comparison between theory and the results of four different experimental investigations is given in Tables I through IV. The chromatographic columns used in these investigations were as follows:

Table I—experimental data of Moore and Ward (19), alumina packed column.

Table II—experimental data of Carter and Smith (2), alumina packed column.

Table III—experimental data of Mohnke and Saffert (17), leached glass capillary column.

Table IV—experimental data of Haubach, Knobler, Katorski, and White (12), alumina column on which xenon was pre-adsorbed.

As previously mentioned, two parameters, y and D, need to be fixed in order to make a comparison with experiment. In Tables I and II it can be seen that the three different sets of y and D are equally acceptable potential parameters. Although the overall agreement is no better than a few percent, it should be pointed out that the uncertainty in the experimental data is of the same order of magnitude. It is clear, however, that the sensitivity of the separation factors and heats of adsorption to rather large changes of the parameters of the potential function is not very great—certainly not at temperatures in the vicinity of the boiling point of liquid nitrogen where the data given in Tables I, II, and III were obtained. In Table III, the comparison between theory and experiment is given for a particular value of y and D. Like the results in Tables I and II, there are other choices of the parameters which give nearly the same agreement between theory and experiment.

In Table IV, separation factors for several of the isotopic hydrogens at considerably lower temperatures are given. The values of y and D in this Table were chosen to fit the experimental ortho-para separation factor of hydrogen at the lowest temperature, $27°K$. Even though fair agreement between theory and experiment is obtained for all of the

Table I. Comparison of Experimental[a] Heats of Adsorption and

		ΔH_{p-H_2} (kcal. mole^{-1})	ΔH_{0-H_2} (kcal. mole^{-1})
Experimental Results		1.40	1.55
Calculated Values for following potential parameters			
y	D (kcal. mole^{-1})		
1.80	2.00	1.44	1.50
2.10	2.10	1.36	1.45
2.40	2.40	1.42	1.53

[a] Experimental data of Moore and Ward, Reference 19.

Table II. Comparison of Experimental[a] Separation Factors of

		S_{0-H_2}	S_{HD}	S_{0-D_2}	S_{p-D_2}
Experimental Results		1.37	—	2.25	—
Calculated Values for following potential parameters					
y	D (kcal. mole^{-1})				
1.80	2.40	1.36	1.64	2.59	2.88
2.10	2.00	1.38	1.67	2.61	2.94
2.40	1.70	1.37	1.66	2.51	2.90

[a] Experimental data of Carter and Smith, Reference 2.

separation factors, irrespective of the choice of y and D, this is not the case for the heat of adsorption. This latter quantity limits the choice of the potential parameters to a rather narrow range in the vicinity of $y = 2$ and $D = 2$. The advantage of low temperature chromatographic data in establishing the parameters of the surface potential is clear. On the other hand, the low temperature data also points to a deficiency in the model chosen for the adsorbed layer. It should be noted that in Table IV, the separation factors were given at a specific sample volume equal to 0.04 cc. The reason for this is that both the separation factors and heats of adsorption are strongly dependent on surface coverage, as illustrated in Figures 6 and 7. This dependency, to a large extent, can be attributed to surface heterogeneity. The purpose of the preadsorbed xenon was to smooth out the heterogeneity (11). The isoteric heats of adsorption, Figure 7, show

Ortho-Para Separation Factor of Hydrogen at 77.4°K. with Theory

ΔH_{HD} (kcal. mole⁻¹)	ΔH_{o-D_2} (kcal. mole⁻¹)	ΔH_{p-D_2} (kcal. mole⁻¹)	$S_{o-H_2, p-H_2}$
1.51	1.58	1.65	1.34
1.53	1.64	1.66	1.30
1.49	1.60	1.64	1.40
1.68	1.72	1.77	1.53

Various Isotopic Hydrogens (relative to p-H$_2$) at 77.4°K. with Theory

S_{HT}	S_{DT}	S_{p-T_2}	S_{o-T_2}	ΔH_{p-H_2} (kcal. mole⁻¹)	ΔH_{o-D_2} (kcal. mole⁻¹)
2.01	3.30	3.86	—	—	—
1.90	3.24	3.90	3.98	1.73	1.99
1.97	3.29	4.05	4.15	1.30	1.53
1.97	3.19	3.89	4.09	0.98	1.20

that this was accomplished at high surface coverage but certainly not at the low coverage where the chromatographic experiments were performed.

Undoubtedly, surface heterogeneity was a factor in all of the experiments discussed above. However, it is only at low temperatures, where the Boltzmann factors determining the distribution of particles among the regions of different surface activity show large selectivity, that this effect becomes observable. It is, however, encouraging that in spite of the surface heterogeneity there is a choice of parameters y and D which gives a good agreement between theory and experiment (Table IV). These parameters must now represent some average for the surface coverages used in the chromatographic experiments. It should be mentioned that the retention time and heats of adsorption for different sample vol-

Table III. Comparison of Experimental[a] Separation Factors of as a Function of

	Temp. (°K.)	S_{o-H_2}	S_{HD}	S_{o-D_2}	S_{p-D_2}
Experimental	77.6	1.39	1.51	2.04	2.23
Calculated y = 2.40 D = 2.40 kcal. mole^{-1}		1.31	1.64	2.12	2.41
Experimental	70.2	1.52	1.64	2.33	2.68
Calculated y = 2.40 D = 2.40 kcal. mole^{-1}		1.37	1.61	2.41	2.80
Experimental	67.8	1.40	1.51	2.36	2.88
Calculated y = 2.40 D = 2.40 kcal. mole^{-1}		1.39	1.65	2.53	2.96

[a] Experimental data of Mohnke and Saffert, Reference 17. [During the verification of the data in this paper an apparent error was found in Mohnke and Saffert's paper (17). If the respective retention times are correct, the α for o,p-H_2 at 67.8°K. should be 1.40 rather than 1.653. This error also appeared in Katorski and White's paper (16) and since the succeeding S values in that paper (16) were computed from the α for o,p-H_2, all values for S at 67.8°K. in Table IV of Reference 16 are incorrect. The correct values appear in Table III of the current paper.]

Table IV. Comparison of Experimental[a] Separation Factors of Various

Potential Parameters for Calculated Values		Temperature = 27°K. Sample Volume = 0.04cc.		
y	D (kcal. mole^{-1})	S_{o-H_2}	S_{o-D_2}	$S_{p-D_2,o-D_2}$
Experimental		4.6	38.6	2.1
Calculated				
1.50	3.28	4.6	37.8	2.3
1.80	2.56	4.6	36.8	2.4
2.10	2.14	4.6	39.0	2.4
2.40	1.87	4.6	44.0	2.5
2.70	1.74	4.6	43.0	2.5

[a] Experimental data of Haubach, Knobler, Katorski and White, Reference 12.
[b] Represents the differential heat of adsorption of equilibrium H_2 at surface coverage

umes (Figures 6 and 7) can be accounted for, provided the parameters of the potential function are assumed to depend on the surface coverage. A more detailed examination of the effect of surface heterogeneity is discussed in the next section.

There have been several other comprehensive investigations of the separation of the isotopic hydrogens by preferential adsorption—Refer-

Hydrogen Isotopes (relative to p-H$_2$) and Heats of Adsorption Temperature with Theory

ΔH_{p-H_2} (kcal. mole^{-1})	ΔH_{o-H_2} (kcal. mole^{-1})	ΔH_{HD} (kcal. mole^{-1})	ΔH_{o-D_2} (kcal. mole^{-1})	ΔH_{p-D_2} (kcal. mole^{-1})
—	—	—	—	—
0.85	0.91	0.94	1.04	1.08
0.77[b]	0.93[b]	0.92[b]	1.00[b]	1.09[b]
0.84	0.90	0.93	1.03	1.06
—	—	—	—	—
0.84	0.90	0.94	1.04	1.07

[b] The experimental heats of adsorption represent averages over the temperature range 67.8° to 77.6°K.

Isotopic Hydrogens (relative to p-H$_2$) at 27° and 55°K. with Theory

Temperature $= 55°K.$
Sample Volume $= 0.04cc.$

S_{o-H_2}	S_{HT}	S_{o-D_2}	ΔH_{p-H_2} at 65°K. (kcal. mole^{-1})
1.9	2.8	5.9	1.35[b]
1.8	3.0	4.9	2.53
1.8	3.1	5.0	1.77
1.8	3.4	5.2	1.31
1.8	3.6	5.4	1.04
1.9	3.7	5.4	0.83

corresponding to approximately 0.04 cc. sample volume averaged over the temperature range 50° to 80°K.

ences 3 and 9. These have been at higher temperatures and therefore are not included in the comparison of theory with experiment, since the calculation of the partition function for the adsorbed phase requires the inclusion of a large number of excited rotational-vibrational states. It is, however, interesting to note that the trend of the separation factors, well above the boiling point of liquid nitrogen, is the same as in the low temperature experiments.

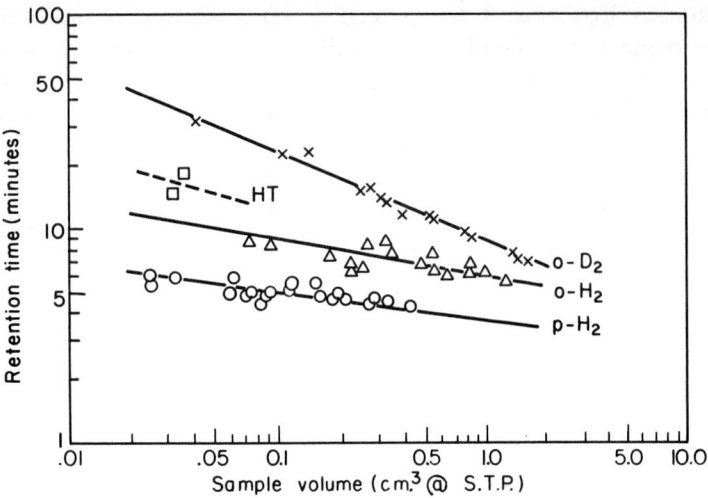

Figure 6. Chromatographic retention times for several isotopic hydrogens as a function of sample volume. T = 55°K. and column packed with γ-alumina on which 3/8 monolayer of xenon adsorbed

Surface Heterogeneity

A heterogeneous surface implies the existence of a barrier to center of mass and angular motions, of an adsorbed diatomic molecule, in the plane of the surface. It is, however, still possible to discuss this situation in terms of the proposed model for the adsorbed layer, provided certain simplifying approximations are made. Let us assume that the heterogeneous surface consists of a large number of planar regions, each of dimensions much larger than the size of the adsorbed molecule but differing in surface-molecule binding energy. If the potential of interaction is represented by the Morse type function, Equation 8, then the parameters of these interactions differ in each of the surface regions. The model is, therefore, one in which the molecules confined to a given surface area move essentially freely in the plane of the surface but the vibrational frequencies normal to the surface and the magnitude of the rotational perturbations are determined by their location on the surface.

The simplest case to consider is one in which the adsorption is confined to a monolayer and where the intermolecular (molecule-molecule) interactions are assumed to be very small compared with the molecule-surface interactions. The properties of an adsorbed monolayer can then be determined from the distribution function giving the number of surface regions of a given binding energy as a function of binding energy and the energy levels of the adsorbed molecule calculated from the

Hamiltonian Equation 4 for potentials characteristic of each of the surface regions. For simplicity we will assume the parameter, y, of the potential energy Equation 8 is the same in each surface region but the parameter, D, giving the depth of the potential well varies. A minor modification of the theory of localized unimolecular adsorption by Hill (*14*) can then be used to calculate the distribution of ortho-para or isotopic species on a surface in equilibrium with a gaseous mixture of the same species.

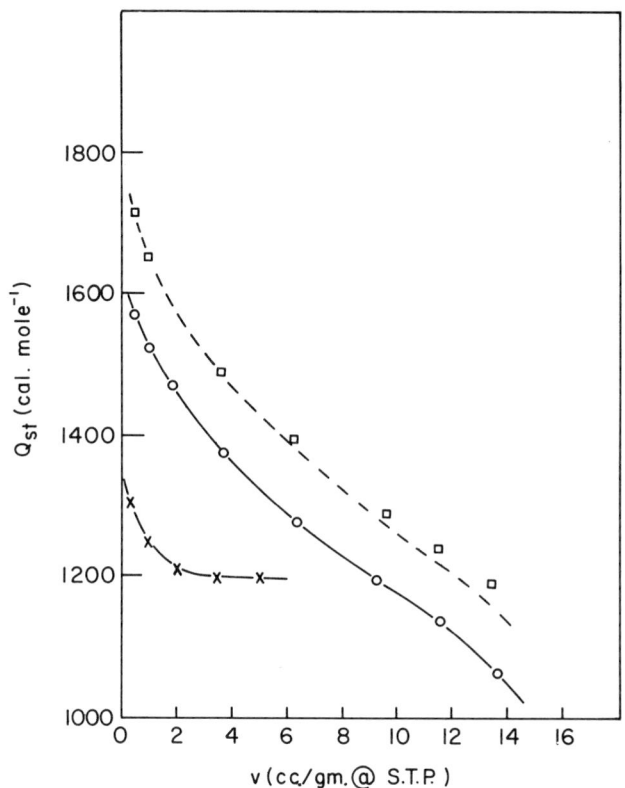

Figure 7. Isosteric heats of adsorption as a function of surface coverage

--- ☐ --- *equilibrium D_2 adsorbed on γ-alumina, broken line is calculated curve from H_2 data*
⊙ *equilibrium H_2 adsorbed on γ-alumina*
X *equilibrium H_2 adsorbed on γ-alumina plus 3/8 monolayer of xenon*

Let $\sigma_i{}^1$, $\sigma_i{}^2$ be the fraction of the ith surface region occupied by molecular species 1 and 2 respectively at equilibrium. This region is characterized by a particular surface-molecule interaction—*i.e.*, a fixed D in Equation 8. Then for every different region of the surface it can be shown that in the limit of complete surface coverage (monolayer)

$$\frac{\sigma_i^1/P_1}{\sigma_i^2/P_2} = \frac{Q^a{}_{i1}/Q^a{}_{i2}}{Q_1{}^g/Q_2{}^g} \tag{33}$$

which is just the separation factor, $S_{1,2}(D_i)$ of the ith region of the surface. P_1 and P_2 are the partial pressures of species 1 and 2 respectively in equilibrium with the adsorbed phase. The separation factor for the entire monolayer, $\overline{S}_{1,2}$ expressed in terms of the separation factors for each of the different surface regions is

$$\overline{S}_{1,2} = \frac{(\overline{X_1/X_2})_a}{(\overline{X_1/X_2})_g} = \frac{\displaystyle\int_{D_{min}}^{D_{max}} \frac{S_{1,2}(D_i)f(D_i)\,dD_i}{1 + (X_1/X_2)_g S_{1,2}(D_i)}}{\displaystyle\int_{D_{min}}^{D_{max}} \frac{f(D_i)\,dD_i}{1 + (X_1/X_2)_g S_{1,2}(D_i)}} \tag{34}$$

$(\overline{X_1/X_2})_a$ is the mole fraction ratio of species 1 and 2 for the entire monolayer and $f(D_i)$ a continuous distribution such that $f(D_i)dD_i$ gives the number of surface regions having a potential minimum for the surface-molecule interaction in the range $D_i \to D_i + dD_i$. In the limit when

$(X_1/X_2)_g \to 0$

$$\overline{S}_{1,2} = \int_{D_{min}}^{D_{max}} S_{1,2}(D_i)f(D_i)\,dD_i \tag{35}$$

and as $(X_1/X_2)_g \to \infty$

$$\frac{1}{\overline{S}_{1,2}} = \int_{D_{min}}^{D_{max}} \frac{1}{S_{1,2}(D_i)} f(D_i)\,dD_i. \tag{36}$$

The calculation of the monolayer separation factor from Equation 34 depends on a knowledge of the $S_{1,2}(D_i)$'s, which are given in the previous section, and the distribution function $f(D_i)$ characteristic of the adsorbent. The latter can be obtained from experimental isosteric heats of adsorption. A comparison between experimental and calculated monolayer separation factors for hydrogens adsorbed on γ-alumina is presented below.

The isosteric heats of adsorption, Q_{st}, of equilibrium hydrogen adsorbed on γ-alumina as a function of surface coverage are shown in Figure 7. These were determined from vapor pressure measurements in the temperature range 50° to 80°K. using a calorimeter described by Johnston and Kerr (*15*). The γ-alumina used in these experiments was the 20 Cr Al sample described in References 4 and 5. It was impregnated with 1.1×10^{-4} moles of Cr_2O_3 to give rapid ortho-para equilibration;

however, its isothermal behavior at 20.4°K. (volume per gram adsorbed as a function of pressure) was within experimental error identical with the unimpregnated material (4, 5). The difference in energy between the gas and the adsorbed phase at the absolute zero $(E^g - E^a)_0$ as a function of the moles adsorbed on the surface N_s is obtained from the isosteric heats using the expression

$$(E^g - E^a)_0 = \frac{1}{N_s}\int_0^{N_s} Q_{st}C_{ns} - \frac{1}{Ns}\int_0^{N_s}\left[\int_0^T C_p{}^g dT\right] dN_s$$

$$+ \frac{1}{N_s}\int_0^{N_s}\int_0^T \frac{dC_{ns}}{dN_s} dTdN_s \tag{37}$$

where C_{ns} is the heat capacity of N_s moles of adsorbate and $C_p{}^g$ the heat capacity of the gaseous adsorbate. Assuming that the variation of $(E^g - E^a)_0$ with surface coverage is caused by a distribution of surface-molecule binding energies, the distribution function is then given by $dN_s/d(E^g - E^a)_0$ (6).

The normalized distribution function for para-H_2 (eqm. $- H_2$ at $T = 0$) is shown in Figure 8. The heat capacities, C_{ns}, used in the calculation were measured in the same calorimeter employed for the isosteric heat experiments (20). The distribution function, Figure 8, can now be transformed into the function $f(D_i)$ using the tables in References 15 and 21. These tables give the ground state energy of adsorbed para-H_2 as a function of D for various values of y.

The apparatus used to determine separation factors for an adsorbed monolayer was similar to that used by Cunningham, Chapin, and Johnston (4, 5) but was modified to minimize the dead space and ensure good thermal equilibrium between the feed gas and the adsorbent. The inner copper cylindrical chamber was filled with 67 grams of the same γ-alumina used in the isosteric heat of adsorption experiments for the establishment of the distribution function. The γ-alumina was, however, free of any paramagnetic material to permit ortho-para separation factor measurements.

The separation experiments at 20.4°K. were performed as follows. With the γ-alumina in thermal contact with the liquid hydrogen, feed gas of known composition was passed through the adsorbent until equilibrium was established—i.e., the composition of the feed gas was identical to that of the effluent. The pressure of the feed gas during the equilibration process was maintained constant at a value of P/P_0, of approximately 0.06, where P_0 is the saturation pressure of the mixture. This is the ratio which gives a monolayer as determined from a B.E.T. plot of the isotherm (*see* References 4 and 5). The adsorbed monolayer was then removed by thermally isolating and heating the adsorbent. Samples of the desorbed isotopic or ortho-para mixture were then analyzed mass spectrometrically or by the micro thermal conductivity method described by Grilley (*10*). The experimental results of three different separation experiments at 20.4°K. are shown in Figures 9, 10, and 11. The composition of the desorbed monolayer is given as a function of the fraction of the surface stripped. The rate of desorption changes the form of the composition dependence on fraction of surface stripped (Figures 9 and 10). The areas under the curves corresponding to different rates of desorption, which gives the overall composition of the monolayer are, however, rate independent. Figure 11 clearly illustrates the effect of ortho-para composition on isotopic separations. This was discussed in the previous section and the present results are in accord with the predictions of the theory (*see* Figure 5). The experimental factors for the monolayer at 20.4°K., calculated from the ratios of the mole fractions in the adsorbed and gas phases are summarized in Table V.

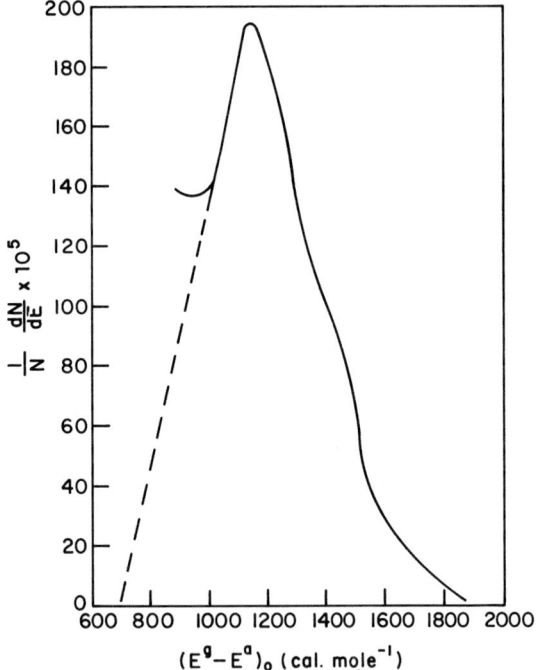

Figure 8.   The distribution of the energy of adsorption of para-hydrogen on γ-alumina

A comparison between theory and experiment is also shown in Table V. The distribution function $f(D_i)$ was determined from the

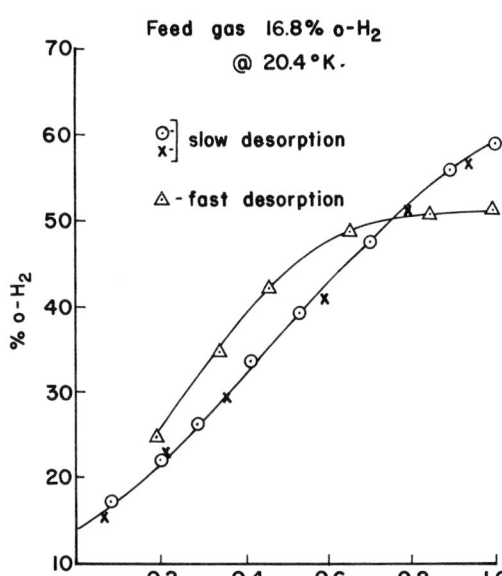

Figure 9. Percentage ortho-hydrogen as a function of fraction of surface stripped for two rates of desorption

distribution of the binding energy of para-H_2 on the surface (Figure 8) on the assumption that the parameter y of the potential function (Equation 8), was constant over the entire surface and equal to 1.40. The value of 1.40 was chosen to fit the experimental ortho-para separation factor of hydrogen (Table V). The agreement between theory and experiment for the remainder of the separation factors given in Table V is fairly good. The large differences in separation factors between the two isotopic mixtures of different ortho-para composition, predicted by the theory, is borne out in the experiments. The experimental difference is, however, not as large as the calculated one.

The choice of the potential parameter $y = 1.40$ and the resulting distribution function $f(D_i)$ permits a calculation of the distribution of binding energies on the surface of any isotopic molecular hydrogen in its ground state (rotational-center of mass vibrational). This has been done in the case of deuterium and the results used to calculate the isosteric heat of absorption of equilibrium-D_2 on γ-alumina (Equation 37). A comparison of the calculated and measured isosteric heats is shown in Figure 7. The agreement is quite good at low surface coverages but shows appreciable deviations at higher coverages.

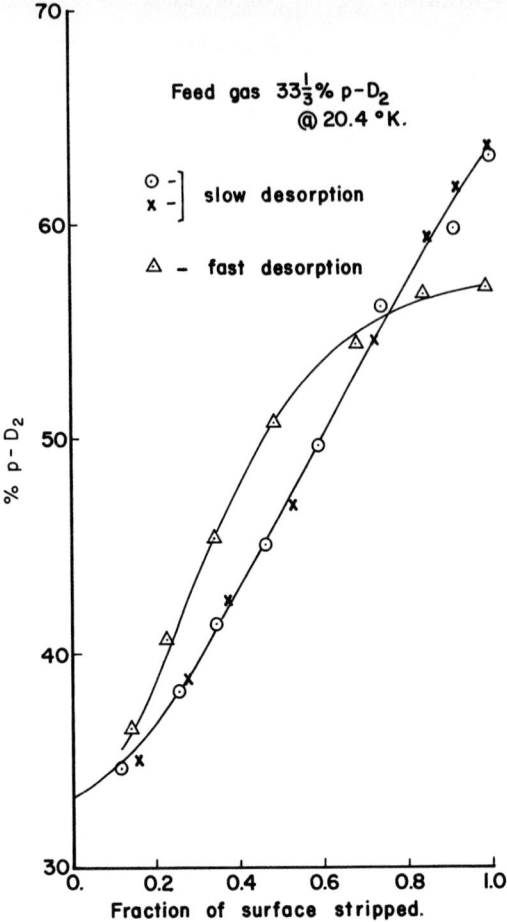

Figure 10. Percentage of para-deuterium as a function of fraction of surface stripped for two rates of desorption

Although the above model for adsorption on a heterogeneous surface gives fairly good agreement with the experimental separation factors involving two or more isotopic or nuclear spin species, it is far from adequate in describing the thermodynamic properties of a single component adsorbed on the surface. For example, it is difficult to quantitatively account for the isothermal behavior of adsorbed hydrogen (isotherm References 4 and 5) or deuterium (Reference 20) as well as the measured heat capacities as a function of surface coverage (Reference 20). Perhaps one reason for the good agreement with the experimental separation factors is the fact that this quantity involves a ratio of partition functions of two adsorbed species which results in a partial cancellation of error.

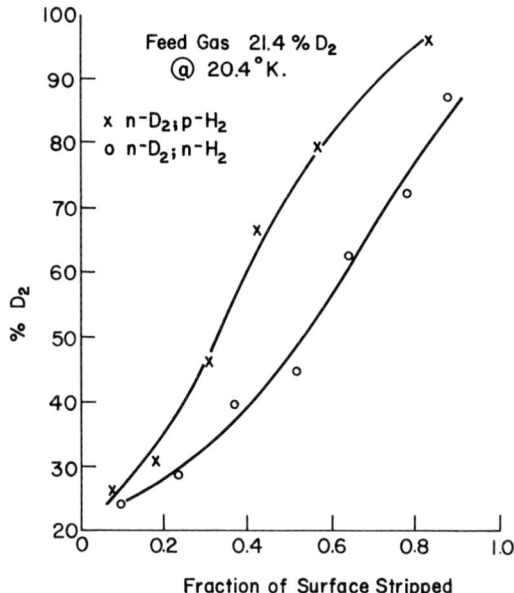

Figure 11.   *Percentage of deuterium as a function of fraction of surface stripped*
Upper curve, separation of normal-D_2 from para-H_2.
Lower curve, separation of normal D_2 from normal H_2

Table V.   Monolayer Separation Factors at 20.4°K. Comparison of Theory with Experiment

Species Separated		Mole Fraction Vapor Phase[b]	Experimental Separation Factor	Calculated Separation Factor[a]
(1)	(2)	X_1	$S_{1,2}$	$S_{1,2}$
ortho-H_2	para-H_2	0.168	3.0	3.0[a]
para-D_2	ortho-D_2	0.333	1.9	1.8
normal-D_2	para-H_2	0.214	7.1	10.2
normal-D_2	normal-H_2	0.214	3.6	4.1

[a] Calculated from the distribution function Figure 8 assuming potential parameter $y = 1.40$. The value of y was chosen to fit the experimental ortho-para separation factor of hydrogen.
[b] Feed gas composition.

There are certain obvious improvements that can be introduced in the model. The isothermal behavior (References 4 and 5) shows clearly that restriction to monolayer adsorption is not realistic. Furthermore, the potential of interaction does not include: molecule-molecule interactions;

a barrier to rotation in the ϕ direction which would certainly be characteristic of any surface consisting of a periodic lattice; constraints to translation motions in the x-y plane; a difference in the parallel and perpendicular polarizability of the adsorbed diatomic molecule; etc. Until more direct information is available on the nature of the surface-molecule interactions, it does not seem worthwhile to extend the present, relatively simple calculations, to more complex models.

Literature Cited

(1) Babloyantz, A., *Mol. Phys.* **2**, 39 (1959).
(2) Carter, E. H., Jr., Smith, H. A., *J. Phys. Chem.* **67**, 1512 (1963).
(3) Conti, M. L., Lesimple, M., *J. Chromatography* **29**, 32 (1967).
(4) Cunningham, C. M., Johnston, H. L., *J. Am. Chem. Soc.* **80**, 2377 (1958).
(5) Cunningham, C. M., Chapin, D., Johnston, H. L., *J. Am. Chem. Soc.* **80**, 2382 (1958).
(6) Drain, L. E., Morrison, J. A., *Trans. Faraday Soc.* **48**, 316 (1952).
(7) Evett, E., *J. Chem. Phys.* **31**, 565 (1959).
(8) Friedman, H., *Advan. Chem. Phys.* **4**, 225 (1962).
(9) Gant, P. L., *Trans. Am. Nucl. Soc.* **7**, 335 (1964).
(10) Grilley, E. R., *Rev. Sci. Instr.* **24**, 72 (1953).
(11) Halsey, G. D., Jr., *J. Chem. Phys.* **22**, 979 (1954).
(12) Haubach, W. J., Knobler, C. M., Katorski, A., White, David, *J. Phys. Chem.* **71**, 1398 (1967).
(13) Hill, T. L., *J. Chem. Phys.* **16**, 181 (1948).
(14) *Ibid.*, **17**, 762 (1949).
(15) Johnston, H. L., Kerr, E. C., *J. Am. Chem. Soc.* **72**, 4733 (1950).
(16) Katorski, A., White, David, *J. Phys. Chem.* **40**, 3183 (1964).
(17) Mohnke, M., Saffert, W., "Gas Chromatography," p. 216, M. vanSwaay, Ed., Butterworth's Scientific Publications, Ltd., London, 1962.
(18) Moore, W. R., Ward, H. R., *J. Am. Chem. Soc.* **80**, 2909 (1958).
(19) Moore, W. R., Ward, H. R., *J. Phys. Chem.* **64**, 832 (1960).
(20) Rhadakrishna, P., Cryogenic Laboratory, The Ohio State University (unpublished results).
(21) Sandler, Y. L., *J. Phys. Chem.* **58**, 58 (1954).
(22) White, David, Lassettre, E. N., *J. Chem. Phys.* **32**, 72 (1960).

RECEIVED March 7, 1968. This work was supported in part by the Chemistry Branch, Division of Research, U. S. Atomic Energy Commission, Washington, D. C.

Isotope Separation by Gas Chromatography

W. ALEXANDER VAN HOOK

University of Tennessee, Knoxville, Tenn.

Gas chromatographic techniques for separating isotopically substituted stable molecules are discussed as is the theory of the separations. The discussion focuses on both gas-liquid and gas-solid chromatographic separations of small hydrocarbons substituted with hydrogen and deuterium or tritium, but one $^{12}C-^{13}C$ separation is cited. The examples treated in detail are selected from the literature and/or from our laboratory. These include acetylene-deuteroacetylene(s), ethane-deuteroethane(s) and methane-deuteromethane(s). The available data from these systems agree with the predictions of the statistical theory of isotope effects in condensed phases. Other systems of interest are also mentioned.

Chromatographic separation of isotopically substituted isomers of simple molecules, like all chromatographic separations, is a relatively new technique. In fact, the first separation of a deuterated hydrocarbon from its protiated analog was reported only some ten years ago (40). Even so, most of the literature in the field dates from within the past five years (except for separations of the isotopic and spin isomers of hydrogen which are explicitly excluded from this report).

Chromatographic separations of the isotopic isomers of molecules are of interest first because they afford a convenient technique for analysis of mixtures, secondly because scale up in the future might afford economically feasible separations of macroscopic amounts of material, and finally because the values of the separation factors and their temperature coefficients are of intrinsic theoretical interest. This last follows because such data are straightforwardly related to the understanding of isotope effects on solution and adsorption processes and of the intermolecular forces which give rise to these effects. We have approached the general problem of chromatographic separations of isotopic isomers because of our interest in such solution and adsorption processes, and consequently our experimental program has been directed to the simple determination of the separation factors as a function of temperature rather than to the optimization of the chromatographic parameters such as resolution, analysis time, etc. In the present paper some of our results together with some results from the literature will be discussed in the light of the applicable theory.

Discussion

Condensed Phase Isotope Effects. The chromatographic results discussed later in the paper will be interpreted with the use of the statistical theory of isotope effects in condensed systems attributed to Bigeleisen (6). With the application of a cell model to the condensed phase and the assumption of harmonic frequencies for all $3N$ modes the theory leads to:

$$\ln\left(\frac{\gamma' P^{o'}}{\gamma P^o}\right) = \ln\left(\frac{P'}{P}\right) = \sum_{\substack{\text{internal} \\ \text{frequencies}}}^{3N-6} \times \ln\left\{\frac{(u/u')_c}{(u/u')_g}\frac{e^{(u'-u)_c/2}}{e^{(u'-u)_g/2}}\cdot\frac{(1-e^{-u_c'})/(1-e^{-u_c})}{(1-e^{-u_g'})/(1-e^{-u_g})}\right\}$$

$$+ \sum_{\substack{\text{external} \\ \text{frequencies}}}^{6} \ln\left\{\left(\frac{u}{u'}\right)(e^{(u'-u)/2})\frac{(1-e^{-u'})}{(1-e^{-u})}\right\} \tag{1}$$

$$+ \frac{1}{RT}(P'V' - PV) + \left\{\left(B_oP + \frac{1}{2}C_oP^2\right) - \left(B_oP + \frac{1}{2}C_oP^2\right)'\right\} - G(\sigma,\sigma')_g$$

Here c and g refer to condensed and gaseous phases, $u = h\nu/kT$, and the prime signifies the lighter isotope.

Equation 1 relates the force fields describing the motions of the molecule in the condensed and in the gaseous phase with the activity ratio. These fields are different owing to the effect of the intermolecular forces which are operative in the condensed phase. The intermolecular forces are exclusively "solute-solute" forces in the pure state (where the ratio P'/P reduces to $P^{o'}/P^o$, the vapor pressure isotope effect, $VPIE$), but in infinitely dilute solution they are exclusively "solvent-solute," and in the dilute surface-absorbed state they are exclusively "surface-adsorbate." The latter two cases are nicely approximated in gas-liquid and gas-solid chromatography respectively, and it thus follows that chromatographic studies can be directed to yield information on the connection between intermolecular forces and isotope effects.

Van Hook and Phillips (34) and Van Hook (37) have discussed the application of Equation 1 to gas-liquid and gas-solid chromatography respectively. First consider the corrective terms. The third term in Equation 1 corrects for the isotope effect on the partial molal volumes of the condensed phase. In the case of the two dimensional adsorbed film the term should be rewritten in terms of the surface tension and the molar coverage. In either event the correction is expected to be of the same order of magnitude as that for the pure liquids (where it reduces simply to the isotope effect on molar volumes). These corrections are negligibly small. They amount to only about 0.1% of the total isotope effect per D atom for representative hydrocarbons (35). Similarly, the fourth term which corrects for the isotope effect on the nonideality of the gas phase is readily shown to be negligibly small (31, 35) under normal chromatographic conditions.

The last corrective term is that for non-classical rotation in the gas phase. This correction is negligibly small for massive rotors but will amount to several percent of the effect for light molecules such as methane (10, 17, 18) and of course more for hydrogen (20, 22, 39). We are not concerned here with hydrogen, but it is clear that even for methane any complete theoretical analysis must include a consideration of this correction and take proper account of the relative amounts of ortho, meta, and para isomers in both the gaseous and condensed phases. Even so, some applications of the theory will be made in an effort to illuminate specific experimental results not of themselves sufficiently precise to demonstrate spin effects. One such example is the treatment of methane isotope effects cited later in this paper. Here, in view of the fact that no effects owing to spin isomerization were observed experimentally, such small corrections were ignored in both the gas and condensed phases. This should have the effect of slightly shifting the force constants used to describe the effective harmonic frequencies, but since the corrections are in any event small, it does not change the force of the arguments.

We are, then, led in the harmonic approximation under the assumption of a cell model and the neglect of gas phase nonclassical rotation, molar volume, and gas imperfection corrections to Equation 2. We choose to call this the "complete equation."

$$
\frac{\gamma' P'_{\,0}}{\gamma P_{\,0}} = \frac{P'}{P} = \prod_{\substack{\text{internals}}}^{3N-6} \times \left[\frac{(u/u')_c}{(u/u')_g}\right] \left[\frac{e^{(u'-u)_c/2}}{e^{(u'-u)_g/2}}\right] \left[\frac{(1-e^{-u_c'})/(1-e^{-u_c})}{(1-e^{-u_g'})/(1-e^{-u_g})}\right]
$$

$$
\times \prod_{\substack{\text{externals}}}^{6} \left[\frac{u}{u'}\right]_c \times \left[e^{(u'-u)_c/2}\right] \left[\frac{1-e^{-u_c'}}{1-e^{-u_c}}\right]
$$

(2)

If the $3N$ frequencies in Equation 2 can be factored into two distinct sets, this equation reduces to

$$\ln \frac{P'}{P} = \ln \frac{V}{V'} = \frac{A}{T^2} - \frac{B}{T} \tag{3}$$

where we have identified the ratio of thermodynamic activities P'/P with the ratio of corrected chromatographic retention times, V/V' (21). The A term is interpreted as a first order quantum correction for the low-lying modes $u \ll 2\pi$. It takes the form:

$$A = \frac{1}{24}\left(\frac{h}{k}\right)^2 \left\{ \sum_{u_a \leqslant 2\pi} (v'^2_{ac} - v^2_{ac}) \right\} \tag{4}$$

while the B term accounts for the contribution of the change in zero point energy of the higher $(u_b > 2\pi)$ frequencies on condensation.

$$B = \frac{h}{2k}\left\{ \sum_{u'_b > 2\pi} (v'_{bg} - v'_{bc}) - \sum_{u'_b > 2\pi} (v_{bg} - v_{bc}) \right\} \tag{5}$$

Here in Equations 4 and 5 we have particularized to the common case where the low-lying modes in the condensed phase are the six external motions, three hindered translations and three hindered rotations or librations. These are, of course, zero frequencies in the gas phase. The A term is thus attributed to the motion of the molecule as a whole and necessarily corresponds to a normal $(P_{(\text{light})} > P_{(\text{heavy})})$ isotope effect, but the B term arises from the shift in internal frequencies on condensation and depending on the details of the solute-solvent interaction can be either positive or negative in sign (normal or inverse). For hydrocarbons dissolved in nonpolar media there is a net red shift in the internal frequencies on condensation and the B contribution is larger than that from A over a broad temperature range. Accordingly inverse isotope effects (with concomitant maxima), deviations from the rule of the mean, and isotope effects between equivalent isomers are expected and observed. Examples will be pointed out later in the paper. From this point of view it becomes apparent that as one changes the environment of the condensed phase molecule by changing the solvent or substrate, marked differences in both the A and the B terms and hence in the isotopic separation factors are to be expected. In particular, for hydrocarbons one expects that as the polarity of the solvent is increased the magnitude of the inverse isotope effect should decrease because the hydrogenic motions of the solute molecule stiffen (blue shift) with respect to their values in nonpolar solvents. This is a consequence of the strong directed intermolecular forces in polar solvents. Examples of this correlation will be pointed out in later sections.

It is to be noted carefully that quite often one is faced with a condensed phase molecule where some of the frequencies fit neatly into neither the A nor the B class. In such an event any meaningful calculations should employ the complete equation, at least if the particular frequency or frequencies are strongly isotope dependent. Nonetheless, Equation 3 is still useful even in such cases because it is more readily associated with a physical picture of the condensation process. Often an approximate "forcing" of the data into T^{-2} and T^{-1} terms facilitates the selection of approximate parameters to be employed in calculations using the complete Equation 2. These parameters are then subject to later refinement. Such a technique is described below and in Reference 37 where the theory is applied to chromatographic data for the isotopic methanes.

The above discussion of Equations 2 and 3 has been predicted on the assumption of harmonic frequencies for all $3N$ modes. More realistically, these are at best described as slightly anharmonic frequencies which we approximate with an effective harmonic force field. For lattice frequencies in particular, anharmonicity is expected to be important; here it arises both from the anharmonic curvature in the potential and from the expansion of the lattice on warming. Consequently, the force constants used to describe the lattice modes become temperature dependent. The approach amounts to a simple extension of the ideas at the basis of the pseudo-harmonic theory of solid lattices (2, 3) to the condensed phases which interest us. One phenomenological result of such anharmonicity is that Equation 3 now takes the form:

$$\ln \frac{P}{P'} = \frac{C_2}{T^2} + \frac{C_1}{T} + C_0 \qquad (6)$$

Alternatively, such effects can be treated in the context of equations of type 2 by the expedient of introducing temperature dependent force constants. Specific cases are discussed in detail by Van Hook (33, 35), but in general we shall find that the available chromatographic data is simply not precise enough to allow the definition of such fine points as anharmonic corrections.

[One sees from the above development that our eventual interest lies in correlating the observed isotope effects with the detailed motions of the molecule in the condensed and vapor phases—i.e., with a microscopic model. Others—e.g., see References 8, 9, 11, 12, and 15—have made the alternate choice of bypassing a model and reporting the results directly in terms of the isotope effects on the thermodynamic parameters for the solution process, $\Delta(\Delta G)$, $\Delta(\Delta S)$, and $\Delta(\Delta H)$. Clearly, if the partition functions obtained in the model calculation reproduce the observed isotope effects, then the thermodynamic parameters can be obtained from them using appropriate statistical thermodynamic formulae.]

Chromatographic Considerations. The experimental problem is now reduced to the far from trivial one of determining the ratio of the retention volumes of the two isotopically substituted molecules. Consider a typical chromatogram for two difficultly resolvable isomers such as is sketched in Figure 1. Here t_0 is the time from injection that a completely inert nonadsorbed material is eluted; t_2 and t_1 are the corrected retention times $(P_2/P_1 = t_1/t_2)$ (21); t is the average residence time in the column and w is the peak width.

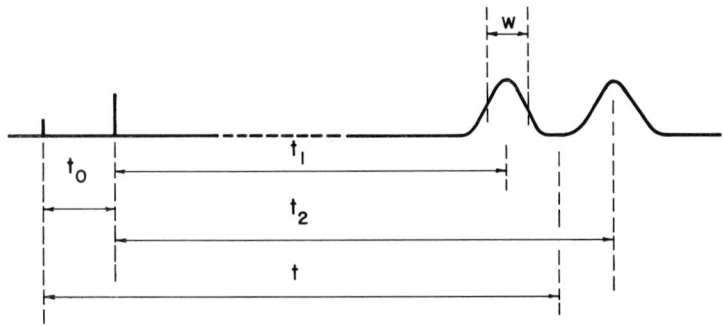

Figure 1.   A chromatogram. The ordinate shows detector response
See text for definition of symbols

For difficult separations such as we discuss in this paper, $t_2 \approx t_1 \approx t \gg t_0$, and the chromatographic parameters of interest are the resolution $R\left(R = \dfrac{(t_2 - t_1)}{2w}\right)$, and the number of theoretical plates (assumed the same for both isotopes), $n \approx 4\left(\dfrac{t}{w}\right)^2$. Next we define the separation factor $\alpha = \dfrac{t_2}{t_1}$ and the column capacity $K = \left(\dfrac{t}{t_0} - 1\right)$ where K can also be shown (21) to be related to the Henry's Law constant, K', characterizing the column, $K = K'\dfrac{V_g}{V_c}$, V_g the volume of gas in the column, V_c the volume of condensed phase. A little manipulation leads to

$$\frac{R^2}{n} \cong \frac{1}{16}\left(\frac{\alpha - 1}{\alpha}\right)^2 \left(\frac{K}{K + 1}\right)^2 \tag{7}$$

Now we particularize the column to the usual operating conditions in the linear range of the plate height $vs.$ gas velocity curve. Then $n = \dfrac{L}{HETP} \approx \dfrac{L}{Cu}$ where L is the column length, u is gas velocity, and C is a constant characterizing the apparatus. Also $u = L/t_o = L/t(K + 1)$ so

$$\frac{R^2}{t} \approx \frac{1}{16}\frac{1}{C}\left(\frac{\alpha - 1}{\alpha}\right)^2 \frac{1}{K} \approx \frac{1}{16}\frac{V_g}{V_L C}\left(\frac{\alpha - 1}{\alpha}\right)^2 \frac{1}{K'} \qquad (8)$$

Bruner, Cartoni, and Liberti (8) have discussed the use of this equation in optimizing chromatographic conditions for separation—$i.e.$, in maximizing R^2/n. In general, C, α, and K' are all temperature dependent but α and K' much more so than C. We have already seen that α goes as $1/T$ or $1/T^2$ generally increasing as the temperature drops, while K', the Henry's Law constant, goes approximately as $K' = K'_o e^{+b/T}$ and gets exponentially larger as the temperature drops. The two criteria then conflict on the question of the most judicious choice of temperature, and it is necessary to determine the best compromise. Generally, this will be found at subambient temperatures and accordingly low temperature chromatographic techniques are dictated. Note from Equation 8 that with K' and α fixed by the selection of the operating column and the temperature, that R^2/t is proportional to V_g/V_c, that is for maximum resolution open tubular columns are indicated. This is hardly an unexpected result.

Bruner, Cartoni, and Liberti (8) have discussed the design of a low temperature chromatograph suitable for studies of isotopic separations. A similar somewhat modified apparatus is in use in our laboratory at the present time. It essentially consists of a double walled chamber in which the column, a thermostatted heater, a fan, and a number of thermocouples are set in an air bath. The space between the walls of the chamber is evacuated, and it is placed in a large Dewar which can be filled with either dry ice–acetone, or liquid nitrogen in which case the level is maintained with a liquid level controller. The temperature is easily maintained to within about a tenth of a degree centigrade over a temperature range extending from $\sim273°K.$ to $\sim90°K.$ The injector port and the detector portion of a Perkin-Elmer F-11 gas chromatograph are placed immediately over the Dewar. A flame ionization detector is employed and the unit is adaptable to either packed or open tubular columns. Helium gas is employed as a carrier.

In most of the work described below our interests have been directed toward simply determining α as a function of temperature on various substrates, not in optimizing column conditions or temperature. In many

of these experiments packed 1/8- or 1/4-inch columns were employed.
The setup was essentially that diagramed except that temperature control was effected with a simple bath and a hot wire or thermistor catharometer was employed.

Results

In this section we shall discuss chromatographic data for a number
of systems together with the theoretical interpretation of that data.

Ethane–Deuteroethanes. Chromatographic separation of ethane and
perdeuteroethane was first reported by Van Hook and Kelly (*32*) using
packed columns loaded with methylcyclopentane at subambient temperatures. These authors also reported the partial resolution of protioethane from mono and di-deuteroethanes. The chromatographic properties of the perdeutero-ordinary system were further investigated on a
variety of liquid substrates using packed column GLC techniques by
Van Hook and Phillips (*34*) and on an open tubular etched glass column
with a wetted wall (subsequently called "wet glass" in this paper) by
Bruner, Cartoni, and Liberti (*8*).

The available data are plotted in Figure 2. They display the features
expected in the light of the earlier discussion in the first part of the
Discussion section, including curvature in the $\ln \dfrac{V}{V'}$ *vs.* $\dfrac{1}{T}$ plots which is
particularly evident for the wet glass and alcohol columns. (An immediate consequence is that interpretation of the slopes of such plots in terms
of isotope effects on enthalpies of vaporization, etc., should be made
only with extreme caution since in general a straight line relationship is
not to be expected). It is unfortunate that data could not be obtained
to a lower temperature on the alcohol column but this was prevented by
the freezing of the liquid. However, some lowering of the temperature
was obtained by going to a two-component ethyl alcohol-acetaldehyde
liquid phase.

In Figure 2 the vapor pressure isotope effect is plotted as the solid
line, and it is to be noted that the deviations from ideality are in the
expected direction—*i.e.*, as the polarity of the solvent increases, the
magnitude of the inverse isotope effect falls off. Clearly, on this basis
the wet glass column must be considered as quite polar, a conclusion
which is consistent with the results for other systems found on this column.
It is unfortunate that the data of Figure 2 are not precise enough
to allow meaningful detailed fits to Equations 3 or 6 to be made (but
note the improvement in precision in going from the packed to the open

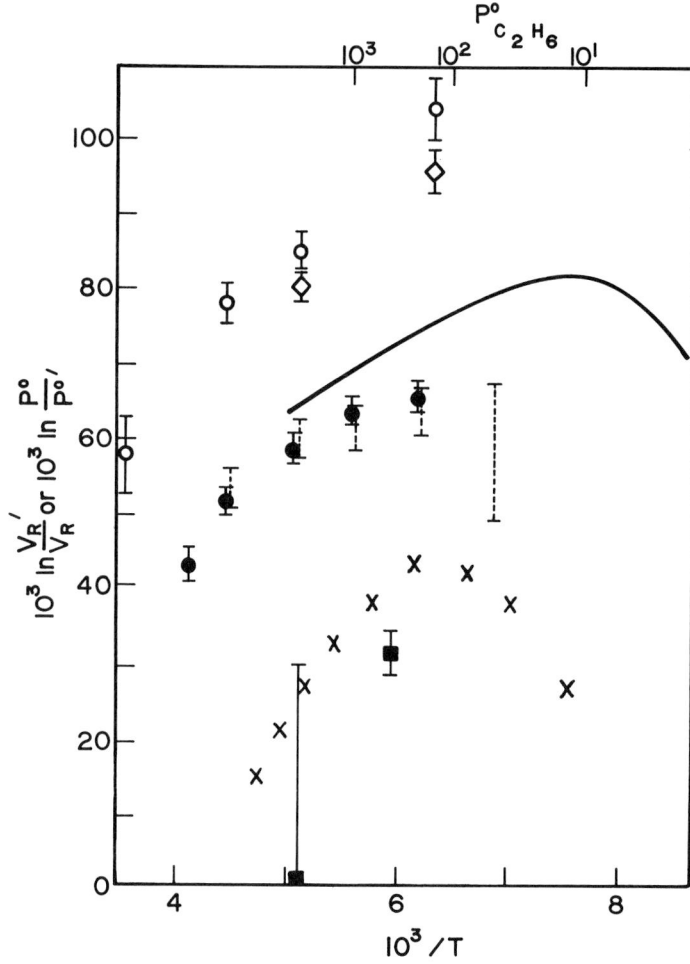

Figure 2.   Separation factors for the system C_2D_6–C_2H_6

■ *15% acetaldehyde on firebrick* (34)
X *open tubular glass column with wetted walls* (8)
● *33% ethyl alcohol on firebrick* (34)
Ɨ *20% 8:2 ethyl alcohol–acetaldehyde on firebrick* (34)
— *vapor pressure ratios of pure liquids* (33)
◇ *13% 2,3,4 trimethyl pentane on firebrick* (34)
○ *15% methylcyclopentane on firebrick* (32)

tubular glass columns) in order to define the changes in A and B which occur on changing the solvent. It is also to be regretted that no independent spectroscopic data on the zero point energy shifts on condensation of ethane into solution exist; therefore, comparisons between spectroscopically and chromatographically determined zero point energy terms are impossible. Even so it can be demonstrated (34) that significant changes must occur at least in the zero point energy shifts on condensation (B terms) as the solvent is varied from the nonpolar methyl cyclopentane or trimethylpentane to the very polar acetaldehyde or wetted glass columns. The ethane data thus is in good qualitative agreement with the theory but has not been subjected to quantitative evaluation.

Methane–Deuteromethanes–$^{13}CH_4$. A good deal of data on the chromatographic isotope effects of methane is now available. All to date has been obtained by gas-solid adsorption chromatography and most of this on the CH_4–CD_4 system but these results are available on a variety of columns and over a broad temperature range. In addition, separation factors at selected temperatures have been measured for a number of the intermediate isomers, both deuterated and tritiated, and for $^{14}CH_4$.

The results which are presently available for the CH_4–CD_4 system are shown plotted in Figure 3 together with the vapor pressure ratios measured by Armstrong, Brickwedde, and Scott (1). The data shown include those of Gant and Yang (16) on activated charcoal packed column between 270° and 425°K., of Bruner, Cartoni, and Liberti (8) between 85° and 150°K. on wetted glass wall tubular columns, and of Phillips and Van Hook (26) between 110° and 273°K. on a packed column loaded with thoroughly dried porous glass (96% silica glass) chips. In addition, single points on molecular sieve packed (28) and empty copper tubular (38) columns are included for completeness. The lines on the diagram (except those showing the VPIE itself) are calculated and will be discussed below.

Let us first consider the data of Bruner et al. (8) on wet glass together with their results on the separation factors of intermediate isomers (and $^{13}CH_4$) taken at 85°K. on a similar column (7). The results for the intermediate isomers are shown in Table I. When considered together with the CD_4 results they offer a good test of the theory (37). We proceed by first fixing the force fields which describe the $3N - 6$ internal modes of the molecule in both phases and thus define the B term. It is unfortunate that no spectroscopic values are available for the shifts which occur during the condensation process from the vapor to the wet glass surface. Even so, an experimental value for the B term is available from the fit to the CH_4–CD_4 temperature coefficient ($B_{CD_4-CH_4} = 13.8°K.$) (8), and it is reasonable to assume that the distribution of these shifts between the various internal modes is the same as that found for the condensation process to the liquid (13, 29) (where $B_{CD_4-CH_4}$ is 8.9°K.). We have compared calculations where each of these choices of $B_{CD_4-CH_4}$ has been used to define force fields for the $3N - 6$ internal frequencies of the adsorbed methane. Values of the force constants and further details are found in Reference 37. With the internal condensed and gas phase (19) fields selected it is a simpler matter to calculate the vibrational frequencies of all isotopes in both phases and hence determine the B contribution to the adsorption isotope effect for all of the isotopic isomers. [We are indebted to M. Wolfsberg and J. Schactschneider for the use of their computer programs which make possible the calculation of these isotope effects using the complete equation. In the final calculations (once both the internal and external portions of the force field were selected) the complete equation (Equation 2) was employed and the calculation performed in $3N$ coordinates.]

Table I. Relative Isotopic Separations[a] on Wetted Glass Tubular Columns

	Isomer	Observed[b]	Calc.[c] (B_{liq})	Calc.[d] (B_{exp})	Calc.[e] (Free Rot.)
Relative Separations at 85°K.	$^{13}CH_4$	(0.13)	(0.13)	(0.13)	(0.13)
	CH_3D	0.42	0.37	0.41	0.25
	CH_2D_2	0.67	0.66	0.75	0.50
	CHD_3	0.87	0.86	0.88	0.75
	CD_4	(1.00)	(1.00)	(1.00)	(1.00)
Temperature Dependence of CH_4-CD_4 Isotope Effect	85°K.	0.082[f]	0.078	0.078	
	100°K.	0.038	0.044	0.037	
	125°K.	0.003	0.015	0.003	
	150°K.	−0.014	0.000	−0.013	
	200°K.	−0.025	−0.011	−0.024	

[a] We define a separation here as $\ln(V/V')$ where V is the corrected retention volume of the substituted isomer and V' that of normal CH_4. A normal isotope effect is thus positive in this table.
[b] Reference 7.
[c] Assuming B term is equivalent to that obtained on condensation to the liquid.
[d] Assuming B obtained from temperature dependency of CD_4-CH_4 data (8, 37).
[e] Relative retentions calculated on the assumption of free rotation on the surface.
[f] Obtained from best fit (8, 37): $\ln \dfrac{P_{CH_4}}{P_{CD_4}} = \dfrac{-13.82}{T} + \dfrac{1766}{T^2}$.

We now turn our attention to the A term which is the predominant one over most of the temperature range. For the case of methane we can write

$$A = \frac{1}{24}\left(\frac{h}{k}\right)^2 \left\{ 3\nu'^2_{tr}\left(1 - \frac{M'}{M}\right) + \sum_{i=1}^{3} \nu'^2_R\left(1 - \frac{I'_i}{I_i}\right) \right\} \qquad (9)$$

where ν'_{tr} and ν'_R signify the hindered translational and rotational frequencies of ordinary methane and M, M', and I, I' the masses and moments of inertia of the substituted and ordinary molecules. One of the most interesting points of the data on the intermediate isomers is that the difference between the $^{13}CH_4$ and the $^{12}CH_3D$ effects enables a clear distinction to be drawn between the relative contributions of the hindered translations and the hindered rotations to the lattice (A) term. This because the moments of inertia of $^{13}CH_4$ and $^{12}CH_4$ are identical so that $A_{^{13}CH_4}$ is a direct measure of the translational contribution to the partition function. This contribution can be easily evaluated from the data in Table I and $B_{^{13}CH_4}$ (calculated above) using Equation 3. It is obvious from Equation 9 that $A_{^{13}CH_4}^{trans} = A_{^{12}CH_3D}^{trans}$ and with $B_{^{12}CH_3D}^{rot}$ known (above) $A_{^{12}CH_3D}$ is deduced. A^{rot} and A^{trans} can then be found for all of the other isomers using Equation 9 and their isotope effects calculated. The data on the intermediate isomers and on the temperature coefficient of the CD_4 effect serve as a test of the theory. For numerical orientation using the calculation based on the zero point energy shifts for the liquid where $B_{^{13}CH_4} = 1.01°K$. one finds $A_{^{13}CH_4} = 94°K$. This corresponds to $A_{CD_4}^{trans} = 321°K.[2]$ and $A_{CD_4}^{rot}$ follows as $1094°K.[2]$. If these lattice contributions are interpreted as harmonic frequencies corresponding to three isotropic translations and three isotropic librations in the condensed phase, $\nu_{CH_4}^{trans} = 77$ cm.$^{-1}$ and $\nu_{CH_4}^{rot} = 91$ cm.$^{-1}$. It is interesting to compare this result for hindered rotation with the 63 cm.$^{-1}$ suggested by Ewing (14) for the liquid. It would appear that a significant increase in the barrier hindering rotation occurs in going from the liquid to the wet glass surface.

The results for all of the intermediate isomers are compared with the experimental data in Table I. The agreement is excellent both for the intermediate isomer effects and for the CD_4 isotope effects over a broad temperature range. A comparison is also given with the results that would be calculated for intermediate isomers if free surface rotation was assumed. It is concluded that hindered rotation is occurring on this surface. This is an important result. (A similar conclusion concerning the existence of hindered rotation in the liquid phase of methane recently has been drawn by Jeevanandam, Craig, and Bigeleisen (18) from an analysis of new and published vapor pressure data.) Note that the calculated effects are not particularly sensitive to the choice of B because for this particular system the A factor is by far the predominant term. This is even true for the calculation of the temperature dependency of the CD_4 effect where there is actually very little reason to choose between the two calculations cited in Table I. The one based on B_{exp} is shown plotted as the solid line in Figure 3.

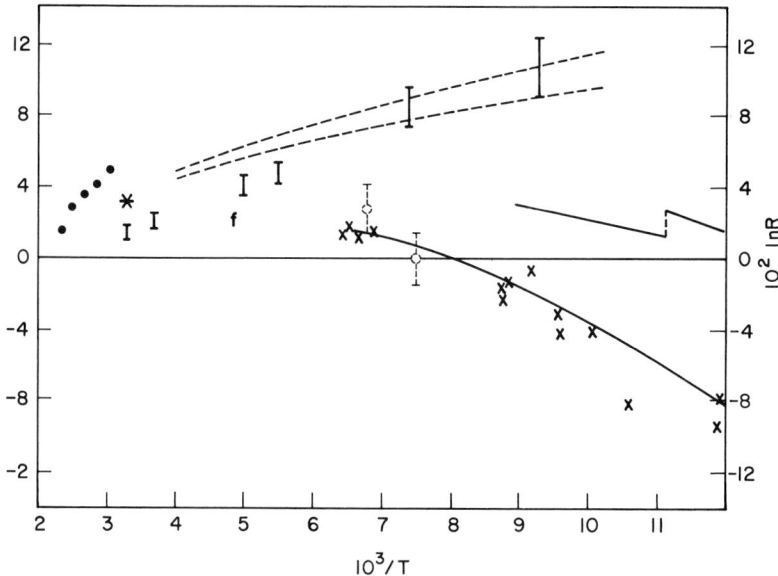

Figure 3.   Separation factors for the system CD_4–CH_4

    — *Vapor pressure isotope effect* (1)
  I *Dry porous glass, packed column* (26)
  Φ *Wet porous glass, packed column* (26)
  X *Open tubular glass column with wetted wall* (8)
  • *Activated charcoal packed column* (16)
  * *Molecular sieve packed column* (28)
  f *Uncoated copper tubular column* (38)

We now turn our attention to the results shown in the upper part of Figure 3. The experiments of Phillips and Van Hook (26) on packed porous glass columns (plotted as the bars) were designed because spectroscopic values were available for the frequency shifts on condensation to the dry glass (29) (albeit only at liquid nitrogen temperatures) and the B term could thus be determined independently of the chromatographic experiments. It is interesting that the value calculated from the spectroscopic shifts is 12.7°K., a number not significantly different from that deduced from the wet glass chromatographic data. In view of the fact that the isotope effects are of opposite sign, this is a surprising result and one that can only be explained if the A contribution on the dry surface is very small. The dotted lines in Figure 4 show the results of sample calculations (Equation 2) using the spectroscopic B term and two different and rather small A terms (upper line $\nu_{\text{trans-x}} = \nu_{\text{trans-y}} = 0$; $\nu_{\text{trans-z}} = 73$ cm.$^{-1}$; $\nu_{\text{rot-x}} = \nu_{\text{rot-y}} = \nu_{\text{rot-z}} = 0$; lower line $\nu_{\text{trans-x}} = \nu_{\text{trans-y}} = 50$ cm.$^{-1}$; $\nu_{\text{trans-z}} = 73$ cm.$^{-1}$; $\nu_{\text{rot-x}} = \nu_{\text{rot-y}} = 25$ cm.$^{-1}$; $\nu_{\text{rot-z}} = 0$). Agreement with experiment is evidenced at the lower temperatures but it worsens as the temperature is raised. This could be because of a change in condensed phase force constants with temperature (thus on this glass ν_3 for acetylene varies by 30% on warming from 90° to 300°K.) or to other anharmonicities. The calculations were, of course, made in the harmonic approximation. In a second set of experiments a dry glass column was wet by equilibrating it with a stream of moist helium for several hours. The separation factors obtained on the wet column (Figure 3) were significantly lowered and in satisfactory agreement with the results of Liberti, *et al.*, on their wetted open tubular columns. The experiments then indicate that the presence of water makes the two columns essentially different. On the wet surface the lattice contribution is markedly larger than on the dry, but the zero point energy contributions (B terms) are roughly the same for both surfaces. Unfortunately, the resolution of the packed columns was very poor and experimental difficulties precluded measurements of relative retentions of $^{12}CH_4$, $^{13}CH_4$, and $^{12}CH_3D$ which would have allowed the magnitude of the lattice contribution to be more precisely estimated.

Finally, consider the high temperature (273° to 423°K.) data of Gant and Yang (*16*) taken with an activated charcoal column. This data is plotted to the extreme left of Figure 3. No spectroscopic assessment of the phase frequency shifts is available but the slope is about twice that for the dry glass experiment indicating a B term of at least 25°K. The authors also measured separation factors for the intermediate deuterium and tritium isomers as well as for $^{14}CH_4$. Some relative effects at 25°C. calculated from their results are shown in Table II. It appears that within experimental error the relative isotope effects are equal to those predicted by the law of the mean (0.25, 0.50, and 0.75 for mono, di, and tri substitution), and that therefore any contribution which is made by hindered rotation to the partition function is negligible as compared with the zero point energy contribution. The authors (*16*) prefer an explanation in terms of a D or T isotope effect on the polarizability of methane (*41*) rather than pointing directly to vibrational effects.

Acetylene and Deuteroacetylene. Van Hook and Phillips (*36*) have reported successful analytical and preparative separations of small amounts of C_2H_2, C_2HD, and C_2D_2 using packed columns. They investi-

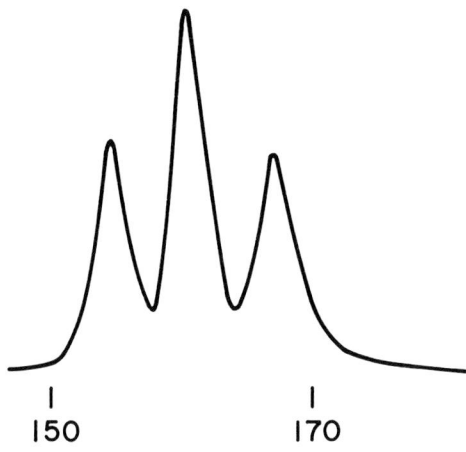

*Figure 4.   Separation of equilibrium mix-
ture of the protio-deutero isomers of acetylene (D:H::1:1)*

Order of appearance (left to right)
C_2H_2:C_2HD:C_2D_2
*Column: 24 ft. 18% $(C_2H_5)_3N$ at $-78°C.$,
He carrier at $\sim$15 cc./min.*

*Measured separation factors $R_{C_2H_2/C_2D_2} = 1.085$;
$R_{C_2H_2/C_2HD} = 1.032$*

Time is entered in minutes

gated a series of liquid phases at $-78°C.$ and observed successful analytical separations using liquid phase materials expected to complex with acetylene. The separation factors (V/V') were 1.08 ± 0.01 for a number of different amines and alcohols. The isotope effects were normal in agreement with theoretical expectations for the case where complexing between sample and substrate occurs in the condensed phase. A marked temperature coefficient was also observed (for CH_3OH columns, 1.088 at $-78°C.$, 1.075 at $-69°C.$ and 1.038 at $-45°C.$). It is interesting to note that vapor pressure isotope effects on methylacetylene (35) and on acetylene (23) itself are normal and can be interpreted as being caused by complexing in the condensed phase. A chromatogram of an equilibrium mixture of the acetylenes (D:H::1:1) is shown in Figure 4.

One purpose of the study was to prepare a macroscopic sample of pure C_2HD which had not previously been isolated from the equilibrium mixture. This was accomplished by making multiple injections into a long 1/4-inch preparative column loaded with 18% $(C_2H_5)_3N$ on chromsorb P and held at $-78°C$. Extensive tailing occurred because of the formation of the acetylene-amine complex which accounts for the separation. However, several rechromatographings of laboriously accumulated intermediate product sufficed to produce a small amount ($\sim$2cc.) of approximately 99% C_2HD. Some analyses of successive runs are shown in Reference 36. The purity of the final material was checked by infrared spectroscopy (24). The application of preparative scale chromatography to this system would be particularly appropriate because a direct synthesis of C_2HD which avoids equilibration between C_2D_2 and C_2H_2 has not yet been reported.

Table II.   Separation of Isotopic Methanes on a Charcoal Column[a]

Isomer	Relative Effect[b]
$^{14}CH_4$	0
CH_3D	0.25
CH_2D_2	0.49
CHD_3	0.70
CD_4	1.00
CH_3T	0.20
CH_2T_2	0.46
CHT_3	0.71
CT_4	1.00

[a] Reference 16.

[b] $\ln \left(\dfrac{V_{CH_4}}{V_{D \text{ or } T}} \right) \Big/ \ln \left(\dfrac{V_{CH_4}}{V_{CD_4} \text{ or } V_{CT_4}} \right).$

In spite of the successful separation above, we have found that the inordinate amount of labor involved in the many rechromatographings of intermediate precludes the separation of really useful amounts of material. This is because of the very pronounced tailing which develops as the sample size increases, this tailing in turn owing to the very large value of the equilibrium constant describing the complexing, K in Equation 8. The result is that the column approaches ideality only at extremely light loadings. Note that an attempt to improve the situation by raising the temperature, thus lowering K, is self-defeating because the isotope effect itself, α in Equation 8, has a strong inverse temperature dependence. The example is perhaps an extreme one because of the unusually strong complexing of acetylene in the condensed phase. It does, however, point directly to the kind of problem to be expected when ideal or nearly ideal separations of microscopic amounts of material are scaled up. It is appropriate to reemphasize at this point that the theoretical analysis discussed earlier is limited to the case of ideal chromatography. Following general practice in the field, the criteria for this approach to ideality is taken in terms of the symmetry of the eluted peaks.

Some Other Systems. A number of other investigations where the chromatographic isotope effect has been studied as both a function of temperature and of substrate are in the literature. In 1962 Falconer and Cvetanovic (15) measured separations of a number of different deuterated paraffins from their protio analogs on a capillary column loaded with squalane. They found inverse effects which averaged 0.72% per D at 25°C. decreasing to 0.50% per D at 100°C. Unfortunately, the vapor pressure isotope effect ($VPIE$) has not been measured on the compounds they employed so that activity coefficients cannot be calculated. Liberti and co-workers (8, 25) have extensively investigated a number of different hydrocarbon systems including C_6H_6–C_6D_6, C_6H_{12}–C_6D_{12}, and $C_6H_5CH_3$–$C_6D_5CD_3$ between 0° and 50°C. on squalane, Dow-Corning 702 silicone oil and dinonylphthlate columns (with some $C_6H_5CH_3$–$C_6D_5CD_3$ data on wetted glass in addition). In each instance the effects were in the theoretically expected order. That is, the inverse isotope effect decreased as the polarity of the column material increased (squalane $>$ $VPIE$ $>$ DC 702 silicone $>$ dinonylphthalate $>$ wetted glass). In fact, the effect on wetted glass, measured only for the toluene system, had already changed sign and become normal. This same group (9) has looked at separations of $(CD_3)_2C$=O $-$ $(CH_3)_2C$=O, CD_3OH $-$ CH_3OH and C_2D_5OH $-$ C_2H_5OH over the range from 25° to 50°C. on Ucon Ux-550, tetraethylene glycol and diglycerol columns. While these materials are all polar, it is to be noted that the position of isotopic substitution is still paraffinic and the isotope effects remain inverse rather than changing sign and becoming normal as would be expected if the position of isotopic substitution was directly complexed with the condensed phase. Once again the inverse isotope effect falls in order of increasing substrate polarity (Ucon Ux-550 $>$ tetraethylene glycol $>$ diglycerol). Vapor pressure data available only for CD_3OH (4) places the pure liquid (still inverse at ∼0.7%) between the TEG (∼1.5%) and the diglycerol columns (∼−1%). The deutero acetone and deutero ethanol compounds are all comfortably inverse. In yet another study (9) on $CDCl_3$–$CHCl_3$, again around room temperature, it was found on squalane that ln (V_H/V_D) is about 10% larger than the $VPIE$ which is itself about 1% inverse (27), but on wetted glass the effect drops markedly to a normal effect of about 0.3%. This observation is consistent with our previous experience.

Cvetanovic, Duncan, and Falconer (11) and Cvetanovic, Duncan, Falconer, and Irwin (12) have made extensive investigations of the separation of isotopically substituted olefins as a function of temperature on ethylene glycol-silver nitrate columns. The separation is caused by the formation of a strong silver-olefin pi complex in the condensed phase which results in an unusually large normal isotope effect which is most logically discussed in a different context than that used in this paper.

Finally we emphasize that a number of interesting separations have been reported at isolated temperatures and for this reason have not been mentioned in the brief summary comprising this section. Examples include separations of $O_2{}^{16}$ from $O_2{}^{18}$, (8), deuterated from non-deuterated trimethylsilyl derivatives of sugars (5), some assorted hydrocarbon separations on safrole (28), and a partial separation of the nitrogen isotopes (30).

Conclusion

The experimental results discussed in this paper indicate that chromatographic studies of separation factors between isotopic isomers afford a convenient method for investigating isotope effects in solution and adsorption processes. In general, there are significant isotope effects on the activity coefficients which are both temperature and solvent dependent, but these effects are at least qualitatively consistent with the predictions of the theory both in regard to the temperature and to the solvent dependency. This is an important result because it establishes a foundation for the rational selection of columns and operating temperatures for separations of isotopic molecules. It is unfortunate that much of the data is not precise enough, or is not yet available over a broad enough temperature range to permit detailed calculations and interpretation on several different systems. Even so, those results now available do substantiate the theory and thus point out the importance of consideration of the details of molecular structure in the understanding of these separation factors.

From a more practical standpoint it is clear that chromatographic techniques afford a cheap, rapid, and convenient method for the analysis of mixtures of isotopic molecules. Also preparative scale chromatography might in the future afford one route towards isolating useful amounts of isotopic isomers which are difficult or impossible to synthesize as pure compounds.

Acknowledgment

This research was supported in major part by the Petroleum Research Fund, administered by the American Chemical Society. Some of the equipment used was constructed with funds from NASA Sustaining University Grant NGR 43-001-021.

Literature Cited

(1) Armstrong, G. T., Brickwedde, F. G., Scott, R. B., *J. Res. Natl. Bur. Std.* **55**, 39 (1955).
(2) Barron, T. H. K., *Discussions Faraday Soc.* **40**, 69 (1965).
(3) Barron, T. H. K., "Lattice Dynamics," p. 247, R. F. Wallis, Ed., Pergamon Press, Inc., London, 1965.
(4) Beersmans, J., Jungers, J. C., *Bull. Soc. chim. Belges.*, **56**, 72 (1947).
(5) Bentley, R., Saha, N. C., Sweeley, C. C., *Anal. Chem.* **37**, 1118 (1965).
(6) Bigeleisen, J., *J. Chem. Phys.* **34**, 1485 (1961).
(7) Bruner, F., Cartoni, G. P., *J. Chromatography* **18**, 390 (1965).
(8) Bruner, F., Cartoni, G. P., Liberti, A., *Anal. Chem.* **38**, 298 (1966).
(9) Cartoni, G. P., Liberti, A., Pela, A., *Anal. Chem.* **39**, 1618 (1967).
(10) Curl, R. F., Jr., Kasper, J. V., Pitzer, K. S., Sathiandam, K., *J. Chem. Phys.* **44**, 4636 (1966).
(11) Cvetanovic, R. J., Duncan, F. J., Falconer, W. E., *Can. J. Chem.* **41**, 2095 (1963).
(12) Cvetanovic, R. J., Duncan, F. J., Falconer, W. E., Irwin, R. S., *J. Am. Chem. Soc.* **87**, 1827 (1965).
(13) Crawford, M. F., Welsh, H. L., Harrold, J. H., *Can. J. Phys.* **30**, 81 (1952).
(14) Ewing, G. E., *J. Chem. Phys.* **40**, 179 (1964).
(15) Falconer, W. E., Cvetanovic, R. J., *Anal. Chem.* **34**, 1064 (1962).
(16) Gant, P. L., Yang, K., *J. Am. Chem. Soc.* **86**, 5063 (1964).
(17) Hopkins, H. P., Kaspar, J. V., Pitzer, K. S., *J. Chem. Phys.* **46**, 218 (1967).
(18) Jeevanandam, M., Craig, B., Bigeleisen, J., *J. Chem. Phys.* **47**, 4335 (1967).
(19) Jones, L. H., *Mol. Spectro.* **3**, 632 (1959).
(20) Katorski, A., White, D., *J. Chem. Phys.* **40**, 3183 (1964).
(21) Keulmans, A. I. M., "Gas Chromatography," p. 172, Rheinhold Publishing Corp., New York, New York, 1959.
(22) King, J., Jr., Benson, S. W., *J. Chem. Phys.* **44**, 1007 (1966).
(23) Klemenc, A., Von Frugnoni, O., *Naturwiss.* **22**, 465 (1934).
(24) Lafferty, W. J., Plyler, E. K., Tidwell, E. D., *J. Chem. Phys.* **37**, 1983 (1962).
(25) Liberti, A., Cartoni, G. P., Bruner, F., *J. Chromatography* **12**, 8 (1963).
(26) Phillips, J. T., Van Hook, W. A., *J. Phys. Chem.* **71**, 3276 (1967).
(27) Rabinovich, I. M., Nikolaev, P. N., *Russ. J. Phys. Chem.* **34**, 1087 (1960).
(28) Root, J. W., Lee, E. K. C., Rowland, F. S., *Science* **143**, 678 (1964).
(29) Shepard, N., Yates, D. J. C., *Proc. Roy. Soc.* **A238**, 69 (1956).
(30) Sideman, S., Giladi, J., "Gas Chromatography," M. Von Swaay, Ed., Butterworths, Washington, 1962.
(31) Thomaes, G., von Steenwenkel, R., *Mol. Phys.* **5**, 307 (1962).
(32) Van Hook, W. A., Kelley, M. E., *Anal. Chem.* **37**, 508 (1965).
(33) Van Hook, W. A., *J. Chem. Phys.* **44**, 234 (1966).
(34) Van Hook, W. A., Phillips, J. T., *J. Phys. Chem.* **70**, 1515 (1966).
(35) Van Hook, W. A., *J. Chem. Phys.* **46**, 1907 (1967).

(36) Van Hook, W. A., Phillips, J. T., *J. Chromatography* **30**, 211 (1967).
(37) Van Hook, W. A., *J. Phys. Chem.* **71**, 3270 (1967).
(38) Van Hook, W. A., Appleton, G. T. (unpublished data).
(39) White, D., ADVAN. CHEM. SER. **89**, 73 (1969).
(40) Wilzbach, K., Riesz, R., *Science* **126**, 748 (1957).
(41) Yaris, R., Sams, J. R. Jr., *J. Chem. Phys.* **37**, 571 (1962).

RECEIVED July 27, 1967.

8

Preparation of 99.5% Nitrogen-15 by Chemical Exchange between Oxides of Nitrogen in a Solvent Carrier System

M. JEEVANADAM[1] and T. I. TAYLOR

Columbia University, New York, N. Y.

Solvents such as CCl_4 and n-heptane increased the single stage enrichment factor α for the distribution of nitrogen-15 between the gas and liquid phase for the NO–N_2O_3 exchange system. A further increase resulted when donor molecules such as 1,4-dioxane were present in the solution. It was shown that the changes in composition of the phases could account for the increases in α. The use of solvents as carriers in exchange columns for the NO–N_2O_3 system resulted in marked increases in the overall separations for nitrogen-15. Besides their effect on α, solvents improved the interphase exchange rate and decreased the hold-up of exchangeable material. A cascade of two columns was constructed and 99.5% nitrogen-15 was produced to test the reflux process for the solvent carrier systems.

Isotope exchange reactions involving the oxides of nitrogen have been found to be particularly useful for the concentration of nitrogen-15. Two chemical exchange systems have been used successfully in our laboratory for the preparation of over 99.5% nitrogen-15. These involved the exchange of oxides of nitrogen with $10M$ HNO_3 (*12, 39, 43*) at 25°C. and with liquid N_2O_3 (*31, 32*) at −9°C. The principal exchange reactions in these systems are:

$$^{15}NO + H^{14}NO_3 \rightleftharpoons {}^{14}NO + {}^{15}HNO_3 \ (\alpha = 1.055 \pm 0.005,$$
$$\text{HETP} = 2.8 \text{ cm.}) \qquad (1)$$

$$^{15}NO + {}^{14}N_2O_3 \rightleftharpoons {}^{14}NO + {}^{14}N^{15}NO_3 \ (\alpha = 1.031 \pm 0.002,$$
$$\text{HETP} = 1.15 \text{ cm.}) \qquad (2)$$

---

[1] Present address: Chemistry Division, Bhabha Atomic Research Centre, Bombay 74, India.

Other oxides of nitrogen are present in these systems, and they affect the single stage enrichment factor $\alpha = (^{15}N/^{14}N)_{liquid}/(^{15}N/^{14}N)_{gas}$ as well as the interphase transfer rate as measured by the height of the column equivalent to a theoretical plate (HETP).

In their simplest form, the exchange systems for the above reactions consist of a packed column with a refluxer attached to the bottom end where the nitrogen-15 concentrates. The liquid phase with normal abundance (0.365 atom %) of N-15 is fed to the upper end of the column and, as will be described later, the refluxer converts the nitrogen quantitatively to gaseous oxides of nitrogen which flow upward countercurrent to the liquid phase. In both systems the reflux involves the reaction of the liquid phase with sulfur dioxide to form primarily nitric oxide and sulfuric acid.

For a practical system it is important that α be reasonably large and HETP be small since the overall separation S_∞ in a column length z at steady state with no production is given by

$$S_\infty = \alpha^n = \alpha^{z/\text{HETP}} \simeq e^{(\alpha-1)z/\text{HETP}} \qquad (3)$$

or

$$\ln S_\infty = (\alpha - 1)z/\text{HETP} \text{ and } z = \ln S_\infty(\text{HETP}/(\alpha - 1)) \qquad (4)$$

where n is the number of theoretical plates in the column and S_∞ is given by $(^{15}N/^{14}N)_{product}/(^{15}N/^{14}N)_{feed}$. Thus, the length of column required for a given overall separation is proportional to $(\text{HETP})/(\alpha - 1)$. In cases where α is near unity and the atom fraction N_0 of nitrogen-15 in the feed material is small, consideration of material balances in the system will show that the maximum transport T in gram atoms ^{15}N/minute is given approximately by

$$T = LN_0(1 - N_0)(\alpha - 1) = AL'N_0(1 - N_0)(\alpha - 1). \qquad (5)$$

Here L is the interstage flow (gram atoms N/min.) of exchangeable nitrogen in the liquid phase and L' is the same quantity per cm.^{2} of column area. For a given transport and feed concentration, the area A required will be proportional to $1/L'(\alpha - 1)$ so that the size (volume) of the system required will be proportional to $\text{HETP}/L'(\alpha - 1)^2$. These considerations show the importance of even small increases in $(\alpha - 1)$ or of a decrease in HETP. Similar considerations to be discussed later will show that the equilibrium time is also dependent on $1/(\alpha - 1)^2$.

The value of α in the exchange Reactions 1 and 2 is significantly affected by the relative concentration of the different oxides of nitrogen (29, 30, 31, 32, 42). For the NO–HNO$_3$ system, the composition of the gas phase is most conveniently controlled by the nitric acid concentration, although it is also affected by temperature and pressure. It was found that the optimum value for $\text{HETP}/L'(\alpha - 1)^2$ was obtained with approximately $10M$ HNO$_3$ (43). The interphase exchange rate, as measured by HETP, as well as $(\alpha - 1)$ are significantly affected by the composition of the phases so that a compromise is necessary between $(\alpha - 1)$ which is higher for the lower acid concentrations and the exchange rate which is greater for the more concentrated acid solutions.

In the case of the $NO-N_2O_3$ system, the composition of the phases and consequently the value of α is determined primarily by the temperature and the pressure. At atmospheric pressure it is necessary to operate the exchange columns at about $-10°C$. for optimum results. Even at this temperature the interphase exchange rate is much higher (HETP = 1.15 cm.) than that for the $NO-HNO_3$ system (HETP = 2.8 cm.). To obtain a given concentration of nitrogen-15, the relative lengths of exchange columns for the two systems as given by $(HETP)/(\alpha - 1)$ is significantly in favor of the $NO-N_2O_3$ system even though $(\alpha - 1)$ is appreciably smaller, 0.031 compared with 0.055. The relative sizes (length $\times$ cross sectional area) of exchange columns to produce 99.5% nitrogen-15 at a fixed rate as given by $HETP/L'(\alpha - 1)^2$ are about the same. However, the necessity for refrigeration of the $NO-N_2O_3$ is a definite disadvantage. Thus, any method of operation that would either improve the single stage enrichment factor or allow operation of the $NO-N_2O_3$ system at higher temperatures would be of interest.

Monse, Kauder, and Spindel (*31*) have considered the possibility of using pressures greater than one atomosphere to alter the composition of the phases and thereby increase α for operation at higher temperatures. Increasing the pressure from one atmosphere at $23°C$. to seven atmospheres, for example, markedly reduced the concentration of N_2O_4, NO_2, and N_2O_3 in the gas phase and increased the concentration of N_2O_4 in the liquid phase. The measured value of α at $23°C$. was 1.030 which is about the same as that for one atmosphere at $-10°C$.

The present investigation was undertaken to determine the influence of inert (non-donor) solvents with and without complexing agents (donor molecules) on the concentration of NO_2 and N_2O_4 in the gas phase and on the single stage separation factor α. Preliminary experiments in short exchange columns showed that a solvent as a carrier significantly improved the performance of the system. Consequently, a two column cascade was set up to prepare 99.5% nitrogen-15.

Effect of Solvent on α

When NO is added to liquid N_2O_4 until the pressure in the vessel is 1 atm., the gas phase consists of N_2O_3, N_2O_4, NO, and NO_2 at partial pressures of p_1, p_2, p_3, and p_4 atm. respectively. The liquid phase is primarily N_2O_3 and N_2O_4 of mole fractions M_1 and M_2. For a fixed pressure of 1 atm., the composition of the phases is determined by the temperature and this fixes the effective fractionation factor, $\alpha =$ $(^{15}N/^{14}N)_{\text{liquid}}/(^{15}N/^{14}N)_{\text{gas}}$. When a non-donor solvent such as CCl_4 or of the solvent along with a complexing agent (donor molecule) such as 1,4 dioxane is added, the composition of the phases is significantly changed with a corresponding change in the effective fractionation factor.

Although isotope exchange occurs among all the species in the gas and liquid phase, it has been shown previously (29, 30,, 31) that the effective fractionation factor can be evaluated in terms of three independent exchange reactions:

$$^{15}NO + {}^{14}N_2O_3 \rightleftharpoons {}^{14}NO + {}^{14}N^{15}NO_3, \alpha_{13}(1.037 \text{ at } -10°C.) \qquad (6)$$

$$^{15}NO + {}^{14}N_2O_4 \rightleftharpoons {}^{14}NO + {}^{14}N^{15}NO_4, \alpha_{23}(1.084 \text{ at } -10°C.) \qquad (7)$$

$$^{15}NO + {}^{14}NO_2 \rightleftharpoons {}^{14}NO + {}^{15}NO_2, \alpha_{43}(1.051 \text{ at } -10°C.) \qquad (8)$$

This formulation assumes negligible isotope effect between the same species in the gas and liquid phase and between N_2O_3 and N_2O_4 which are assumed to be the principal species in the liquid phase. Further, if the concentration of ^{15}N is small compared with that of ^{14}N, the effective fractionation factor α can be expressed in terms of α_{13}, α_{23}, and α_{43} as follows (30, 31)

$$\alpha = \frac{\alpha_{13}M_1 + \alpha_{23}M_2}{\alpha_{13}m_1 + \alpha_{23}m_2 + m_3 + \alpha_{43}m_4} \qquad (9)$$

where m_1, m_2, m_3, and m_4 are the atom fractions of total nitrogen of the gas phase in the N_2O_3, N_2O_4, NO, and NO_2 species respectively, and M_1 and M_2 are the atom fractions of total nitrogen of the liquid phase in N_2O_3 and N_2O_4 respectively. For example,

$$m_1 = \frac{2p_1}{2p_1 + 2p_2 + p_3 + p_4} \qquad (10)$$

and M_1 would be equal to the mole fraction of N_2O_3 in the liquid phase.

As will be shown later, addition of a solvent to the system at a given temperature reduces m_4, m_1, and m_2 in the gas phase and increases M_2 in the liquid phase. From Equation 9 and the individual values of α_{13}, α_{23}, and α_{43}, it can be seen that this should result in an increase in α. Further, the addition of a donor molecule which selectively complexes N_2O_4 or N_2O_3 in the liquid phase should produce an even larger effect on α.

Determination of α. The procedure for the determination of α in the presence of solvents was similar to that used previously (31) for the $NO–N_2O_3$ system alone. In order that the initial isotopic abundances in both phases be the same, N_2O_4 was prepared from the NO by reaction with excess oxygen. A quantity of the N_2O_4 (from 2 to 4 grams) was transferred to a jacketed equilibration vessel (146 cc.) which was evacuated and cooled with dry ice. The actual quantity transferred was determined by weighing the vessel before and after addition of the N_2O_4. Dry nitrogen was admitted to the frozen N_2O_4 and a calculated volume of spectro-grade solvent was introduced with a hypodermic syringe. The vessel was cooled with dry ice and evacuated to 10^{-3} mm. Hg. Three cycles of melting, then freezing the mixture, and finally evacuating the vessel, served to outgas the solution.

The vessel was connected to the transfer system shown in Figure 1 and thermostatically regulated coolant was circulated through the jacket. Tank NO was purified by freezing it with liquid nitrogen, pumping off the non-condensible gases, and then collecting the center fraction in a storage vessel as the NO slowly vaporized. Measured quantities of the NO were introduced into the vessel from a gas burette until there was no further absorption of NO and the total pressure in the vessel was 1 atm. With constant agitation of the liquid by a magnetic stirrer, the saturation was completed in about one half hour and the equilibration was continued for ten hours or longer. Samples of gas (about 5 cc.) were then withdrawn and reduced to N_2 by passing the sample through a mixture of copper-oxide and reduced copper wire at 720°–750°C. (*43*). A sample of the initial NO used for the equilibration was reduced to N_2 in the same way.

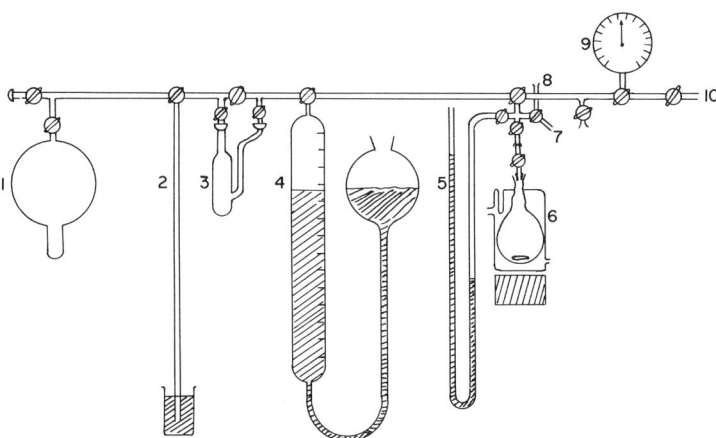

Figure 1. Vacuum line and transfer system for the determination of single stage fractionation factors and composition of the phases: (1) storage bulb for purified NO; (2) manometer; (3) silica gel tube for further purification of NO; (4) gas burette containing mercury covered with a layer of α-bromonaphthalene; (5) manometer; (6) equilibrium vessel; (7) connection for mechanical pump; (8) connection for sample tube; (9) stainless steel Helicoid gage; (10) connection to mercury diffusion pump

The abundance ratios 29/28 for mass 29 to mass 28 corresponding to $^{15}N^{14}N/^{14}N^{14}N$ were determined for both samples with a single collector Nier-type mass spectrometer (35, 36). Since the initial ^{15}N concentrations were the same in both phases, α can be calculated from the analysis of the gas phase alone by the equation

$$\alpha = \frac{R_2}{R_1} + \frac{m}{M}\left(\frac{R_2}{R_1} - 1\right) \tag{11}$$

where R_1 is the abundance ratio 29/28 in the N_2 from the NO before equilibration and R_2 is the abundance ratio 29/28 in the N_2 from the gases after equilibration. m/M is the ratio of total exchangeable nitrogen in the gas phase to that in the liquid phase. This ratio was from 0.02 to 0.1 in the above experiments as estimated from the quantities of NO and NO_2 added to the system and from the volume and approximate composition of the gas phase at equilibrium. When m/M is small, the second term of Equation 11 is small, and small uncertainties in the composition of gas phase result in only small errors in α. For each determination, several abundance ratios, 29/28, were obtained for duplicate samples and the spread in the values of α was about ± 0.003.

Composition of the Phases. In a separate series of experiments the compositions of the gas and liquid phases were determined by a combination of material balances and spectrophotometric determinations of the concentration of NO_2 in a sample withdrawn from the vessel. The procedure was similar to that described for the determination of α, except that the NO was purified further by passing it through silica gel (12) at dry ice temperature as the gas burette was filled. Measured quantities of NO were introduced to the equilibration vessel until the total pressure was 1 atm. as described previously. After equilibration a sample was withdrawn into a borosilicate glass optical cell, 2 cm. $\times$ 1.8 cm. diameter ($\sim$5 cc.). The absorbance of the sample at $\sim$25°C. was determined with a Cary Model 11 spectrophotometer at 4360A. Using an absorbtivity of 0.0105 $\pm$ 0.002 (mm. Hg)$^{-1}$ cm.$^{-1}$ as determined by calibration at a series of NO_2 pressures at 25°C. as has been done previously (10, 18, 22, 24), the partial pressure of NO_2 in the optical cell was calculated.

The known total pressure P in the optical cell is given by

$$P_{\text{atm}} = p_1' + p_2' + p_3' + p_4' + p_5'. \tag{12}$$

The partial pressure p_4' of NO_2 is known from the absorbance measurements and p_5' is the known vapor pressure of the solvent at the temperature of equilibration. From the equilibrium constants (9, 23, 26, 47) for the reactions

$$N_2O_3 \rightleftharpoons NO + NO_2 \quad K_1 \quad (1.89 \text{ at } 25°C.) \tag{13}$$

$$N_2O_4 \rightleftharpoons 2NO_2 \qquad K_2 \quad (1.49 \times 10^{-1} \text{ at } 25°C.) \tag{14}$$

the partial pressure of N_2O_4 is given by

$$p_2' = (p_4')^2/K_2 \tag{15}$$

$$p_3' = K_1 p_1'/p_4' \tag{16}$$

Substitution for p_3' into Equation 12 and solving for p_1', the partial pressure of N_2O_3, gives

$$p_1' = \frac{P - (p_2' + p_4' + p_5')}{1 + K_1/p_4'} \tag{17}$$

Thus, with these equations the concentration of each species in the optical cell at 25°C. can be calculated. The atom fraction of the nitrogen in the 4+ oxidation state is $x = (p_1' + 2p_2' + p_4')/(2p_1' + 2p_2' + p_3' + p_4')$ and that in the 2+ oxidation state is $(1 - x) = (p_1' + p_3')/(2p_1' + 2p_2' + p_3' + p_4')$ or a ratio $x/(1 - x) = (p_1' + 2p_2' + p_4')/(p_1' + p_3') = B/A$ where $B = p_1' + 2p_2' + p_4'$ and $A = p_1' + p_3'$. This is also the ratio of 4+ nitrogen to 2+ nitrogen in the gas phase of the equilibration vessel from which the sample was withdrawn into the optical cell.

The partial pressure of each nitrogen species in the equilibration vessel at temperature t can be calculated from the above values of A and B as follows. Since the ratio of 4+ nitrogen to 2+ nitrogen in the equilibration vessel is the same as that in the optical cell, $A = p_1 + p_3$ and $B = p_1 + 2p_2 + p_4$ where p_i refers to the partial pressures at temperature t. From these relations and the expressions for the equilibrium constants at t, the following equation is obtained for p_4, the partial pressure of NO_2:

$$(p_4)^3 + (p_4)^2 \left[\frac{K_2}{2} + K_1 \right] + p_4 \left[\frac{K_2}{2} (K_1 + (A - B)) \right] - \frac{K_2 K_1 B}{2} = 0 \tag{18a}$$

From the calculated value of p_4 from this equation and from the known total pressure P (1 atm.), the partial pressures p_2, p_1, and p_3 of N_2O_4, N_2O_3, and NO can be calculated using Equations 15, 16, and 17. The values of K_1 (9) and K_2 (23) as a function of temperature are given by

$$\log K_1 = -2107.6/T + 7.3471$$

and

$$\log K_2 = -2979.2/T + 9.1677.$$

The composition of the liquid phase can be obtained from a material balance on the initial moles of NO_2 and NO admitted to the equilibration vessel by means of the equation,

$$X = (n_1 - Dx)/(n_1 + n_2 - D) \tag{18b}$$

where n_1 and n_2 are the initial total moles of NO_2 and NO introduced; D is the gram atoms of nitrogen in the gas phase; x is the atom fraction of 4+ nitrogen in the gas phase; and X is the atom fraction of 4+ nitrogen in the liquid phase. If one assumes that the liquid phase consists of N_2O_3 and N_2O_4, the atom fraction M_2 of nitrogen present as N_2O_4 is

$$M_2 = 2X - 1 \qquad (19)$$

and the atom fraction M_1 of nitrogen present as N_2O_3 is

$$M_1 = 2(1 - X). \qquad (20)$$

M_2 and M_1 are also the mole fractions of N_2O_4 and N_2O_3 in the liquid phase. Plots of x and X against temperature are shown in Figure 2 for N_2O_4 alone and for the CCl_4 solutions. The results in absence of solvent are in good agreement with previously reported values (11, 37) indicating that the analytical method and calculations described here give reliable results. The significant effect of the solvent on the mole fraction of 4+ nitrogen in the gas phase is evident from the curves in Figure 2. The changes in the liquid phase concentrations are smaller.

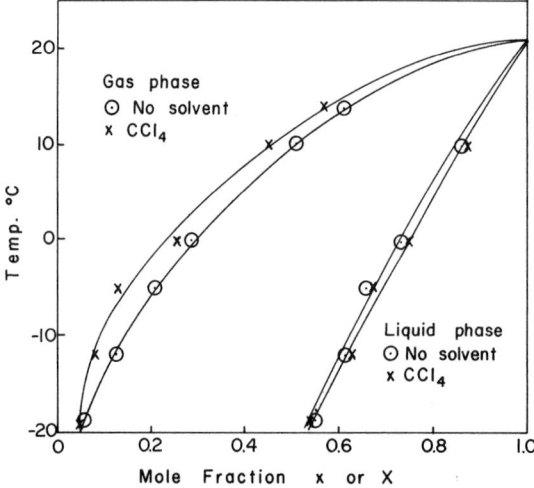

Figure 2. Effect of solvent on the mole fraction x of nitrogen in the gas phase that is in the 4+ oxidation state; X is the same quantity for the liquid phase

Results for α and Compositions. The fractionation factor α for the $NO-N_2O_3$ system in the presence of a number of non-donor solvents are summarized in Table I, and some results for solutions of complexes of N_2O_4 with donor molecules are given in Table II. The values listed for the $NO-N_2O_3$ system in the absence of solvents were taken from plots

Table I. Effect of Non-donor Solvents on the Single Stage Enrichment Factor α_{exp} for Solutions with an Initial Mole Fraction of N_2O_4 of Approximately 0.5 to which NO was Added until the Total Pressure in the Equilibration Vessel (146cc.) was 1 atm.

Temp. °C.	Solvent	Initial Mole Fraction N_2O_4	Moles NO added per mole NO_2	α_{exp} ±0.003
−14	none	—	—	1.035
−14	n-heptane	0.50	0.76	1.033
−14	$CCl_4:C_2Cl_4F_2$	0.52	0.61	1.032
−5	none	—	—	1.025
−5	n-heptane	0.50	0.44	1.030
−5	CCl_4	0.45	0.45	1.032
0	none	—	—	1.020
0	n-heptane	0.50	0.36	1.024
0	$CCl_4:C_2Cl_4F_2$	0.52	0.33	1.024
0	CCl_4	0.45	0.37	1.028
0	nitromethane	0.50	0.40	1.030
10	none	—	—	1.012
10	n-heptane	0.50	0.13	1.021
20	n-heptane	0.50	0.06	1.013

Table II. Single Stage Enrichment Factors α_{exp} for Solutions of Complexes of N_2O_4 with Donor Molecules in Solvents After Addition of NO until the Pressure in the Equilibrium Vessel (146cc.) was 1 atm.

Temp. °C.	Solvent	Donor	mmoles N_2O_4:Donor per ml. solvent	Moles NO added per mole NO_2	α_{exp} ±0.003
0	CCl_4	tetrahydrofuran	1.0	0.57	1.019
0	CCl_4	1,2 dimethoxymethane	1.0	0.31	1.020
0	CCl_4	dimethylsulfoxide	1.0	0.39	1.024
0	CCl_4	1,3 dioxane	1.0		1.030
0	CCl_4	1,4 dioxane	1.0	0.46	1.038
10	1,4 dioxane	1,4 dioxane	1.0	0.61	1.033
10	1,4 dioxane	1,4 dioxane	2.0	0.56	1.037
10	n-heptane	1,4 dioxane	1.0	0.24	1.037
10	CCl_4	1,4 dioxane	2.0	0.35	1.040
20	CCl_4	1,4 dioxane	2.0	—	1.029
20	1,4 dioxane	1,4 dioxane	1.0	0.49	1.031
20	n-heptane	1,4 dioxane	1.0	0.27	1.034
20	1,4 dioxane	1,4 dioxane	2.0	—	1.036
25	1,4 dioxane	1,4 dioxane	2.0	—	1.006
25	n-heptane	1,4 dioxane	1.0	—	1.009
25	n-heptane	1,4 dioxane	1.0	—	1.012

of previous measurements (29, 32, 42). Tables III and IV give the experimental results for the effect of solvents on the composition of the phases along with calculated values for α. A plot of all the determinations with CCl_4 and with CCl_4–$C_2Cl_4F_2$ was used to obtain values of α at temperatures of interest in the experiments with the exchange columns to be described later.

Table III.   Effect of Solvent on the Composition of the Gas and Liquid Phases as a Function of Temperature for the NO–NO$_2$ System[a]

Temp. °C.	Solvent	N_2O_3 p_1	N_2O_4 p_2	NO p_3	NO_2 p_4	Solvent p_5	x	X
−19	none	0.036	0.009	0.950	0.005	—	0.056	0.544
−19	CCl_4	0.033	0.006	0.943	0.004	0.014	0.048	0.543
−12	none	0.066	0.031	0.889	0.014	—	0.129	0.618
−12	CCl_4	0.045	0.014	0.914	0.009	0.018	0.079	0.623
−5	none	0.073	0.068	0.832	0.027	—	0.203	0.657
−5	CCl_4–$C_2Cl_4F_2$	0.053	0.032	0.855	0.019	0.041	0.130	0.664
0	none	0.079	0.108	0.769	0.044	—	0.286	0.734
0	CCl_4	0.073	0.087	0.757	0.040	0.043	0.257	0.737
0	CCl_4–$C_2Cl_4F_2$	0.076	0.080	0.761	0.039	0.044	0.247	0.739
10	none	0.078	0.251	0.567	0.104	—	0.515	0.859
10	CCl_4–$C_2Cl_4F_2$	0.066	0.186	0.580	0.090	0.078	0.450	0.869

[a] The concentrations of the initial solutions were 1 mole N_2O_4 per 100 ml. of solvent. The partial pressures are in atmospheres. x is the fraction of the nitrogen of gas phase that is in the 4+ oxidation state; X is the same quantity for the liquid phase.

Table IV.   Effect of Solvents on the Enrichment Factor Calculated from the Compositions of the Phases and the Values of α for the Individual Exchange Reactions[a]

Temp. °C.	Solvent	Gas Phase				Liquid Phase		
		N_2O_3 m_1	N_2O_4 m_2	NO m_3	NO_2 m_4	N_2O_3 M_1	N_2O_4 M_2	$\alpha_{calc.}$
−19	none	0.069	0.017	0.909	0.0048	0.912	0.088	1.040
−19	CCl_4	0.064	0.012	0.920	0.0039	0.914	0.086	1.041
−12	none	0.120	0.057	0.810	0.013	0.764	0.236	1.039
−12	CCl_4	0.087	0.027	0.878	0.0086	0.754	0.246	1.044
−5	none	0.128	0.119	0.729	0.024	0.686	0.314	1.036
−5	CCl_4:$C_2Cl_4F_2$	0.102	0.061	0.819	0.018	0.672	0.328	1.042
0	none	0.133	0.182	0.648	0.037	0.532	0.468	1.035
0	CCl_4	0.104	0.156	0.678	0.036	0.526	0.474	1.037
0	CCl_4:$C_2Cl_4F_2$	0.137	0.144	0.684	0.035	0.522	0.478	1.038
10	none	0.117	0.338	0.427	0.078	0.282	0.718	1.027
−10	CCl_4:$C_2Cl_4F_2$	0.112	0.317	0.494	0.077	0.262	0.738	1.032

[a] m_i is the atom fraction of the nitrogen of the gas phase present as species i; M_i is the same quantity for the liquid phase.

Except at $-14°C.$, there is a small but significant increase in α for the $NO-N_2O_3$ system when an inert non-donor solvent is present in approximately equal molar quantities with the initial N_2O_4. At $-14°C.$ and lower temperatures, the gas phase is over 90% NO even in the absence of the solvent and no significant effect would be expected. At the higher temperatures, the differences among the solvents is within the uncertainty of the measurements except that nitromethane with a dielectric constant of 37 seems to have a slightly greater effect on α at $0°C.$ than n-heptane. Although solvents such as nitromethane increase the extent of self-ionization of N_2O_4 to NO^+ and NO_3^- as measured by conductivity ($1, 21$), the fraction ionized is very small. The dissociation ($20, 41$) of N_2O_4 to NO_2 is very much less in liquid N_2O_4 ($K_c' = 10.5 \times 10^{-5}$ moles/liter at $20°C.$) than in the gaseous phase ($K_c = 394 \times 10^{-5}$ moles/liter at $20°C.$). In solvents such as CCl_4 ($K_c' = 8.1 \times 10^{-5}$ moles/liter at $20°C.$), the dissociation is affected by the nature of the solvent and increases with dilution, but it is still small. These effects may influence the rate of isotope exchange since they significantly affect the chemical reactivity of the system ($2, 21$), but their effect on the equilibrium concentrations of the principal species and on α should be small.

Evidence that the increase in α can be attributed to the effect of the solvent on the composition of gas and liquid phases is supported by the results in Tables III and IV. The values of m_1, m_2, m_3, and m_4 were calculated from the partial pressures of the oxides of nitrogen in the gas phase (Table III). (*See* Equation 10). Similarly M_1 and M_2 were calculated from Equations 19 and 20, and the results are given in Table IV. For temperatures higher than $-19°C.$, the presence of CCl_4 or of an equal volume mixture of CCl_4 and FCl_2CCCl_2F (Freon 112) decreases the partial pressures of N_2O_3, N_2O_4, and NO_2 in the gas phase and increases the mole fraction of N_2O_4 in the liquid phase. The corresponding values of m_i and M_i change in the same way. Thus, the 4+ nitrogen species are decreased in the gas phase and increased in the liquid phase. Qualitatively these results are expected since the mole fraction of N_2O_3 and N_2O_4 in the liquid phase is reduced by the presence of the solvent (4), and this should reduce their partial pressures in the gas phase. The concentration of NO will be affected very little by the small quantity of solvent since the solubility of NO is small. Measurements at $0°C.$, for example, gave the following solubilities in cc. of NO per ml. of solvent: n-heptane, 0.57 cc./ml.; CCl_4, 0.63 cc./ml.; and nitromethane, 0.52 cc./ml.

The significance of the changes in concentration of the species in the two phases is illustrated by calculations of the theoretical values for $\alpha_{calc.}$ (Table IV). Monse *et al.* (29) have used spectroscopic data to calculate the enrichment factors for the three exchange Reactions 6, 7, and 8, and their results over the temperature range of interest here are given by log α_{13} = 7.340/T − 0.01168; α_{23} = 14.400/T − 0.01903; and log α_{43} = 8.9253/T − 0.01197. Using values from these expressions in Equation 9, calculated values of α ($\alpha_{calc.}$ in Table IV) were obtained for the system alone or with the solvent at each temperature. Except at −19°C., $\alpha_{calc.}$ is significantly higher in the presence of the solvents. The maximum effect is in the temperature range from −5° to −12°C. which also corresponds to the maximum changes in composition of the gas phase (Figure 2).

The values of α (Table IV) calculated from the experimentally determined composition of the phases and the theoretically calculated values of α for Reactions 6, 7, and 8 are in reasonable agreement with those measured experimentally but in general are slightly higher. This could arise in part from the assumptions involved in the derivation of Equation 9 which neglects isotope effects among the species in the condensed phase and between the same molecules in the gas and liquid phase. Also the oxides of nitrogen in the liquid phase were assumed to be only N_2O_3 and N_2O_4 when, as mentioned previously, it is known that N_2O_4 is slightly dissociated to NO_2. Furthermore, some NO is present owing to the dissociation of N_2O_3 and to the solubility of NO. No attempt was made to determine whether or not consideration of such effects would improve the agreement between the calculated and the experimental values of α.

Effect of Donor Molecules on α. The experimental values of α in Table II indicate that the presence of donor molecules can significantly enhance the fractionation factor, particularly at the higher temperatures. In these experiments, the millimoles of donor added was equal to the millimoles of N_2O_4. A solvent was then added to give the concentrations listed, after which NO was added as previously described until the pressure in the equilibration vessel was 1 atm. Because of the limited solubility of the complexes in some of the solvents, it was necessary to use more dilute solutions than those of Table I.

The experiments at 0°C. (Table II) involved a series of donor molecules that form 1 : 1 complexes with N_2O_4 whose melting points are in the following order (40): 1,4-dioxane, 45.2°C.; dimethylsulfoxide, 38.0°C.; 1,3-dioxane, 2.0°C.; tetrahydrofuran, −20.5°C.; 2,2 dimethoxyethane, < −60°C. The nature and stability of complexes such as these have been investigated rather extensively (2, 3, 4, 5, 6, 7, 8, 28, 38, 40, 48). 1,4-dioxane forms a relatively stable complex with N_2O_4 and of those complexes listed above, it has the largest effect on α. For this reason it was selected for the experiments at higher temperatures and with the other solvents.

When the N_2O_4 : 1,4-dioxane complex is equilibrated with some excess gaseous NO_2 at 25°C., there is a small isotope effect of 1.008 which increases to 1.012 at 20°C. for a solution of 2 millimoles of the complex per ml. of 1,4-dioxane as a solvent. This is about the magnitude of the effect expected for the isotope exchange of NO_2 with N_2O_4 (29). The solution of the complex is light brown as a result of a small amount of dissociation to NO_2. After saturation with NO at 10°C. until pressure is 1 atm., the solution is blue but the gas phase is practically colorless indicating rather low concentrations of NO_2 in the gas phase relative to those observed for N_2O_4 in non-donor solvents. The fact that α at 10°C. is about the same for a solution of the N_2O_4 : 1,4-dioxane complex in n-heptane or CCl_4 as it is in excess 1,4-dioxane as a solvent indicates that one mole of 1,4-dioxane per mole of N_2O_4 is sufficient effectively to complex N_2O_4.

Since the value of α for N_2O_4 : 1,4-dioxane complex at 20°C. is about the same as that for N_2O_4 alone in CCl_4 at -5°C., its use in an exchange column would have the advantage of not requiring refrigeration. However, it was found that the 1,4-dioxane was slowly attacked when used in the exchange column. This probably occurs in the thermal reflux system to be described in the following section. A more stable donor molecule would be of interest in this respect.

Experiments with Exchange Columns

The Solvent Carrier Exchange System. The results of the previous section showed that the single stage fractionation factor α for the $NO-N_2O_3$ system could be increased by the addition of inert solvents with or without donor molecules. A small exchange column, as described in this section, was used to study the behavior of these solvent systems and to determine the optimum operating conditions for concentrating nitrogen-15. The arrangement was similar to the solvent carrier system used by Narten and Taylor (34) for the exchange of NO with non-aqueous solutions of the $NO-CuCl_2$ complex. However, it was necessary to add an additional section to the thermal reflux system to convert nitrogen in the 4+ oxidation state to NO as was done by Monse, Taylor, and Spindel (32) for the $NO-N_2O_3$ system.

The exchange column and reflux system are shown in Figure 3. The jacketed exchange column B (1.0 cm. i.d.) was packed for a length of 100 cm. with small rectangular coils of stainless steel wire. For most of the initial experiments Helipak (Podbielniak, Inc., Franklin Park, Ill.) No. 3013, 0.050 inches $\times$ 0.100 inches $\times$ 0.100 inches was used as a packing although, as will be discussed later, the smaller size Helipak No. 3012, 0.035 inches $\times$ 0.050 inches $\times$ 0.050 inches, was more efficient in this 1.0 cm. i.d. column. Foam rubber was used to insulate the jacketed sections of the system, and the temperatures were controlled by circulating coolant from two separate thermostatically regulated baths. One bath regulated to ±0.5°C. supplied coolant at R_3, R_4, and R_5 for the exchange column and the thermal refluxer. The other bath at temperatures between $-12°$ and $-16°$C. supplied coolant at R_1, R_2, and R_6.

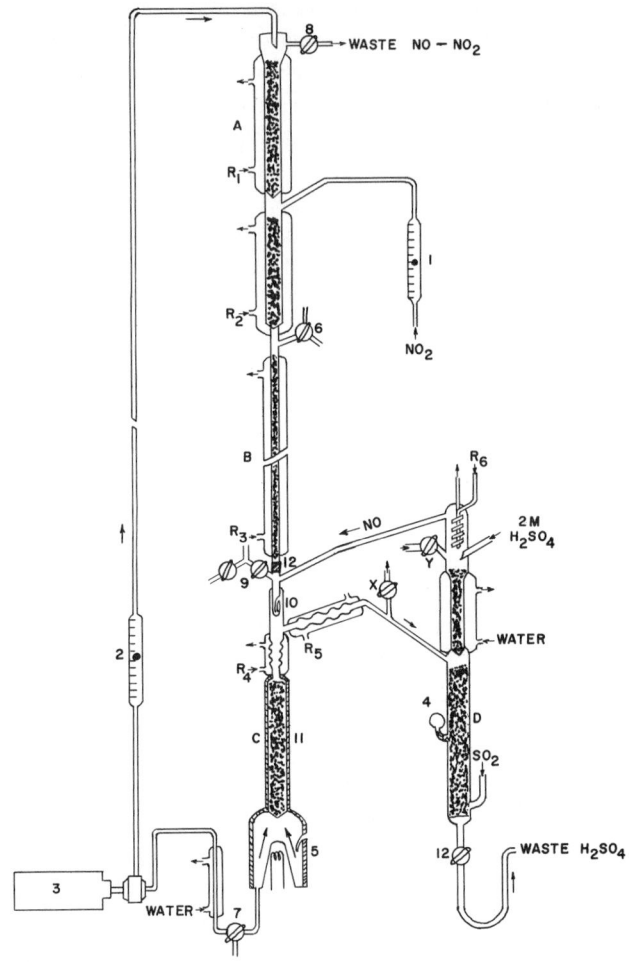

Figure 3. Exchange column, thermal refluxer, and reflux reactor for the NO-N_2O_3 solvent carrier system. The parts of the system are discussed in the text. X and Y indicate the positions to which connections are made when two columns are operated in cascade

Gaseous NO_2 flows from a tank of N_2O_4 through a calibrated Rota-meter flow meter and a heated ($28°$–$30°$C.) stainless steel tube to the center part of section A at the top of the exchange column (*see* Figure 3). Here the NO_2 condenses to N_2O_4 and dissolves in the solvent entering at the top of section A. Reaction of the N_2O_4 with part of the ascending NO forms a solution of N_2O_3 and N_2O_4. The remainder of the NO with some

NO$_2$, determined by the temperature of the top condenser, leaves as waste through stopcock (no. 8) and is discarded after reaction with air and water to form nitric acid in a short packed column (not shown in Figure 3).

As the solution of N$_2$O$_3$–N$_2$O$_4$ flows downward through the packing, isotope exchange occurs with the ascending gaseous mixture of oxides of nitrogen. The liquid phase is enriched in nitrogen-15 which accumulates at the lower end of the column. The solution flows through the liquid seal (no. 10) into the thermal reflux section C where the oxides of nitrogen are expelled from the solvent. This section consists of a boiler (no. 5); a packed stripping column (no. 11) (20 cm. long, 22 mm. i.d., packed with 1.6 mm. i.d. glass helices); and the two condensers. The solvent, free of oxides of nitrogen, is pumped by a Sigmamotor (Sigmamotor, Inc., Middleport, N. Y.) finger pump (no. 3) through a flowmeter (no. 2) to the top of section A.

The oxides of nitrogen expelled from the solvent in the thermal refluxer pass into the reactor D (60 cm. long, 30 mm. i.d., packed with glass helices) where the nitrogen in the 4+ oxidation state reacts with a descending stream of 2M H$_2$SO$_4$ (1-3 cc./minute) and an ascending stream of SO$_2$ according to the following reactions

$$3NO_2 + H_2O \rightarrow 2HNO_3 + NO$$

$$\frac{2HNO_3 + 3SO_2 + 2H_2O \rightarrow 3H_2SO_4 + 2NO}{3NO_2 + 3H_2O + 3SO_2 \rightarrow 3H_2SO_4 + 2NO} \tag{21}$$

The use of 2M to 4M H$_2$SO$_4$ instead of water improves the performance of this part of the reflux system (*31*). An optical cell 4 with a photo-electric relay was used for automatic control of the flow of SO$_2$ (*39, 43*) by opening a solenoid valve to increase the flow of SO$_2$ when the brown colored reaction zone descended to the optical cell. The NO produced by the above reactions, along with that present in the liquid phase as N$_2$O$_3$, passed into the exchange column B through a jacketed section at −12° to −16°C. which condensed and returned most of the unreacted NO$_2$ to the reactor.

The waste sulfuric acid from the bottom of the reactor was collected, measured, and titrated for H$_2$SO$_4$ content to obtain the flow in millimoles of H$_2$SO$_4$/minute. The difference between the total flow of H$_2$SO$_4$ and the flow of H$_2$SO$_4$ into the top of the reactor is the millimoles of H$_2$SO$_4$/minute produced by Reaction 21. This is equal to the millimoles/minute of NO$_2$ reduced to NO, that is the mg. atoms/minute of 4+ nitrogen reduced to 2+ oxidation state. Since the mg. atoms/minute of 4+ nitrogen entering the refluxer is the difference between the flow of 4+ nitrogen in the liquid and gas phase (*31*),

$$(LX - Lx) = L_{H_2SO_4}$$

or

$$L = \frac{L_{H_2SO_4}}{X - x} \tag{22}$$

where L = interstage flow in mg. atoms N/minute, $L_{H_2SO_4}$ is the millimoles/minute of H$_2$SO$_4$ produced in the reactor; X and x are the atom fractions of 4+ nitrogen in the total nitrogen of the liquid and the gas phase respectively at the temperature of the exchange column. Values for X and x at various temperatures, with and without solvent, are known from spectrophotometric measurements as described in a previous section.

The interstage flow could also be calculated from material balance considerations at the top end of the system. When no product is being withdrawn, the mg. atoms of 4+ and 2+ nitrogen leaving as waste must be equal to the total feed flow L_f in mg. atom N/minute as NO_2 or N_2O_4. The mg. atoms N/minute of 2+ nitrogen as NO in the waste stream is then $L_f(1 - x')$ which must be equal to the 4+ nitrogen that entered the refluxer and was reduced to NO; thus,

$$LX - Lx = L_f(1 - x')$$

or

$$L = \frac{L_f(1 - x')}{(X - x)} \tag{23}$$

where x' is the atom fraction of 4+ nitrogen in the total nitrogen of the gas phase at the temperature of the top condenser. The results for the interstage flow measurements by the two methods agreed within $\pm 3\%$.

Typically, to start a run, a short section of thin-walled Teflon tubing (no. 12) between the exchange column and the refluxer was pinched with a screw clamp. The boiler was charged with 250 cc. of the solvent which was pumped to the top of section A until the exchange column was flooded. After adjusting the pumping rate to that desired for the experiment, the solvent was slowly drained from the column by adjusting the screw clamp. With continuous pumping of solvent at the desired rate, the power to the boiler was turned on and the temperatures of the circulating coolant in the jackets were adjusted. N_2O_4 was then admitted and the run was considered started when the oxides of nitrogen entered the reactor D and the SO_2 had formed a stable reaction zone near the optical cell.

The progress of the enrichment of nitrogen-15 was followed by periodically withdrawing gas samples from the top of the exchange column through stopcock (no. 6) and from the bottom through stopcock (no. 9). These samples were converted to N_2 and analyzed with the mass spectrometer as described previously. The overall separation S, is given by $S = R_p/R_o$ where R_o is the ratio of the peak height at mass 29 to that at mass 28 for the sample from the upper end of the exchange column and R_p is this ratio for the product from the lower end. If no product is withdrawn, other than a negligible amount for samples, the overall separation S_∞ at the steady state can be used to calculate the number of "theoretical plates" n in the column from Equation 3. The height of column equivalent to a theoretical plate (HETP) is then z/n where z is the length of the exchange column.

Although values of S_∞, HETP and α can be used to select the optimum operating conditions, Cohen's (15, 16) equations for countercurrent isotope exchange columns can be used to examine the effect of the variables in more detail. Since the distribution of isotopes between the phases is displaced from equilibrium by the order of α during the operation of the exchange column, there will be a transfer of F moles/sec.-cc. of nitrogen-

15 across the phase boundary in a 1 cm. length of column per cm.^{2} of cross section as given by

$$F = k_T a[\alpha(n)(1 - N) - N(1 - n)] \tag{24}$$

where

$$\frac{1}{k_T a} = \frac{1}{kcC} + \frac{1}{(dca/b)} + \frac{1}{(DCa/B)} \tag{25}$$

In the above equations n and N are the atom fractions of nitrogen-15 species in the gas phase and the liquid phase respectively; c (moles/cc.), d (cm.^{2}/sec.), b (cm.) for the gas phase are respectively the concentration of oxides of nitrogen, the diffusion coefficient, and the thickness of the boundary layer, while C, D, and B are the same quantities for the liquid phase; k (cc./moles-sec.) is a rate constant for the exchange of oxides of nitrogen between the gas and liquid phase. The specific transfer rate k_T (moles/sec.-cm.^{2}) when multiplied by the interfacial area a (cm.^{2}/cc.) in a 1 cm. length of column per cm.^{2} of cross-sectional area gives an interphase transfer rate $k_T a$ (moles/sec.-cc.). If chemical reaction is rate limiting, $k_T a$ will be determined by the first term of Equation 25, otherwise it will be determined by the diffusion terms.

For steady-state operation with no production in cases where α is near unity, the overall separation is given by (*15*)

$$\ln S_\infty = (k_T a)z(\alpha - 1)/L' \tag{26}$$

where z (cm.) is the length of the column, and L' (moles/sec.-cm.^{2}) is the interstage flow of exchangeable species per unit cross-sectional area of the column. This equation can be rearranged to $k_T a = (\ln S_\infty)L'/z(\alpha - 1) = L'/$HETP from which an interphase transfer rate per unit volume of column can be calculated. In the solvent carrier system, this rate will be affected primarily by such factors as the concentration of oxides of nitrogen in the liquid, the temperature, and the interfacial area per unit volume of packing.

If $k_T a$ and $(\alpha - 1)$ do not change with interstage flow, Equation 26 shows that ln S_∞ should vary as $1/L'$. Alternatively Equation 26 can be written as $z(\alpha - 1)/\ln S_\infty = L'/k_T a =$ HETP or as $(\ln S_\infty)L' = k_T a z(\alpha - 1)$. Thus, HETP should vary linearly with L' or $(\ln S_\infty)L'$ should be constant if $k_T a$ and $(\alpha - 1)$ remain constant. However, if the liquid flow is too low, the packing may not be properly wet and the interfacial area per cc. of packing will be low so that $k_T a$ may decrease at low liquid flow rates. It was shown in a previous section that the presence of a solvent affects the composition of the phases resulting in small changes in $(\alpha - 1)$. Thus, a change in mole fraction of oxides of nitrogen by changes in the ratio of N_2O_4 feed flow to solvent flow can affect $(\alpha - 1)$. However, as the following sections will indicate, the principal effect of the solvent is its influence on the interphase transfer rate $k_T a$, HETP, and hold-up of exchangeable species.

A considerable amount of data would be required to evaluate the effect of all of the variables in the operation of the exchange column. The results for a limited number of experiments on the effect of solvent, flow rates and temperature are summarized in sections A-D of Table V.

Table V. Effect of Solvent, Feed Flow, Solvent of Nitrogen-15 in a 100 cm. × 1.0 cm.

Solvent	Column Temp. °C.	Top Temp. °C.	Solvent ml./min.	Feed, L_f mg. atoms N/min.
				A. Effect of
none	-14	-12	0	20
CCl_4	-14	-12	1.0	20
$CCl_4:C_2Cl_4F_2$	-14	-12	1.0	20
none	0	-14	0	20
CCl_4	0	-14	1.0	20
$CCl_4:C_2Cl_4F_2$	0	-14	1.0	20
none	14	-14	0	20
CCl_4	14	-14	1.0	20
$CCl_4:C_2Cl_4F_2$	14	-16	1.0	20
				B. Effect of
none	-14	-12	0	10
none	-14	-12	0	20
CCl_4	-14	-14	0.9	10
CCl_4	-14	-12	1.0	20
$CCl_4:C_2Cl_2F_2$	0	-14	1.0	10
$CCl_4:C_2Cl_2F_2$	0	-14	1.0	20
$CCl_4:C_2Cl_2F_2$	0	-14	1.0	30
				C. Effect of
CCl_4	-14	-14	0.9	10
CCl_4	-14	-14	2.0	10
CCl_4	-14	-12	5.0	10
				D. Effect of
none	-14	-12	0	20
none	0	-14	0	20
none	14	-14	0	20
CCl_4	-14	-12	1	20
CCl_4	0	-14	1	20
CCl_4	14	-14	1	20

[a] Values of α were interpolated from plots of available data and the interstage flows

Effect of Solvent. The marked effect of the solvent carrier on the overall separation is shown in section A of Table V. At $-14°$C., for example, S_∞ was 2.8 with the $NO–N_2O_3$ system alone, but at the same feed flow, a solvent flow of 1 cc./min. increased the overall separation to 7.6 for CCl_4 and to 9.1 for an equal volume mixture of CCl_4 and $C_2Cl_4F_2$. A similiar improvement is observed at $0°$C. but at $14°$C. the effect is

**Flow and Temperature on the Overall Separation
i.d. Column Packed with Helipak 3013** [a]

Interstage, L mg. atoms N/min.	S_∞	α	HETP cm.	$k_Ta \times 10^4$ gram-atoms N sec.–cc.
Solvent				
35	2.8	1.035	3.41	2.19
36	7.9	1.034	1.58	4.64
37	9.1	1.034	1.51	4.96
41	2.3	1.020	2.38	3.62
40	7.1	1.028	1.41	5.94
40	7.6	1.029	1.41	5.79
54	1.7	1.008	1.50	7.60
50	3.2	1.018	1.53	6.86
75	3.5	1.019	1.51	10.50
Feed Flow				
18	2.4	1.035	3.93	0.96
35	2.8	1.035	3.41	2.19
(18)	3.4	1.034	2.73	1.53
36	7.9	1.034	1.62	4.64
20	4.5	1.029	1.60	2.26
39	7.6	1.029	1.41	5.79
54	5.1	1.029	1.75	6.44
Solvent Flow				
(18)	3.4	1.034	2.73	1.53
(18)	3.0	1.034	3.04	1.30
18	2.3	1.034	4.01	0.94
Temperature				
35	2.8	1.035	3.41	2.19
41	2.3	1.020	2.38	3.62
54	1.7	1.008	1.50	7.60
36	7.9	1.034	1.62	4.64
40	7.1	1.028	1.41	5.94
50	3.2	1.018	1.53	6.86

are the averages of the values from the two methods referred to in the text.

somewhat less. At $-14°C.$, where the value of α is not significantly affected by the solvent, there is a large decrease in HETP from 3.4 to 1.5 cm. and an increase in k_Ta from 2.2 to 5.0×10^{-4} moles/sec.-cc. Thus, the effect of the solvent seems to be primarily caused by improved inter-phase transfer apparently as a result of more complete wetting of the packing to give greater interfacial area, lower film resistance, or faster chemical exchange rates.

At 0°C. the presence of the solvent increases α from about 1.020 with no solvent to 1.029 with CCl_4–$C_2Cl_4F_2$ present. Since S_∞ for no solvent was 2.3, the number of plates in the 100 cm. column was 42 (Equation 3). This same number of plates for CCl_4–$C_2Cl_4F_2$ with $\alpha = 1.029$ at 0°C. would result in an overall separation of only 3.3 instead of 7.6 observed. Thus, at this temperature also, besides improving α, an important effect of the solvent is to decrease HETP thereby increasing the number of theoretical plates in the column.

Besides CCl_4 and an equal volume mixture of CCl_4 and $C_2Cl_4F_2$, a number of other solvents and solutions were tested in the exchange column. These included n-hexane, n-heptane, n-octane, nitromethane, 1-2 dimethoxyethane, $1M$ 1,4-dioxane in CCl_4, and $1M$ tetrahydrofuran in CCl_4 (27). Among the hydrocarbons, n-heptane gave the highest overall separations and seemed to be reasonably stable, but it was not as effective as CCl_4 or CCl_4–$C_2Cl_4F_2$. The other solvents and mixtures listed above were slowly attacked by the oxides of nitrogen. Comparisons of a solution of a strong complexing agent such as 1,4-dioxane with a solution of a less stable one such as tetrahydrofuran were of interest because of their favorable effect on the value of α (Table II). However, during the operation of the exchange column both of these donor molecules were slowly attacked, probably in the boiler of the thermal reflux system. By withdrawing samples from stopcock 7 (Figure 3) at the lower end of the thermal reflux system it was confirmed that the lower separation with the solvents other than CCl_4 and CCl_4–$C_2Cl_4F_2$ was caused by reaction with oxides of nitrogen. These were examined by mass spectrometry, gas chromatography or infrared spectrometry. Of the solvents investigated CCl_4, CCl_4–$C_2Cl_4F_2$, and n-heptane were the most satisfactory with respect to physical properties and chemical stability.

Effect of Flow Rates. In the solvent carrier system used here, it is possible to vary independently the feed flow of N_2O_4 and the solvent flow. The optimum flow rates can be determined by holding one of the flows constant and changing the other. Section B of Table V shows the results of a limited number of experiments on the effect of increasing the feed flow while holding the solvent flow constant at approximately 1 cc./min. With CCl_4 at −14°C. there is a marked increase in overall separation when the feed flow was increased from 10 to 20 mg. atoms N/min. Similarly at 0°C. with CCl_4–$C_2Cl_4F_2$ there was a maximum in the overall separation at a feed rate of 20 mg. atoms N/min. From these results the optimum flows appear to be about 20 mg. atoms N/min. (10 millimoles N_2O_4/min.) and a solvent flow of 1 cc./min. (10.4 millimoles CCl_4/min.).

In the case of CCl_4 at −14°C., a feed flow of 20 mg. atoms N/min. resulted in an interstage flow of 36 mg. atoms N/min. This higher flow results from the reactions $2NO + N_2O_4 \rightleftharpoons 2N_2O_3$ at the top of the column so that the total nitrogen flow in the liquid phase is greater than expected from the feed flow alone. The interstage flow is also influenced by the composition of the gas phase and the temperature of the jackets at the top of the column as shown by Equation 23 since at lower temperatures less NO_2, N_2O_3, and N_2O_4 leaves the column with the waste NO. With the above feed and interstage flows at −14°C., the liquid phase will consist of approximately 83 mole % N_2O_3 and 17 mole % N_2O_4 (Table IV) or 15 millimoles of N_2O_3 and 3 millimoles of N_2O_4 in 10.4 millimoles of CCl_4 resulting in a molarity of about 9 moles/liter. The mole fraction of the oxides of nitrogen is about 0.63 and the percent by volume of CCl_4 is about 50%. The total liquid flow is about 2 cc./min. or 2.55 cc./cm.^{2}-min. These optimum flows are for a 1.0 cm. i.d. column packed with Helipak 3013. As will be shown later, considerably higher separations are obtained with a smaller size packing in the same column and the optimum flows are not quite the same.

The relative values of S_x, HETP, and $k_T a$ for the experiments in Table V-B indicate that volumetric flows below 2 cc./min. or mole fractions of oxides of nitrogen in the solvent below 0.6 (concentration ~9 moles/liter), result in poorer performance of this exchange column. Normally, according to Equation 26, an increase in interstage flow L results in an increase in HETP. However, for the two experiments with no solvent where this equation should apply, HETP decreased when the interstage flow increased from 18 to 35 mg. atoms N/min. The lower flow apparently does not wet the packing effectively as is also indicated by the low value for $k_T a$.

Increasing the solvent flow from 0.9 to 5 ml./min. while maintaining the feed flow constant at 10 mg. atoms N/min. (Table V-C) decreases the concentration of oxides of nitrogen in the liquid phase from about 6.5 to 1.6 moles/liter. The decrease in overall separation or the increase in HETP was not as large as expected for $k_T a$ proportional to concentration C. The change in $k_T a$ is more nearly proportional to $C^{1/2}$ which, under some circumstances would indicate that the process is reaction rate controlled (*17*). Thus, for the more dilute solutions, the process may be limited partially by reaction rate while for concentrations greater than 9 moles/liter, it may be limited by diffusion although not enough data are available to establish these relations.

Effect of Temperature. The principal effect of increasing the temperature from $-14°$ to $+14°C$. is a large decrease in the overall separation (Table V-D). However, the increase in temperature is expected to increase the rate of interphase transfer $k_T a$ primarily because of changes in diffusion constants, viscosity and reaction rates. A plot of ln $k_T a$ *vs.* $1/T$ results in an activation energy of about 2 kcal./mole for the CCl_4 solution and about 6 kcal./mole when no solvent is present. The low value for these CCl_4 solutions, in which the concentration of the oxides of nitrogen were 9 to 10 moles/liter, is more characteristic of a diffusion controlled process than one that is limited by reaction rate. Examination of the results listed in Table V indicates that the optimum temperature of operation for the solvent carrier system is between $-14°$ and $0°C$.

Effect of Column Packing. The column packing chosen for the experiments described above was Helipak 3013 ($1.27 \times 2.54 \times 2.54$ mm.) since it allowed a wider range of flow rates than the smaller size packing, Helipak 3012 ($0.89 \times 1.78 \times 1.78$ mm.). Usually for a minimum HETP, the size of the packing should be about 1/8 the diameter of the column (*19*) so that the smaller size is more appropriate for a 1.0 cm. i.d. column. The results of a number of experiments for the two packings in the same column are summarized in Table VI. Although the conditions in the experiments for the two packing materials are not precisely the same in all cases, it is evident that the use of the smaller size packing (3012) results in appreciably higher separations and lower values for HETP. The maximum separation obtained with the 3013 packing was 9.1 while the maximum separation obtained with 3012 packing was 22.2 in the same column.

Table VI.   Effect of Size of Packing on the Overall Separation for Nitrogen-15 in a 100 cm. × 1.0 cm. Diameter Exchange Column

Solvent	Temp. °C.	Solvent ml./min.	Feed, L_f mg. atoms N/min.	Packing Helipak No.	S_∞	α	HETP cm.
none	−14	0	10	3013	2.4	1.035	3.93
none	−9	0	10	3012	15.2	1.031	1.12
$CCl_4:C_2Cl_4F_2$	−14	1.0	20	3013	9.1	1.034	1.51
$CCl_4:C_2Cl_4F_2$	−9	0.6	10	3012	19.2	1.033	1.10
$CCl_4:C_2Cl_4F_2$	−9	1.1	10	3012	22.2	1.033	1.05
none	0	0	20	3013	2.3	1.020	2.38
none	0	0	20	3012	2.9	1.020	1.86
$CCl_4:C_2Cl_4F_2$	14	1	20	3013	3.5	1.019	1.50
$CCl_4:C_2Cl_4F_2$	14	1	20	3012	4.2	1.019	1.31

The optimum flows for the 3013 packing in the 1.0 cm. i.d. column (1 cc./min. of CCl_4 and 20 mg. atoms/min. of N_2O_4) frequently resulted in flooding of the 3012 packing. Satisfactory flows for the smaller size packing was 1 cc. of solvent and 10 mg. atoms/min. of N_2O_4 corresponding to a total liquid flow of about 1.6 cc./min.

Comparison With the NO–N_2O_3 and NO–HNO_3 Systems. In order to make a further comparison with NO–N_2O_3 system and to test the operation of the solvent carrier system in a larger diameter column, a 95 cm. × 2.5 cm. i.d. column was packed with Helipak 3013. This was the same column that had been used previously for the NO–N_2O_3 system (*31*) and for the NO–HNO_3 system (*43*). The results for the three systems are summarized in Table VII and the progress of the overall separations with time for typical runs with the NO–N_2O_3 systems are shown in Figure 4. Here again the use of the carrier significantly improved the overall separation. For the NO–N_2O_3 exchange system at the optimum interstage flow of 112 mg. atoms N/min. S_∞ was 13.5 compared to 24.2 with CCl_4 as a solvent. The value of HETP was also significantly improved from 1.12 to 0.96 cm. which means that the interphase transfer rate k_Ta (Table VII) was higher for the solvent carrier system.

An important consideration in a comparison of methods for separating isotopes is the "equilibrium time" or the rate of approach to the steady state. For a given initial and final isotope mole fraction, the equilibrium time is proportional to $h/(\alpha - 1)^2$, where h is the ratio of the hold-up per stage to the interstage flow which is the average processing time per stage (*16*). The measured (*31*) hold-up of column packing (3013) for the NO–N_2O_3 system was 18.6 mg. atoms N/cm. length of column or 20.8 mg. atoms N/stage which, with an interstage flow of 112 mg. atoms N/min., gives a value of 198 for $h/(\alpha - 1)^2$. For this inter-stage flow, the liquid flow was 3.04 ml./min. and the hold-up in ml. of N_2O_3 plus N_2O_4 was 0.105 ml./cc. of packing. The flow of liquid in the column for the $NO-N_2O_3-CCl_4$ system was 3.0 ml./min. of CCl_4 and 2.8 ml./min. of N_2O_3 plus N_2O_4 or a total flow of 5.8 ml./min. of 8.7M solu-tion of the oxides of nitrogen in CCl_4. Measurements of the hold-up of CCl_4 per cc. of column packing at this flow rate with a corresponding counter flow of gas ($\sim$2.5 liter/min.) gave 0.124 ml./cc. If this is taken as the hold-up of the 8.7M solution, the hold-up of solution per cm. length of column is 0.606 ml. or 0.582 ml./stage. Thus, the hold-up for the oxides of nitrogen is 5.06 millimoles or 10.1 mg. atoms N/stage so that $h/(\alpha - 1)^2$ is 92 compared with 198 for the $NO-N_2O_3$ system and 63 for the $NO-HNO_3$ system (Table VII). Consequently, besides increasing α slightly, the use of CCl_4 as a solvent carrier significantly reduces the hold-up of exchangeable material and thereby improves the rate at which overall separation increases with time as is also evident in Figure 4.

Table VII.   Comparison of the Solvent Carrier System with the NO–N$_2$O$_3$ System Alone and the NO–HNO$_3$ System from Experiments in the Same 95 cm. $\times$ 2.5 cm. Diameter Column Packed with Helipak 3013

	$NO-N_2O_3-$ CCl_4	$NO-N_2O_3$ [a]	$NO-HNO_3$ [b]
Temperature, °C.	−9	−9	25
Solvent flow, ml./min.	3	none	none
Feed material	N_2O_4	N_2O_4	10M HNO_3
Feed flow L_f, mg. atoms N/min.	60	60	78
Interstage flow L, mg. atoms N/min.	101	112	$\sim$80
Interstage flow L', mg. atoms N/min.-cm.^{2}	20.6	22.8	16.3
Total liquid flow, ml./min.-cm.^{2}	1.18	0.62	1.60
Overall separation, S_∞	24.2	13.5	6.2
Single stage factor, α	1.033	1.031	1.055
HETP, cm.	0.96	1.12	2.79
k_Ta, gram atoms N/sec.-cc. $\times 10^4$	3.58	3.93	0.97
Hold-up per stage H, mg. atoms N/stage	10.1	20.8	15.4
Processing time/stage, $h = H/L$, min./stage	0.10	0.19	0.19
Relative equilibrium times, $h/(\alpha - 1)^2$	92	198	63
Relative lengths, HETP/$(\alpha - 1)$	29	36	51
Relative areas, $1/L'(\alpha - 1)$	1.47	1.41	1.12
Relative volumes, HETP/$L'(\alpha - 1)^2$	43	51	57

[a] See Reference 31.
[b] See Reference 43.

Other comparisons in Table VII show that the relative lengths and volumes of the column are somewhat more favorable for the solvent carrier system than for the other two systems. In a previous paper (31) comparisons were made of the following exchange systems for concentrating nitrogen-15: $NH_4^+-NH_3$ (*45, 46*); $NO-HNO_3$ (*39, 43*); $NO-N_2O_3$ (*31, 32*) and NO distillation (*13, 14, 33*). From the results of experiments presented here for short columns, somewhat better performance is to be expected for the solvent carrier system relative to the $NO-N_2O_3$ system alone in the preparation of high concentrations of nitrogen-15.

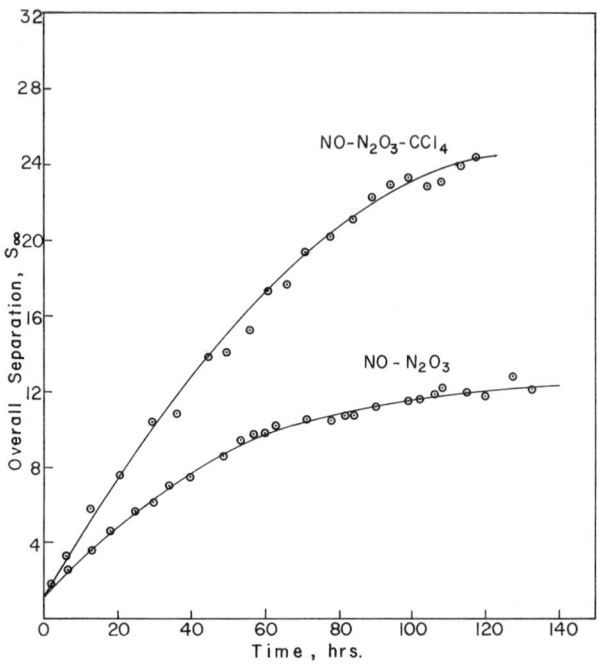

Figure 4.   Progress of the overall separation with time for the $NO-N_2O_3-CCl_4$ and the $NO-N_2O_3$ system in a 95 cm. × 2.5 cm. diameter column packed with Helipak 3013. The curve for the $NO-N_2O_3$ system was reproduced from Reference 3

Preparation of 99.5% Nitrogen Using the Solvent Carrier System

In order to test the calculations based on the data with the small columns and to check the feasibility of the solvent carrier system for preparing 99.5% nitrogen-15, a tapered cascade of two borosilicate glass columns was constructed. It is desirable to prepare high concentrations of nitrogen-15 to establish the applicability of the method since the extent of possible losses or recirculation of exchangeable nitrogen species with the solvent are not easily determined with small columns. The necessity of negligible losses in the reflux system can be seen from the following considerations of the maximum millimoles/min. of product P with a mole fraction of nitrogen-15, N_p, that can be withdrawn for a given interstage flow, L (millimoles/min.). From Equation 5, $T \simeq PN_p \simeq LN_o$-$(1 - N_o) (\alpha - 1)$ so that

$$P \simeq L(N_o) (1 - N_o) (\alpha - 1)/N_p \simeq 120 \times 10^{-6}L \qquad (27)$$

or 120 p.p.m. of the interstage flow. Thus, if small losses occur in the reflux system because of incomplete reaction with SO_2 or because of reaction with the solvent in the thermal refluxer, the overall separation for the system will be reduced and the high concentration of nitrogen-15 will not be obtained.

The overall separation required for 99.5% nitrogen-15 is 54,300 and the minimum number of stages (Equation 3) for $\alpha = 1.033$ is 336. For HETP $= 0.96$ cm./stage, the minimum total length of column with no production would be 3.2 meters, but if product is to be withdrawn, 1.5 to 2 times the minimum number of stages is usually provided. On this basis a total length of 5.5 meters was selected for the two columns, the larger one 2.5 m. $\times$ 25 mm. i.d. and the smaller one 3.0 m. $\times$ 6 mm. i.d. The use of a tapered cascade considerably reduces "equilibrium time" for the system.

Construction and Operation of the Exchange Columns. The construction of the two exchange columns was essentially the same as the one shown in Figure 3 and, except for the reflux system, was about the same as the one used previously for the $NO-N_2O_3$ system (*31, 32, 44*). Details of the characteristics of the cascade are summarized in Table VIII. Column I was first started according to the procedure described for the shorter columns. After about 30 hours of operation when the concentration of nitrogen-15 was about 3.8 atom %, a portion of the enriched oxides of nitrogen was transferred from position X (Figure 3) to the top of column II using a Vanton Flex-i-liner pump (Vanton Pump and Equipment Corp., Hillside, N. J.). The pumping rate was adjusted so that the interstage flow in column II was about 3% of that in column I. The exit gas from column II returned to the bottom of column I at position Y (Figure 3). Waste gases from top of column I were discarded after reaction with air and water as described previously.

Gas samples of the oxides of nitrogen were withdrawn at intervals of about 12 hours for mass spectrometric analysis. The course of the enrichment as a function of time is shown in Figure 5. The irregularities at A and B were because of accidental interruptions of the recirculation of CCl_4. During most of the run, the concentration of nitrogen-15 at the bottom of column II was between 6 and 8 atom %. The concentration of nitrogen-15 in column I reached 50% in 8 days; 90% in 12 days; 95% in 13 days; 99% in 16 days and 99.5% in 17 days. Instead of continuing to let the concentration increase further, some product of maximum con-

centration was withdrawn and then over a period of two days about
1 gram of > 99% and about 4 grams of > 97 atom % nitrogen-15 was
metered to reservoir bulbs at regular intervals. A considerable quantity
of lower concentration material was also obtained while the system was
being shut down.

**Table VIII.   Summary of the Characteristics and Operating Conditions
for the Cascade of Two Exchange Columns for Preparing 99.5%
Nitrogen-15 with the NO–N$_2$O$_3$ Solvent Carrier System**

Item	Column I	Column II
Exchange columns		
Length, meters	2.5	3.0
Diameter, cm.	2.5	0.6
Liquid seal, length, cm.	8	5
Packing, Helipak No.	3013	3012
Top condenser, cm.	20	20
Condenser temp., °C.	−9	−9
Thermal refluxer		
Stripping section, cm.	30 × 4 i.d.	20 × 2.2 i.d.
Packing, glass helices, inches	1/8 i.d.	1/8 i.d.
Boiler capacity, ml.	1000	200
Condenser, cm.	20	18
Condenser temp., °C.	13	13
Reactor		
Lower packed section, cm.	60 × 5 i.d.	55 × 2.5 i.d.
Top packed section, cm.	35 × 5 i.d.	30 × 2.5 i.d.
Packing, glass helices, inches	1/8 i.d.	1/8 i.d.
Condenser, cm.	20 × 3 i.d.	15 × 2.5 i.d.
Condenser temp., °C.	−9	−9
Operating conditions		
Column temperature, °C.	−11	−10
CCl$_4$ flow	3.5 ± 0.2	0.32 ± 0.05
Feed flow, mg. atoms N/min.	100 − 110	—
Interstage flow, mg. atoms N/min.	172	5.3
4M H$_2$SO$_4$, ml./min.	16	0.75
CCl$_4$ loss ml./hr.	~25	—
Atom fraction ^{15}N final	8.5	99.5

Although a steady state was not achieved, HETP calculated from the
overall separation in column II was 1.18. A direct comparison with the
results from the NO–N$_2$O$_3$ system alone (*32, 44*) cannot be made since
in that run column I had already been in operation for several days
before column II was started. Although the operation of the solvent
carrier system was quite satisfactory, it was evident from the initial
start-up of column I that it was not performing as efficiently as the shorter
95 × 2.5 cm. column (Table VII). Inspection of the packing during

operation indicated that it was not being properly wetted, probably because of insufficient cleaning and flooding at the start of the run. If this column had operated properly, the initial prediction 10 to 12 days from the runs with the shorter column would probably have been realized.

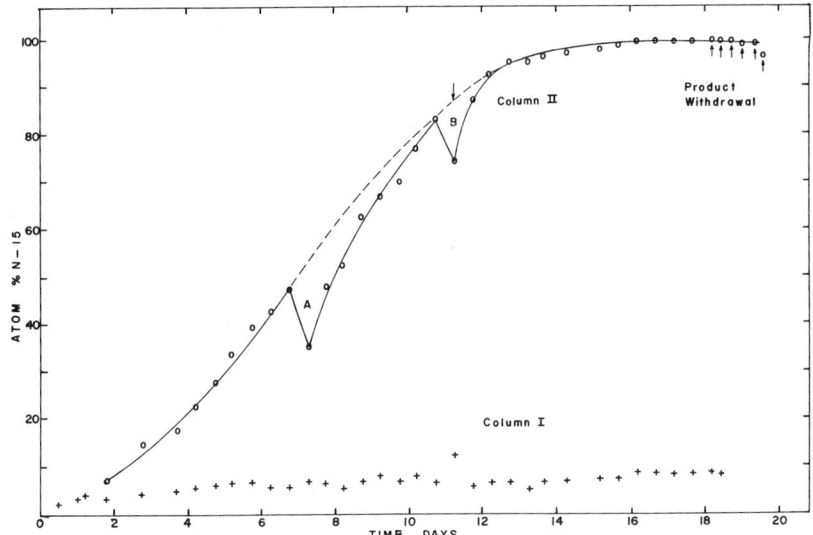

Figure 5. Concentration of nitrogen-15 as a function of time for the cascade of two columns (Table VIII) used to prepare 99.5% nitrogen-15. The irregularities at A and B resulted from interruptions of the recirculation of CCl$_4$

The fact that 99.5% nitrogen-15 was obtained at a transport rate of 0.4 to 0.5 gram nitrogen-15 per day indicates that there was no appreciable loss of enriched material in either the thermal refluxer or the chemical reflux system. Although there was a loss of about 25 cc./hr. of CCl$_4$, most of it could be recovered from the waste sulfuric acid. The solvent carrier system used here required refrigeration to about $-10°$C., but as shown in the experiments on single stage enrichment factors, the use of a sufficiently stable donor molecule that forms a complex with N$_2$O$_4$ would make it possible to achieve the same separation without refrigeration. Similar solvent carrier systems can be used to improve the performance of other exchange reactions for isotope separations.

Acknowledgments

The authors gratefully acknowledge the assistance of Jaime Garbazevich, J. P. Agrawal, Jessie G. Smith, and James Chou in the successful operation of the cascade. We express our appreciation to Karl Schumann for construction of the glass sections of the systems, to Vincent G. Salta-mach for operation of the mass spectrometer and to Gregory Fecho and William C. Zia for some hold-up measurements.

Literature Cited

(1) Addison, C. C., Hodge, N., Lewis, J., *J. Chem. Soc.* **1953**, 2631.
(2) Addison, C. C., Logan, N., "Advances in Inorganic Chemistry and Radio-chemistry," Vol. 6, p. 71, Academic Press, New York, 1964.
(3) Addison, C. C., Lewis, J., *Quart. Rev. (London)* **IX(2)**, 115 (1955).
(4) Addison, C. C., Sheldon, J. C., *J. Chem. Soc.* **1957**, 1937.
(5) *Ibid.*, **1956**, 1941.
(6) *Ibid.*, **1956**, 2705.
(7) *Ibid.*, **1956**, 2709.
(8) *Ibid.*, **1958**, 3142.
(9) Beattie, I. R., Bell, S. W., *J. Chem. Soc.* **1957**, 1681.
(10) Beattie, I. R., Vosper, A. J., *J. Chem. Soc.* **1961**, 2106.
(11) *Ibid.*, **1960**, 4799.
(12) Begun, G. M., Drury, J. S., Joseph, E. F., *Ind. Eng. Chem.* **51**, 1035 (1959).
(13) Clusius, K., Schleich, K., *Helv. Chim. Acta* **41**, 1342 (1958).
(14) Clusius, K., Schleich, K., Vecchi, M., *Helv. Chim. Acta* **44**, 343 (1961).
(15) Cohen, K., *J. Chem. Phys.* **8**, 588 (1940).
(16) Cohen, K., "The Theory of Isotope Separation," McGraw-Hill Book Co., New York, 1951.
(17) Danchkwerts, P. V., Sharma, M. M., *Trans. Inst. Chem. Engrs. (London)* **44**, CE 244 (1966).
(18) Dixon, J. K., *J. Chem. Phys.* **8**, 157 (1940).
(19) Glasebrook, A. L., Williams, F. E., "Technique of Organic Chemistry," Vol. 4, p. 175, Interscience Publishers, New York, 1951.
(20) Gray, P., Rathbone, P., *J. Chem. Soc.* **1958**, 3550.
(21) Gray, P., Yoffe, A. D., *Chem. Rev.* **55**, 1069 (1955).
(22) Hall, T. C., Jr., Blacet, F. E., *J. Chem. Phys.* **20**, 1745 (1952).
(23) Hisatsume, I. C., *J. Phys. Chem.* **65**, 2249 (1961).
(24) Holmes, H. H., Daniels, F., *J. Am. Chem. Soc.* **56**, 630 (1934).
(25) Hughes, E. E., *J. Chem. Phys.* **35**, 1531 (1961).
(26) "JANAF Thermochemical Tables," The Dow Chemical Co., Midland, Mich. (1965).
(27) Jeevanandam, M., Ph.D. Thesis, Columbia University (1965).
(28) Ling, W. H., Sisler, H. H., *J. Am. Chem. Soc.* **75**, 5191 (1953).
(29) Monse, E. U., Kauder, L. N., Spindel, W., *J. Chem. Phys.* **41**, 3898 (1964).
(30) Monse, E. U., Kauder, L. N., Spindel, W., *Z. Naturforch.* **18a**, 235 (1963).
(31) Monse, E. U., Spindel, W., Kauder, L. N., Taylor, T. I., *J. Chem. Phys.* **32**, 1557 (1960).
(32) Monse, E. U., Taylor, T. I., Spindel, W., *J. Phys. Chem.* **65**, 1625 (1961).
(33) McInteer, B. B., Potter, R. M., *Ind. Eng. Chem., Process Design Dev.* **4**, 35 (1965).
(34) Narten, A., Taylor, T. I., *J. Phys. Chem.* **65**, 1877 (1961).
(35) Nier, A. O., *Rev. Sci. Inst.* **11**, 212 (1940).
(36) *Ibid.*, **18**, 398 (1947).
(37) Purcell, R. H., Cheesman, G. H., *J. Chem. Soc.* **1932**, 826.
(38) Rubin, R., Sisler, H. H., Schechter, H., *J. Am. Chem. Soc.* **74**, 877 (1952).
(39) Spindel, W., Taylor, T. I., *J. Chem. Phys.* **24**, 626 (1956).

(40) Sisler, H. H., *J. Chem. Ed.* **34,** 555 (1957).
(41) Steese, C. M., Whittaker, A. G., *J. Chem. Phys.* **24,** 776 (1956).
(42) Stern, M. J., Kauder, L. N., Spindel, W., *J. Chem. Phys.* **36,** 764 (1960).
(43) Taylor, T. I., Spindel, W., "Proceedings International Symposium on Isotope Separation," p. 158, North-Holland Publishing Co., Amsterdam, 1958.
(44) Taylor, T. I., *J. Chim. Phys.* **60,** 154 (1963).
(45) Thode, H. G., Urey, H. C., *J. Chem. Phys.* **7,** 34 (1939).
(46) Urey, H. C., Huffman, J. R., Thode, H. G., Fox, M., *J. Chem. Phys.* **5,** 856 (1937).
(47) Verhoek, E. H., Daniels, F., *J. Am. Chem. Soc.* **53,** 1250 (1931).
(48) Whanger, J., Sisler, H. H., *J. Am. Chem. Soc.* **75,** 5188 (1953).

RECEIVED November 9, 1967. This research was supported by the U. S. Atomic Energy Commission.

9

Analysis of Isotope-effect Calculations Illustrated with Exchange Equilibria Among Oxynitrogen Compounds

E. U. MONSE

Rutgers, The State University, Newark, N. J.

W. SPINDEL and MARVIN J. STERN

Belfer Graduate School of Science, Yeshiva University, New York, N. Y.

The applicability of several approximation methods to the prediction and/or temperature extrapolation of isotopic partition-function ratios for, and equilibrium constants for isotope exchange among, some simple ^{15}N- and ^{18}O-substituted oxynitrogen compounds is evaluated. It is shown that some of the approximation methods investigated can lead to reasonable estimates of room-temperature-region values of the isotopic partition-function ratios. However, attempted application of these methods to the prediction of the (near-unity) equilibrium constants, at room temperature, usually produced rather poor results, owing, for the most part, to the prevalence of "anomalies" in the "exact" temperature dependences. The characteristic frequency of the simple gamma-bar-method equation for either a partition-function ratio or an isotope-exchange equilibrium constant is discussed in terms of the contributing isotope-dependent vibrational frequencies.

The correlation of thermodynamic data on equilibrium or kinetic isotope effects with the force fields and structures of the reacting species is based on quantum-statistical expressions (7, 9, 25) which contain the vibrational frequencies as molecular parameters. The individual frequencies are not easily expressed in terms of the force constants and geometry of the molecule but require the rather involved solution of the secular equation which describes the molecular motions. The use of modern digital computers essentially removes the difficulty in calculating the frequencies, once the necessary input data (force constants, geometry, and atomic masses) are available. Often, however, a lack of spectroscopic data, particularly for large molecules and certainly for transition states, makes the exact prediction of an isotope effect impossible.

There exist (4, 5, 8, 9, 27) simple direct relations, between isotope effect, structure, and force field, which do not necessarily require a complete knowledge of all molecular parameters and avoid the solution of the secular equation. These relations are, however, approximations restricted to limited ranges of temperature. [Newer approximation methods, based on expansions in Jacobi polynomials, are applicable over wide ranges of temperatures (6, 16).] In the past, before the ready availability of fast digital computers, tests of the validity of these approximations were usually fairly limited in nature, but recent extensive tests on model calculations of kinetic isotope effects have been carried out (23, 28). In addition, extensive tests of power-series approximations (not considered in the present paper) have now been performed (6, 16).

The present work is concerned with a critical evaluation of the simple approximation methods as applied to isotope-exchange equilibria among various oxynitrogen compounds. The equilibrium constants were calculated using the best available data on actual force fields and geometries. Of particular interest are the temperature behaviors of the equilibrium constants calculated either by an "exact" equation or by an approximation equation. It has been shown (22) that differences in the thermal-excitation-of-vibration contributions frequently give rise to an "anomalous" temperature dependence of the "exact" isotope effect, in contrast to the common assumption that the magnitude of the isotope effect decreases regularly with increasing temperature. The significance of these temperature-dependence "anomalies" to the results obtained by approximation methods is discussed later in this paper.

The "exact" equation for isotopic reduced partition-function ratios $(s_2/s_1)f$, in the harmonic approximation with neglect of effects owing to condensation and quantum-mechanical rotation, is (7, 25)

$$\frac{s_2}{s_1} f = \Pi \frac{u_{2i}}{u_{1i}} \times \exp\left(\Sigma \frac{u_{1i} - u_{2i}}{2}\right) \times \Pi \frac{1 - \exp(-u_{1i})}{1 - \exp(-u_{2i})}$$

$$\frac{s_2}{s_1} f = VP \times ZPE \times EXC,$$

(1)

where: $u_i = h\nu_i/kT$ (h = Planck's constant, ν_i = normal-mode vibrational frequency, k = Boltzmann's constant, T = absolute temperature);

$s =$ symmetry number; and the subscripts 1 and 2 refer to the light and heavy isotopic species, respectively. The products and sums (here and in succeeding equations) are taken over all normal-mode vibrational frequencies of the molecule. In Equation 1, the atomic-mass factor Π_{atoms} $(m_2/m_1)^{3/2}$ has been omitted, since this factor always cancels in the calculation of an isotope-exchange equilibrium constant. In the short-hand notation (28), VP represents the (temperature-independent) product of the ratios of isotopic frequencies, arising *via* the Teller-Redlich product rule from the classical translational and rotational partition-function contributions, ZPE represents the term arising from the isotopic shift in zero-point energy, and EXC represents the term associated with thermal excitation of vibration. (It should be noted, however, that the definition of the product $VP \times ZPE \times EXC$ in Reference 28 refers to a ratio of isotopic partition-function ratios, whereas in the present work the product refers to the isotopic partition-function ratio of a single chemical species.)

At low temperatures EXC approaches unity—*i.e.*, $(s_2/s_1)f \to VP \times ZPE$. The low-temperature approximation (l.t.a.) is then

$$\frac{s_2}{s_1} f \approx \Pi \frac{u_{2i}}{u_{1i}} \times \exp\left(\Sigma \frac{u_{1i} - u_{2i}}{2}\right). \tag{2}$$

Often the l.t.a. has been further modified by omitting the VP term—*i.e.*,

$$\frac{s_2}{s_1} f \approx \exp\left(\Sigma \frac{u_{1i} - u_{2i}}{2}\right). \tag{3}$$

We will refer to Equation 3 as the "zero-point-energy approximation" (z.p.e.a.).

The high-temperature approximation (h.t.a.) for $(s_2/s_1)f$ is given by (4, 7, 25)

$$\ln\left(\frac{s_2}{s_1} f\right) \approx \frac{1}{24} \Sigma(u_{1i}^2 - u_{2i}^2). \tag{4}$$

Because the h.t.a. can be written in terms of simple molecular parameters (force constants, geometries, and atomic masses) (4, 7, 28), it has been modified (4, 9) for use at lower temperatures. This "gamma-bar" $(\bar{\gamma})$ modification of the h.t.a. is given by

$$\ln\left(\frac{s_2}{s_1} f\right) \approx \frac{\bar{\gamma}}{24} \Sigma(u_{1i}^2 - u_{2i}^2), \tag{5}$$

where

$$\bar{\gamma} \equiv \frac{12\, G(\bar{u})}{\bar{u}}, \tag{5a}$$

$$G(\bar{u}) \equiv \frac{1}{2} - \frac{1}{\bar{u}} + \frac{1}{\exp{(\bar{u})} - 1}. \tag{5b}$$

$\bar{u} = h\bar{\nu}/kT$, where $\bar{\nu}$ is some frequency, characteristic of the chemical species and of the isotopic substitution considered.

At very high temperatures, where the u_i are all very small, $ZPE \rightarrow 1$ and $EXC \rightarrow 1/VP$ so that $(s_2/s_1)f$ approaches its classical (infinite-temperature) limit of unity.

For the equilibrium constants reported in this paper, the following convention is used. The equilibrium constant associated with the isotope-exchange reaction

$$A_1 + B_2 \rightleftharpoons A_2 + B_1, \tag{6}$$

where A and B are different *chemical* species, is written $K_{A/B}$. It is related to the partition-function ratios of the individual species by

$$K_{A/B} = \left(\frac{s_2}{s_1} f\right)_A \bigg/ \left(\frac{s_2}{s_1} f\right)_B. \tag{7}$$

$K_{A/B}$ so defined is not a true equilibrium constant but one in which the symmetry-number factor has been omitted (the true $K_{A/B} = f_A/f_B$), since the purely classical symmetry numbers cannot lead to isotopic fractionation (7). $K_{A/B}$, as defined by Equation 7, might more properly be called a "reduced" equilibrium constant.

Method of Calculation of Vibrational Frequencies

In the following section we consider partition-function ratios and equilibrium constants for all possible ^{15}N-exchange and mono-^{18}O-substituted-exchange equilibria among the fourteen chemical species: NO, NO_2, NO_2^-, NO_2^+, NOF, NOCl, NOBr, *cis*-HONO, *trans*-HONO, NO_3^-, NO_2F, NO_2Cl, $HONO_2$, and $FONO_2$. The normal-mode vibrational frequencies were calculated, from the best available force fields, with an I.B.M. 7094 digital computer using Schachtschneider's programs (20), which utilize the FG-matrix method of Wilson (26). The input parameters used in the calculations—i.e., molecular force fields and geometries—are reported in Table I. We wish to emphasize that we do not claim perfection for any of the force fields used in this work. It is true that the exact temperature behavior of an isotope effect is quite sensitive to the molecular parameters. However, small changes in the force fields or geometries will not alter the general conclusions presented. For this reason, we did not repeat our calculations with slightly revised force fields for HONO, which were published after our calculations had been completed. (*See* Footnote j in Table I.)

Table I. -Input Parameters for

Chemical Species	Geometry[a, b]
NO	$r_{NO} = 1.1502$ A.
NO_2	$r_{NO} = 1.197$ A.; $\alpha_{ONO} = 134.25°$
NO_2^-	$r_{NO} = 1.236$ A.; $\alpha_{ONO} = 115.4°$
NO_2^+	$r_{NO} = 1.15$ A.; $\alpha_{ONO} = 180°$
ONF	$r_{NO} = 1.13$ A.; $r_{NF} = 1.52$ A.; $\alpha_{ONF} = 110.2°$
ONCl	$r_{NO} = 1.14$ A.; $r_{NCl} = 1.95$ A.; $\alpha_{ONCl} = 116°$
ONBr	$r_{NO} = 1.15$ A.; $r_{NBr} = 2.14$ A.; $\alpha_{ONBr} = 117°$
cis-HONO	planar; $r_{NO} = 1.21$ A.; $r_{NO'} = 1.46$ A.; $r_{O'H} = 0.96$ A; $\alpha_{ONO'} = 114°$; $\alpha_{NO'H} = 104°$
trans-HONO	planar; $r_{NO} = 1.21$ A.; $r_{NO'} = 1.46$ A.; $r_{O'H} = 0.96$ A; $\alpha_{ONO'} = 118°$; $\alpha_{NO'H} = 104°$
NO_3^-	planar; $r_{NO} = 1.0$ A. [k]; $\alpha_{ONO} = 120°$
NO_2F	planar; $r_{NF} = 1.40$ A.; $r_{NO} = 1.21$ A.; $\alpha_{ONO} = 129.5°$; $\alpha_{ONF} = 115.25°$
NO_2Cl	planar, $r_{NCl} = 1.83$ A.; $r_{NO} = 1.21$ A.; $\alpha_{ONO} = 129.5°$; $\alpha_{ONCl} = 115.25°$
$HONO_2$	planar, $r_{NO} = 1.210$ A.; $r_{NO*} = 1.198$ A.; $r_{NO'} = 1.405$ A.; $r_{O'H} = 0.961$ A.; $\alpha_{ONO*} = 130.22°$, $\alpha_{O'NO} = 115.92°$; $\alpha_{O'NO*} = 113.87°$, $\alpha_{NO'H} = 102.22°$

Oxynitrogen Species Considered

Force Constants[a, c]	*Footnote*

$f_{NO} = 15.477496$ mdyn/A.   [d]

$f_{NO} = 10.50246$ mdyn/A.; $f_{ONO} = 1.562587$ mdyn · A.;   [e]
$f_{NO,NO} = 2.121853$ mdyn/A.; $f_{NO,ONO} = 0.628358$ mdyn

$f_{NO} = 8.26335$, $f_{(NO)ONO} = 1.5582077$, $f_{NO,NO} = 2.82207$,   [f]
$f_{NO,(NO)ONO} = 0.92035$ mdyn/A.

$f_{NO} = 17.32$, $f_{(NO)ONO} = 0.42$, $f_{NO,NO} = 1.14$ mdyn/A.   [g]

$f_{NO} = 15.307284$, $f_{NF} = 3.3289996$, $f_{(NO)ONF} = 0.9304476$,   [h]
$f_{NO,NF} = 0.832692$, $f_{NO,(NO)ONF} = 0.50130$,
$f_{NF,(NO)ONF} = 0.64089$ mdyn/A.

$f_{NO} = 14.271362$, $f_{NCl} = 2.268911$, $f_{(NO)ONCl} = 0.498196$,   [h, i]
$f_{NO,NCl} = 0.319418$, $f_{NO,(NO)ONF} = 0.097702$,
$f_{NCl,(NO)ONCl} = 0.225731$ mdyn/A.

$f_{NO} = 14.2210175$, $f_{NBr} = 2.1652154$, $f_{(NO)ONBr} = 0.38408610$, [h]
$f_{NO,NBr} = 0.170910656$, $f_{NO,(NO)ONBr} = 0.090695374$,
$f_{NBr,(NO)ONBr} = 0.142113608$ mdyn/A.

$f_{NO} = 10.6546$, $f_{NO'} = 4.3640$, $f_{O'H} = 6.5973$ mdyn/A.;   [j]
$f_{ONO'} = 1.8345$, $f_{NO'H} = 0.7773$, $f_{[HO'NO]} = 0.1626$ mdyn · A.;
$f_{NO',ONO'} = 1.2423$ mdyn

$f_{NO} = 12.0364$, $f_{NO'} = 3.0840$, $f_{O'H} = 7.2449$ mdyn/A.;   [j]
$f_{ONO'} = 1.5878$, $f_{NO'H} = 0.7647$, $f_{[HO'NO]} = 0.1332$ mdyn · A.;
$f_{NO',ONO'} = 0.4023$ mdyn

$f_{NO} = 8.064790$, $f_{(NO)ONO} = 0.679723$, $f_{(NO)\{ONOO\}} = 0.489739$, [k]
$f_{NO,NO} = 1.154263$, $f_{(NO)ONO,(NO)ONO} = -0.339861$,
$f_{NO,(NO)ONO(opposite)} = -0.491657$,
$f_{NO,(NO)ONO(adjacent)} = 0.245829$ mdyn/A.

$f_{NF} = 2.6572$, $f_{NO} = 11.2140$ mdyn/A.; $f_{ONO} = 2.2353$,   [l]
$f_{ONF} = 0.65755$, $f_{\{FNOO\}} = 0.5006$ mdyn · A.;
$f_{NO,NO} = 1.5343$ mdyn/A.; $f_{ONF,ONF} = -0.65755$ mdyn · A.;
$f_{NO,ONO} = 1.2894$, $f_{NF,ONO} = -0.8077$ mdyn

$f_{NCl} = 2.4555$, $f_{NO} = 10.4306$ mdyn/A.; $f_{ONO} = 1.3453$,   [l]
$f_{ONCl} = 0.519125$, $f_{\{ClNOO\}} = 0.4428$ mdyn · A.;
$f_{NO,NO} = 1.5692$ mdyn/A.; $f_{ONCl,ONCl} = -0.519125$ mdyn · A.;
$f_{NO,ONO} = 1.1601$ mdyn

$f_{NO} = f_{NO^*} = 8.200$, $f_{NO'} = 3.239$, $f_{O'H} = 7.092$ mdyn/A.;   [m]
$f_{ONO^*} = 3.653$, $f_{HO'N} = 0.8817$, $f_{O'NO} = f_{O'NO^*} = 0.70775$,
$f_{\{O'NOO^*\}} = 0.4968$, $f_{[HO'NO^*]} = 0.1033$, $f_{O'NO,O'NO^*} = -0.70775$
mdyn · A.; $f_{NO,ONO^*} = f_{NO^*,ONO^*} = 0.1695$, $f_{NO',ONO^*} = -1.286$ mdyn

Table I.

Chemical Species	Geometry[a, b]
FONO$_2$	planar; $r_{NO} = r_{NO^*} = 1.29$ A.; $r_{NO'} = 1.39$ A.; $r_{O'F} = 1.42$ A.; $\alpha_{ONO^*} = 125°$; $\alpha_{O'NO} = \alpha_{O'NO^*} = 117.5°$; $\alpha_{NO'F} = 105°$

[a] r refers to a bond distance and α to an angle between two bonds. O refers to a terminal oxygen atom, O' to a central oxygen atom, and O* to a terminal oxygen atom in a *trans* position when there are two nonequivalent terminal oxygen atoms.

[b] Atomic masses (15) used: H = 1.007825, ^{14}N = 14.00307, ^{15}N = 15.00011, ^{16}O = 15.99491, ^{18}O = 17.99916, F = 18.99840, Cl = 34.96885, Br = 78.91830.

[c] Values of the force constants f are given to more significant figures than justified by the precision of the spectroscopic methods used, only to permit replication of the computed results. The force constants are associated with the valence coordinates indicated by the subscripts. The following examples serve to explain the subscripting: AB = change in AB bond distance; ABC = change in ABC angle—*i.e.*, unweighted bending coordinate; (AB)ABC = equilibrium AB bond distance times change in ABC angle—*i.e.*, weighted bending coordinate; {ABCD} = change in out-of-plane wagging angle between AB bond and BCD plane; [ABCD] = change in dihedral (torsion) angle between ABC plane and BCD plane. An f with a single such subscript indicates a diagonal **F**-matrix element; an f with two such subscripts separated by a comma indicates an off-diagonal **F**-matrix element for interaction between motions along the two coordinates indicated. Where applicable, only one torsion coordinate and/or only one out-of-plane-wag coordinate per molecule was used. Force constants for stretching (f_{AB}), bending (f_{ABC}), and interactions between these motions refer to all such valence coordinates possible in the molecule, including redundant bending coordinates.—*e.g.*, f_{NO} in NO$_3^-$ was used with three NO-stretching coordinates. Only the nonzero force constants are listed.

On the other hand, we were concerned with consistency within our calculations. Thus, we used the same values for atomic masses throughout the calculations. (For Cl and Br, the masses of the most abundant isotopes were used.) Therefore, some of our calculated frequencies do not agree exactly with previously published data. Further, again for consistency, the force fields used were based exclusively on fundamental frequencies even though, in a few cases, data for zero-order frequencies are available. In order to permit replication of our results, the force constants actually used in the calculations are reported to as many as nine significant figures, which is, of course, far beyond the precision justified from present spectroscopic methods.

The force fields for NO$_2^-$ and NO$_3^-$, calculated in this work, are based on spectroscopic data for the ^{14}N- and ^{15}N-substituted species (2). The calculations were carried out using symmetry-factored **F** and **G**

(Continued)

| *Force Constants*[a, e] | *Footnote* |

$f_{NO} = f_{NO^*} = 10.7457$, $f_{NO'} = 2.1668$, $f_{O'F} = 3.0992$ mdyn/A.;
$f_{ONO^*} = 1.9727$, $f_{FO'N} = 2.2513$, $f_{O'NO} = f_{O'NO^*} = 0.69195$,
$f_{\{O'NOO^*\}} = 0.5349$, $f_{[FO'NO^*]} = 0.14496$ mdyn · A.;
$f_{NO,NO^*} = 1.7703$ mdyn/A.; $f_{O'NO,O'NO^*} = -0.69195$ mdyn · A.;
$f_{NO,ONO^*} = f_{NO^*,ONO^*} = 1.7044$, $f_{NO',ONO^*} = -0.28496$ mdyn

[d] Shaw (21); force constant calculated from $^{14}N^{16}O$ fundamental, 1876 cm.$^{-1}$.

[e] Structure: Bird (10). Force Field: Bernitt (3), from fundamentals for $^{14}NO_2$ and $^{15}NO_2$ observed by Arakawa and Nielsen (1).

[f] Structure: Carpenter (11). Force field: this work, from fundamentals for $^{14}NO_2^-$ and $^{15}NO_2^-$ observed by Begun and Fletcher (2).

[g] Teranishi and Decius (24).

[h] Devlin (13).

[i] Refined set.

[j] Bernitt (3), July, 1965. A slightly revised normal-coordinate analysis has since been published (18).

[k] Structure: Herzberg (14); r_{NO} was arbitrarily set equal to unity since, because of the symmetry and the fact that weighted coordinates were used, the calculated frequencies are independent of this distance. Force field: this work, from fundamentals for $^{14}NO_3^-$ and $^{15}NO_3^-$ observed by Begun and Fletcher (2).

[l] Structure: Clayton, Williams, and Weatherly (12). Force field: Bernitt (3), from observed fundamentals for the ^{14}N- and ^{15}N-substituted species.

[m] McGraw, Bernitt, and Hisatsune (17).

[n] Structure: Pauling and Brockway (19); molecule taken to be planar [Bernitt (3)]. Force field: Bernitt (3), from observed fundamentals for $FO^{14}NO_2$ and $FO^{15}NO_2$.

matrices (26). The antisymmetric-stretching mode of NO_2^- appears in its own symmetry type (B_1 species). The force constant associated with this motion was taken as the arithmetic mean of the (two) force constants that reproduce, respectively, the corresponding observed isotopic frequencies exactly. The force constants for the symmetric-stretching (A_1') and out-of-plane-wagging (A_2'') motions of NO_3^-, each of which also appears in its own symmetry type, were calculated in an analogous manner. In solving for the three force constants of the 2×2 symmetry block (A_1) formed by the symmetric-stretching and angle-bending motions of NO_2^-, the expression for the determinant of the F-matrix block was set equal to the arithmetic average of the (two) F-matrix determinants obtained, respectively, from the corresponding observed isotopic frequencies. The force constants for the two (identical) 2×2 symmetry blocks (E') formed by the antisymmetric-stretching and angle-bending motions of NO_3^- were again calculated in an analogous manner.

Table II.   Calculated Normal-

ν_{1i} $(cm.^{-1})$	$\Delta\nu_i$ $(cm.^{-1})$		ν_{1i} $(cm.^{-1})$
NO	^{15}NO	N^{18}O	HONO$_2$
1876.25	33.55	49.41	457.51
			572.26
NO$_3^{-c}$	^{15}NO$_3^-$	NO$_2^{18}$O$^-$	652.56
717.05	2.15	16.32	764.30
717.05	2.15	9.20	878.76
830.98	21.66	3.49	1318.66
1049.46	0.00	20.27	1329.07
1375.90	31.83	14.66	1710.32
1375.90	31.83	0.35	3566.04
NO$_2^{-c}$	^{15}NO$_2^-$	NO^{18}O$^-$	FONO$_2$
810.77	8.15	16.68	151.59
1233.15	25.68	16.45	302.35
1324.75	17.85	18.64	455.17
			633.59
NO$_2^+$	^{15}NO$_2^+$	NO^{18}O$^+$	708.80
541.23	12.66	4.61	803.88
541.23	12.66	4.61	927.77
1399.98	0.00	40.57	1301.17
2375.36	55.56	19.62	1760.94
NO$_2$	^{15}NO$_2$	NO^{18}O	NOF
750.34	10.54	12.78	520.95
1318.44	12.48	27.75	766.12
1617.20	35.85	14.16	1844.45
NOCl	^{15}NOCl	N^{18}OCl	NOBr
333.54	2.06	10.81	265.01
594.67	14.26	1.13	542.56
1801.12	32.58	46.74	1801.38
NO$_2$F	^{15}NO$_2$F	NO^{18}OF	cis-HONO
560.09	1.51	11.75	616.81
567.83	0.58	2.21	639.46
741.26	19.39	3.75	853.12
822.50	13.83	11.84	1260.28
1309.69	11.46	27.47	1640.20
1792.47	42.36	13.96	3438.62
NO$_2$Cl	^{15}NO$_2$Cl	NO^{18}OCl	trans-HONO
369.77	0.05	6.24	550.12
409.35	1.53	7.60	589.86
652.66	17.09	3.77	793.44
794.91	14.23	9.70	1268.86

Mode Vibrational Frequencies

$$\frac{\Delta v_i}{(cm.^{-1})}$$

HO^{15}NO$_2$	H^{18}ONO$_2$	HONO^{18}O^a	HONO^{18}O^b
0.11	2.08	0.20	0.35
1.21	10.04	8.26	11.20
1.81	24.23	5.62	2.00
19.70	1.36	4.27	3.56
1.03	0.86	23.60	24.09
23.64	5.84	5.96	12.03
7.43	2.45	8.61	2.34
39.24	1.91	10.77	10.93
0.00	12.16	0.00	0.00

FO^{15}NO$_2$	F^{18}ONO$_2$	FONO^{18}O^a	FONO^{18}O^b
0.03	3.84	1.60	0.61
0.47	0.38	0.08	8.05
1.21	4.00	11.97	2.21
2.45	14.74	4.46	5.14
18.65	1.86	3.74	3.02
11.89	9.91	5.91	8.10
0.06	36.13	3.07	4.01
10.52	0.44	28.24	27.23
42.44	2.31	11.88	12.02

^{15}NOF	N^{18}OF
5.07	13.26
13.28	0.98
32.91	48.57

^{15}NOBr	N^{18}OBr
1.43	10.26
15.21	1.38
32.65	46.64

cis-HO^{15}NO	cis-H^{18}ONO	cis-HON^{18}O
6.27	7.28	14.91
1.95	3.62	1.23
12.47	21.38	2.57
0.57	8.89	6.24
31.54	3.21	31.56
0.01	11.57	0.00

trans-HO^{15}NO	trans-H^{18}ONO	trans-HON^{18}O
1.25	1.11	1.26
2.88	14.91	13.96
15.73	10.76	2.14
1.62	10.02	1.39

Table II.

ν_{1i} (cm.$^{-1}$)	$\Delta\nu_i$ (cm.$^{-1}$)		ν_{1i} (cm.$^{-1}$)
1285.67	12.87	25.66	1698.71
1685.36	38.76	14.00	3603.64

[a] Isotopic position involved in torsion coordinate.
[b] Isotopic position not involved in torsion coordinate.

Results and Discussion

Calculated Frequencies. Table II contains the normal-mode vibrational frequencies ν_{1i} of the light isotopic species, and the frequency shifts $\Delta\nu_i = \nu_{1i} - \nu_{2i}$ upon isotopic substitution, calculated with the force fields listed in Table I. The force field for NO_3^- reproduces the observed frequencies and frequency shifts very well, whereas the calculated frequencies and shifts for NO_2^- differ somewhat from those observed. However, we consider the general quadratic potential used in the calculation the best fit to the observed frequencies. The discrepancy is caused by a disagreement of the observed (2) frequencies with the Teller-Redlich product rule, which is, of course, assumed in the calculations.

Two sets of frequencies are obtained for HONO^{18}O, depending on which terminal oxygen atom is isotopically substituted. The use of a single torsional coordinate, involving only one terminal oxygen atom, with no interaction force constants involving the torsional motion (see Table I), introduces an artificial asymmetry, over and above the asymmetry owing to the slight nonequivalence of the two terminal oxygen atoms. For this reason, in further considerations of HONO^{18}O, the geometric mean of the partition-function ratios resulting from each of the two sets of frequencies is used. The same problem exists for FONO^{18}O, for which an analogous geometric mean is used.

Partition-Function Ratios. The reduced partition-function ratios $(s_2/s_1)f$ of all the possible ^{15}N-substituted and mono-^{18}O-substituted species were calculated, with Equation 1, over the temperature range 20°–2000°K., using the frequencies in Table II. (We obviously do not think that Equation 1 is valid for these molecules over the entire tem-

(Continued)

$$\Delta \nu_i$$
$$(cm.^{-1})$$

32.50	0.27	39.28
0.01	12.17	0.01

[e] Observed (2) fundamentals (cm.$^{-1}$):

ν_{1i}	$\Delta \nu_i$	ν_{1i}	$\Delta \nu_i$
($^{14}NO_3^-$)	($^{15}NO_3^-$)	($^{14}NO_2^-$)	($^{15}NO_2^-$)
716.8 (2)	2.0	808	3
830.9	21.9	1232	24
1049.2	0.0	1326	21
1375.6 (2)	31.9		

perature range considered, nor even that all of these molecules actually exist over the entire range. For our purposes of comparing the "exact" values with values obtained from approximation equations and of examining temperature dependences, it is useful to consider a very large range of temperatures.) These calculations were carried out with computer programs previously described (28). The calculated $(s_2/s_1)f$, shown in Table III, are, as expected (22), smooth, monotonically decreasing, positive-valued functions of temperature, without inflections or sharp bends.

The "exact" reduced partition-function ratios at 298.1°K. are listed in Table IV in order of increasing magnitude for ^{15}N substitution and for ^{18}O substitution, respectively. Since bending forces are usually much smaller than stretching forces, the magnitude of $(s_2/s_1)f$ for ^{15}N substitution should increase roughly with the number of atoms bonded to the (central) nitrogen atom. Thus, the smallest partition-function ratio is found for diatomic nitric oxide. The triatomic molecules, and the tetratomic molecules in which the nitrogen is bonded to two other atoms, have larger partition-function ratios. The other tetratomic molecules and the pentatomic molecules, where the nitrogen is bonded to three other atoms, have the highest partition-function ratios. The only molecule that deviates from this simple ordering into groups is $^{15}NO_2^+$, which has a higher than "normal" partition-function ratio due to its very strong N–O bonds.

The reduced partition-function ratios for ^{18}O substitution are closer to one another than are those for ^{15}N substitution. The $(s_2/s_1)f$ values at 298.1°K. for ^{18}O substitution range from ~ 1.08 to ~ 1.12, while for ^{15}N substitution they range from ~ 1.06 to ~ 1.16. Thus, on the average, the equilibrium constants for ^{18}O exchange between pairs of molecules would be expected to be closer to unity than those for ^{15}N exchange, despite the greater relative mass difference in ^{18}O substitution. The closeness of the reduced partition-function ratios for the ^{18}O-substituted molecules is to be expected if the number of bonds to the isotopically substituted atom is taken as a rough criterion for the magnitude of $(s_2/s_1)f$. The oxygen atoms in all of the molecules are bonded directly to only one or at most two other atoms. Thus, the ^{18}O-substituted molecules listed in Table IV do not fall into simple groups of diatomic, triatomic, etc., species and there is no simple *a priori* way to arrange these molecules in terms of structure to predict the magnitudes of the partition-function ratios.

The values of $(s_2/s_1)f$ obtained by the approximation methods (Equations 2, 3, 4, and 5) are compared with the corresponding "exact" values in Table IV. For both ^{15}N and ^{18}O substitution in these molecules, the l.t.a. equation predicts the magnitude of $(s_2/s_1)f$ fairly well at room temperature. This approximation (Equation 2) neglects effects caused by thermal excitation of vibration. Therefore, the magnitude of the excitation factor EXC determines how closely the l.t.a. reproduces the result obtained by the "exact" equation. The contributions of individual isotope-dependent frequencies to EXC may be estimated by assuming an isotope shift in the frequencies of about 2%, which is fairly representative of the cases considered here. For frequencies of 700, 400, and 100 cm.$^{-1}$, the contributions to EXC at 298.1°K. are about 1.002, 1.007, and 1.016, respectively. Since the oxygen atoms in the molecules considered here are usually terminal atoms, and the lowest-lying bending frequencies are more dependent on isotopic substitution in terminal positions than in central positions, one should expect to find, and does in fact find, that the l.t.a. applied at room temperature does not do as well for the ^{18}O-substituted molecules as for the ^{15}N-substituted molecules. The poorest fits are found for molecules like $F^{18}ONO_2$, $FONO^{18}O$, and $N^{18}OBr$, which have very low-lying oxygen-isotope-dependent frequencies.

Unfortunately, the l.t.a., even in cases where it works satisfactorily, is not of a form particularly well suited for interpreting partition-function ratios in terms of interatomic forces.

The error in omitting the VP term in Equation 1 is in the opposite direction to, but at room temperature much larger than, the error in omitting the EXC term. Thus, in every case considered, the z.p.e.a. does considerably worse than the l.t.a., even when the l.t.a. error is itself large.

The quite poor performance of the h.t.a. at room temperature, even for non-hydrogen-containing species, may appear at first rather surprising. The h.t.a. (Equation 4) contains only the first term of a series expansion of $(s_2/s_1)f$ in terms of even powers of u_{1i} and u_{2i} (4). It is valid only where all isotope-dependent u_i and $\Delta u_i = u_{1i} - u_{2i}$ are small. For the cases at hand, the h.t.a. agrees with the "exact" values of $(s_2/s_1)f$ only at the highest temperatures ($\rightarrow 2000°K.$). As expected, particularly poor agreement for lower temperatures is obtained for those species which possess high isotope-dependent frequencies—e.g., $^{15}NO_2{}^+$, $NO^{18}O^+$, *cis*- and *trans*-$H^{18}ONO$, and $H^{18}ONO_2$, whereas for species with most of the isotope-dependence residing in lower-lying frequencies—e.g., $^{15}NO_2{}^-$, $NO^{18}O^-$, $HONO^{18}O$, $F^{18}ONO_2$, and $NO_2{}^{18}O^-$, the agreement is fair at 500°K.

Table IV also lists, for 298.1° and 500°K., values of the characteristic frequency $\bar{\nu}$ necessary to make the modified high-temperature approximation, or $\bar{\gamma}$ method, reproduce the "exact" $(s_2/s_1)f$ values. The $\bar{\gamma}$ corresponding to these fit-producing $\bar{\nu}$ were calculated according to

$$\bar{\gamma} = \frac{\ln\left[(s_2/s_1)f\right]_{\text{"exact"}}}{(1/24)\Sigma(u_{1i}{}^2 - u_{2i}{}^2)}. \tag{8}$$

The $\bar{\gamma}$ method should be useful for the extrapolation of isotopic partition-function ratios over limited temperature ranges, especially in those cases where the h.t.a. fails. Such extrapolation would require an estimation of either $\bar{\nu}$ or $\Sigma(\nu_{1i}{}^2 - \nu_{2i}{}^2)$ (*cf.*, Equation 5). Since the latter quantity can be expressed in terms of force constants and geometries (4, 7, 28), reasonably accurate estimations of it can be made (4, 9). $\bar{\gamma}$ is then calculated for a given temperature according to Equation 8 and a corresponding characteristic frequency $\bar{\nu}$ is evaluated. This $\bar{\nu}$ may then be used to predict the partition-function ratio at other temperatures; of course, such a procedure implies the constancy of $\bar{\nu}$ over the temperature range considered.

The expected characteristics of $\bar{\nu}$ can best be determined by an examination of the original derivation of the $\bar{\gamma}$ equation. Bigeleisen and Mayer (7) derived the equation

$$\ln (s_2/s_1)f = \Sigma G(u_{2i})\Delta u_i, \tag{9}$$

which is valid if all the Δu_i, but not necessarily the individual u_i, are small. Bigeleisen and Wolfsberg (4, 9) wrote this equation in the form

$$\ln (s_2/s_1)f = \frac{1}{24}\Sigma\gamma_i\Delta(u_i{}^2), \tag{10}$$

where

$$\gamma_i \equiv 12\,G(u_{2i})/u_{2i} \quad [0 < \gamma_i < 1] \tag{10a}$$

and

$$\Delta(u_i{}^2) \equiv u_{1i}{}^2 - u_{2i}{}^2, \tag{10b}$$

Table III. Calculated Reduced

$T(^\circ K.)$

	^{15}NO	$^{15}NO_2$	$^{15}NO_2^-$
20	3.28194	7.93831	6.13358
40	1.79534	2.75331	2.42185
60	1.46832	1.93448	1.77675
80	1.32787	1.62151	1.52183
100	1.25014	1.45859	1.38678
120	1.20086	1.35919	1.30349
140	1.16685	1.29240	1.24708
160	1.14198	1.24452	1.20642
180	1.12301	1.20858	1.17575
200	1.10805	1.18064	1.15183
220	1.09597	1.15834	1.13269
240	1.08600	1.14016	1.11706
260	1.07764	1.12508	1.10408
273.1	1.07285	1.11653	1.09672
298.1	1.06494	1.10254	1.08469
320	1.05908	1.09229	1.07588
340	1.05441	1.08422	1.06898
360	1.05029	1.07716	1.06295
380	1.04662	1.07096	1.05767
400	1.04335	1.06546	1.05301
500	1.03115	1.04555	1.03629
600	1.02339	1.03338	1.02627
700	1.01813	1.02543	1.01984
800	1.01443	1.01997	1.01547
900	1.01173	1.01608	1.01239
1000	1.00971	1.01320	1.01013
1100	1.00815	1.01102	1.00844
1200	1.00694	1.00934	1.00713
1300	1.00597	1.00801	1.00610
1400	1.00519	1.00694	1.00528
1500	1.00456	1.00607	1.00461
1600	1.00403	1.00535	1.00406
1700	1.00358	1.00476	1.00361
1800	1.00321	1.00425	1.00322
1900	1.00289	1.00383	1.00290
2000	1.00262	1.00346	1.00262
	cis-$HO^{15}NO$	$trans$-$HO^{15}NO$	$^{15}NO_3^-$
20	6.36807	6.64382	23.19263
40	2.46381	2.51669	4.62881
60	1.79531	1.82096	2.70505
80	1.53252	1.54895	2.06790
100	1.39371	1.40568	1.76012
120	1.30828	1.31765	1.58085
140	1.25057	1.25825	1.46416
160	1.20907	1.21558	1.38242
180	1.17789	1.18353	1.32214

Partition-Function Ratios[a]

$^{15}NO_2^+$	^{15}NOF	$^{15}NOCl$	$^{15}NOBr$
17.07304	6.03723	5.52967	5.58886
3.98784	2.40210	2.29490	2.30322
2.45592	1.76676	1.71183	1.71408
1.92737	1.51521	1.47856	1.47892
1.66673	1.38186	1.35435	1.35390
1.51323	1.29964	1.27764	1.27683
1.41280	1.24405	1.22580	1.22483
1.34237	1.20407	1.18857	1.18756
1.29049	1.17403	1.16065	1.15965
1.25085	1.15070	1.13901	1.13806
1.21967	1.13210	1.12179	1.12091
1.19457	1.11697	1.10781	1.10700
1.17397	1.10444	1.09625	1.09551
1.16239	1.09736	1.08972	1.08902
1.14356	1.08578	1.07906	1.07843
1.12985	1.07731	1.07126	1.07070
1.11911	1.07066	1.06514	1.06462
1.10975	1.06485	1.05979	1.05932
1.10151	1.05974	1.05508	1.05465
1.09422	1.05521	1.05092	1.05052
1.06762	1.03877	1.03578	1.03551
1.05099	1.02866	1.02645	1.02626
1.03979	1.02199	1.02030	1.02015
1.03186	1.01737	1.01603	1.01592
1.02605	1.01404	1.01296	1.01287
1.02166	1.01157	1.01068	1.01061
1.01828	1.00969	1.00894	1.00888
1.01561	1.00822	1.00759	1.00754
1.01348	1.00707	1.00652	1.00648
1.01175	1.00613	1.00566	1.00562
1.01033	1.00537	1.00496	1.00492
1.00915	1.00474	1.00438	1.00435
1.00815	1.00422	1.00389	1.00387
1.00731	1.00377	1.00348	1.00346
1.00659	1.00340	1.00313	1.00311
1.00597	1.00307	1.00283	1.00282

$^{15}NO_2F$	$^{15}NO_2Cl$	$HO^{15}NO_2$	$FO^{15}NO_2$
22.78932	19.26795	27.31983	21.58746
4.58681	4.21353	5.02357	4.45856
2.68805	2.53854	2.85665	2.63554
2.05779	1.97043	2.15417	2.02641
1.75302	1.69267	1.81861	1.73090
1.57542	1.52978	1.62453	1.55842
1.45982	1.42336	1.49881	1.44606
1.37892	1.34872	1.41110	1.36741
1.31934	1.29369	1.34661	1.30950

Table III.

$T(°K.)$

200	1.15366	1.15863	1.27597
220	1.13434	1.13878	1.23956
240	1.11863	1.12263	1.21019
260	1.10562	1.10927	1.18607
273.1	1.09827	1.10171	1.17249
298.1	1.08626	1.08937	1.15045
320	1.07749	1.08035	1.13445
340	1.07061	1.07328	1.12197
360	1.06461	1.06710	1.11113
380	1.05934	1.06168	1.10166
400	1.05469	1.05689	1.09334
500	1.03792	1.03957	1.06368
600	1.02774	1.02902	1.04603
700	1.02111	1.02214	1.03473
800	1.01657	1.01740	1.02708
900	1.01333	1.01402	1.02168
1000	1.01095	1.01152	1.01773
1100	1.00914	1.00962	1.01476
1200	1.00774	1.00816	1.01247
1300	1.00664	1.00700	1.01067
1400	1.00575	1.00607	1.00924
1500	1.00503	1.00531	1.00807
1600	1.00444	1.00468	1.00711
1700	1.00394	1.00416	1.00631
1800	1.00353	1.00372	1.00564
1900	1.00317	1.00335	1.00507
2000	1.00287	1.00303	1.00458

	$N^{18}O$	$NO^{18}O$	$NO^{18}O^-$
20	5.75665	6.82197	6.13179
40	2.36750	1.55089	2.41705
60	1.76061	1.83775	1.77222
80	1.51827	1.55985	1.51752
100	1.38919	1.41372	1.38263
120	1.30929	1.32400	1.29944
140	1.25505	1.26347	1.24314
160	1.21585	1.21995	1.20257
180	1.18621	1.18722	1.17201
200	1.16301	1.16176	1.14821
220	1.14438	1.14143	1.12920
240	1.12908	1.12486	1.11371
260	1.11630	1.11113	1.10088
273.1	1.10901	1.10335	1.09362
298.1	1.09699	1.09064	1.08178
320	1.08810	1.08134	1.07315
340	1.08104	1.07405	1.06639

(Continued)

1.27378	1.25159	1.29734	1.26523
1.23793	1.21845	1.25856	1.23041
1.20906	1.19178	1.22732	1.20239
1.18539	1.16991	1.20168	1.17942
1.17209	1.15763	1.18726	1.16652
1.15051	1.13770	1.16383	1.14560
1.13486	1.12326	1.14681	1.13043
1.12265	1.11199	1.13351	1.11860
1.11205	1.10222	1.12196	1.10833
1.10278	1.09367	1.11184	1.09935
1.09461	1.08616	1.10293	1.09144
1.06538	1.05929	1.07099	1.06314
1.04777	1.04318	1.05175	1.04611
1.03634	1.03276	1.03929	1.03507
1.02852	1.02566	1.03079	1.02751
1.02295	1.02061	1.02474	1.02213
1.01885	1.01690	1.02029	1.01817
1.01574	1.01410	1.01693	1.01517
1.01333	1.01194	1.01433	1.01285
1.01143	1.01023	1.01228	1.01102
1.00991	1.00886	1.01064	1.00955
1.00867	1.00775	1.00931	1.00835
1.00765	1.00683	1.00821	1.00737
1.00679	1.00607	1.00729	1.00655
1.00608	1.00543	1.00652	1.00585
1.00546	1.00488	1.00586	1.00526
1.00494	1.00441	1.00530	1.00476

$NO^{18}O^+$	$N^{18}OF$	$N^{18}OCl$
11.48524	9.07249	7.76038
3.29740	2.93218	2.70189
2.17528	2.01224	1.90095
1.76681	1.66699	1.59511
1.55960	1.48909	1.43663
1.43527	1.38138	1.34066
1.35274	1.30952	1.27672
1.29414	1.25837	1.23128
1.25049	1.22022	1.19743
1.21678	1.19077	1.17129
1.19001	1.16739	1.15053
1.16828	1.14841	1.13367
1.15030	1.13273	1.11971
1.14014	1.12387	1.11181
1.12353	1.10938	1.09887
1.11138	1.09878	1.08938
1.10182	1.09043	1.08191

Table III.

$T(°K.)$

360	1.07482	1.06768	1.06051
380	1.06930	1.06210	1.05536
400	1.06438	1.05717	1.05083
500	1.04612	1.03941	1.03465
600	1.03454	1.02869	1.02502
700	1.02675	1.02176	1.01886
800	1.02126	1.01703	1.01469
900	1.01727	1.01367	1.01175
1000	1.01428	1.01120	1.00961
1100	1.01199	1.00934	1.00799
1200	1.01020	1.00790	1.00675
1300	1.00878	1.00677	1.00578
1400	1.00763	1.00586	1.00500
1500	1.00669	1.00512	1.00437
1600	1.00591	1.00452	1.00385
1700	1.00526	1.00401	1.00341
1800	1.00471	1.00358	1.00305
1900	1.00424	1.00322	1.00274
2000	1.00384	1.00291	1.00248

	$N^{18}OBr$	$cis\text{-}H^{18}ONO$	$cis\text{-}HON^{18}O$
20	7.59510	7.07674	7.23360
40	2.66352	2.58761	2.61813
60	1.87912	1.85035	1.86582
80	1.57999	1.56470	1.57511
100	1.42546	1.41497	1.42294
120	1.33211	1.32326	1.32985
140	1.27001	1.26154	1.26726
160	1.22590	1.21731	1.22245
180	1.19303	1.18418	1.18890
200	1.16764	1.15853	1.16292
220	1.14745	1.13816	1.14227
240	1.13104	1.12166	1.12550
260	1.11744	1.10807	1.11166
273.1	1.10974	1.10042	1.10384
298.1	1.09712	1.08799	1.09110
320	1.08785	1.07896	1.08181
340	1.08054	1.07191	1.07452
360	1.07413	1.06580	1.06817
380	1.06846	1.06046	1.06260
400	1.06343	1.05576	1.05769
500	1.04497	1.03897	1.03997
600	1.03344	1.02886	1.02924
700	1.02575	1.02227	1.02225
800	1.02039	1.01772	1.01746
900	1.01651	1.01444	1.01404
1000	1.01363	1.01199	1.01153

(**Continued**)

1.09348	1.08314	1.07535
1.08613	1.07670	1.06957
1.07962	1.07100	1.06443
1.05600	1.05017	1.04562
1.04146	1.03725	1.03389
1.03187	1.02866	1.02609
1.02521	1.02269	1.02065
1.02042	1.01837	1.01672
1.01685	1.01515	1.01379
1.01413	1.01270	1.01156
1.01201	1.01079	1.00982
1.01033	1.00928	1.00844
1.00897	1.00805	1.00733
1.00786	1.00706	1.00642
1.00695	1.00623	1.00567
1.00618	1.00554	1.00504
1.00553	1.00496	1.00451
1.00498	1.00447	1.00406
1.00451	1.00404	1.00368

trans-H^{18}ONO	*trans*-HON^{18}O	NO$_2{}^{18}$O$^-$
5.57241	7.64129	9.40491
2.29915	2.69141	2.96036
1.71163	1.90072	2.01376
1.47684	1.59732	1.66088
1.35179	1.43910	1.47960
1.27449	1.34256	1.36993
1.22220	1.27778	1.29672
1.18465	1.23147	1.24457
1.15651	1.19684	1.20568
1.13473	1.17004	1.17568
1.11746	1.14875	1.15193
1.10349	1.13148	1.13275
1.09200	1.11720	1.11701
1.08553	1.10914	1.10817
1.07504	1.09598	1.09384
1.06742	1.08638	1.08349
1.06149	1.07884	1.07544
1.05633	1.07225	1.06849
1.05183	1.06647	1.06244
1.04787	1.06135	1.05714
1.03371	1.04283	1.03848
1.02515	1.03150	1.02757
1.01954	1.02407	1.02068
1.01564	1.01894	1.01605
1.01281	1.01527	1.01281
1.01068	1.01256	1.01045

Table III.

$T(^\circ K.)$			
1100	1.01142	1.01011	1.00962
1200	1.00971	1.00864	1.00815
1300	1.00834	1.00746	1.00699
1400	1.00724	1.00651	1.00606
1500	1.00635	1.00573	1.00530
1600	1.00561	1.00508	1.00467
1700	1.00499	1.00453	1.00415
1800	1.00446	1.00406	1.00371
1900	1.00402	1.00367	1.00334
2000	1.00363	1.00332	1.00302
	$NO^{18}OF$	$NO^{18}OCl$	$H^{18}ONO_2$
20	11.93499	10.23914	8.31008
40	3.32970	3.07079	2.77846
60	2.17571	2.05554	1.92843
80	1.75874	1.68209	1.60662
100	1.54806	1.49205	1.44004
120	1.42198	1.37816	1.33896
140	1.33851	1.30285	1.27151
160	1.27942	1.24967	1.22360
180	1.23557	1.21030	1.18804
200	1.20187	1.18011	1.16077
220	1.17525	1.15630	1.13932
240	1.15377	1.13712	1.12209
260	1.13612	1.12137	1.10802
273.1	1.12621	1.11252	1.10014
298.1	1.11011	1.09816	1.08742
320	1.09844	1.08776	1.07826
340	1.08933	1.07964	1.07115
360	1.08144	1.07260	1.06500
380	1.07454	1.06645	1.05965
400	1.06848	1.06104	1.05497
500	1.04689	1.04178	1.03833
600	1.03401	1.03029	1.02840
700	1.02573	1.02291	1.02195
800	1.02011	1.01789	1.01749
900	1.01613	1.01435	1.01428
1000	1.01321	1.01175	1.01188
1100	1.01101	1.00979	1.01003
1200	1.00932	1.00828	1.00858
1300	1.00798	1.00709	1.00742
1400	1.00691	1.00614	1.00648
1500	1.00604	1.00536	1.00571
1600	1.00532	1.00473	1.00506
1700	1.00473	1.00420	1.00452
1800	1.00422	1.00375	1.00406

(Continued)

1.00905	1.01050	1.00868
1.00775	1.00890	1.00733
1.00672	1.00764	1.00626
1.00588	1.00663	1.00542
1.00518	1.00580	1.00473
1.00460	1.00512	1.00416
1.00411	1.00455	1.00369
1.00369	1.00407	1.00330
1.00334	1.00366	1.00296
1.00303	1.00331	1.00268

HONO^{18}O [b]	F^{18}ONO$_2$	FONO^{18}O [b]
10.30472	12.57075	11.60143
3.09410	3.34836	3.25676
2.07189	2.15822	2.13366
1.69546	1.73525	1.72817
1.50333	1.52374	1.52385
1.38764	1.39811	1.40206
1.31069	1.31542	1.32174
1.25605	1.25719	1.26510
1.21541	1.21421	1.22320
1.18413	1.18137	1.19107
1.15943	1.15561	1.16574
1.13949	1.13498	1.14533
1.12314	1.11817	1.12859
1.11396	1.10880	1.11918
1.09909	1.09372	1.10392
1.08833	1.08292	1.09287
1.07997	1.07458	1.08425
1.07273	1.06742	1.07678
1.06643	1.06123	1.07025
1.06090	1.05584	1.06452
1.04134	1.03711	1.04412
1.02981	1.02636	1.03197
1.02246	1.01966	1.02416
1.01750	1.01520	1.01887
1.01400	1.01209	1.01513
1.01145	1.00985	1.01239
1.00953	1.00817	1.01032
1.00805	1.00689	1.00873
1.00689	1.00588	1.00747
1.00596	1.00508	1.00647
1.00521	1.00443	1.00566
1.00459	1.00390	1.00498
1.00407	1.00346	1.00443
1.00364	1.00309	1.00395

Table III.

$T(°K.)$

| 1900 | 1.00380 | 1.00337 | 1.00367 |
| 2000 | 1.00343 | 1.00305 | 1.00333 |

[a] Reduced partition-function ratios calculated, with Equation 1, from frequencies listed in Table II.

by introducing the additional approximation $\Delta(u_i^2) = 2u_{2i}\Delta u_i$, which is again valid for small Δu_i. The most significant approximation involved "factoring out" a single $\bar{\gamma}$ from the sum in Equation 10 to yield Equation 5. Comparison of Equations 5 and 10 yields

$$\bar{\gamma} = \frac{\Sigma\gamma_i\Delta(\nu_i^2)}{\Sigma\Delta(\nu_i^2)}, \tag{11}$$

where $\Delta(\nu_i^2) = \nu_{1i}^2 - \nu_{2i}^2$. We see then that $\bar{\gamma}$ is a weighted average of the individual γ_i, the weighting factors being the isotopic shifts in the squares of the frequencies. Over a limited range of u, the function $\gamma = 12\ G(u)/u$ can be taken to be approximately linear in u. [An empirical linear approximation for γ is surprisingly good. For example, for $0 < u \leqslant 10$, γ varies from 1.00 to 0.48 and may be represented as $\gamma = 1.038 - 0.059u$ with a standard error of estimate of 0.014. We do not mean to imply, however, that a linear equation is the best approximation to represent the dependence of γ on u. An approximation which is more justifiable from a theoretical standpoint (4) would express γ in terms of an expansion in even powers on u. We use the linear approximation for simplicity; the use of any other function containing u to only one nonzero power would not significantly affect our conclusions.] If we assume that $\bar{\gamma}$ and the γ_i of all the isotope-dependent frequencies obey the same linear equation within the temperature range considered, we obtain (*see Appendix*)

$$\bar{\nu} \approx \frac{\Sigma\nu_{2i}\Delta(\nu_i^2)}{\Sigma\Delta(\nu_i^2)} \equiv \bar{\bar{\nu}}, \tag{12}$$

where $\bar{\bar{\nu}}$ is defined by this equation. We note that $\bar{\nu}$ itself is approximately a weighted average of the ν_{2i}.

Values of $\bar{\bar{\nu}}$ for the molecules considered are included in Table IV. The $\bar{\bar{\nu}}$ calculated from Equation 12 are excellent approximations to the fit-producing $\bar{\nu}$ calculated from Equation 8, except for the three species (*cis*- and *trans*-H^{18}ONO and H^{18}ONO$_2$) which have particularly wide ranges of isotope-dependent frequencies owing to the isotopically substituted atoms being bonded directly to hydrogen atoms. The values of

(Continued)

1.00327	1.00277	1.00356
1.00296	1.00250	1.00321

[b] Geometric-mean terminal ^{18}O.

$\bar{\nu}$ lie, as predicted by the approximation Equation 12, within the ranges of the isotope-dependent frequencies in the molecules. Since the largest isotopic shifts are generally associated with the highest frequencies, $\bar{\nu}$ is generally highest for molecules with high-lying isotope-dependent frequencies.

While Equation 12 predicts $\bar{\nu}$ to be temperature-independent, the actual $\bar{\nu}$ are somewhat temperature-dependent. The temperature dependence of $\bar{\nu}$ derives mainly from the approximation made in going from Equation 10 to Equation 5, and from the assumption of the linearity of γ in deriving Equation 12. Both approximations improve as the range of u_{2i} considered decreases. Thus, one would expect that the $\bar{\gamma}$ method would work best—i.e., $\bar{\nu}$ would be the least temperature-dependent—for species with a narrow range of isotope-dependent frequencies. Table IV does, in fact, show that the species with the widest ranges of isotope-dependent frequencies—viz., cis- and trans-$H^{18}ONO$ and $H^{18}ONO_2$—are the ones whose $\bar{\nu}$ exhibit the largest temperature dependences, while for species with narrow frequency ranges—e.g., ^{15}N- and ^{18}O-substituted NO_2^-, NO_3^-, and, of course, NO—the temperature dependences of $\bar{\nu}$ are small.

With the exceptions of cis- and trans-$H^{18}ONO$ and $H^{18}ONO_2$, the $\bar{\nu}$ values vary by less than ~4% over the temperature range 298.1°–500°K. The generally small temperature dependences of $\bar{\nu}$ justify the use of the $\bar{\gamma}$ method for extrapolation purposes. For example, for $^{15}NO_2Cl$, where $\bar{\nu}$ varies by 3.5% over the temperature interval 298.1°–500°K., extrapolation of $(s_2/s_1)f$ from 298.1°K. to 500°K., using the value of $\bar{\nu}$ at 298.1°K. (1354 cm.$^{-1}$), yields $(s_2/s_1)f_{500°K.} \approx 1.0600$, compared with the "exact" value of 1.0593. Analogous extrapolation from 500°K. ($\bar{\nu} = 1401$ cm.$^{-1}$) to 298.1°K. yields $(s_2/s_1)f_{298.1°K.} \approx 1.1348$, compared with the exact value of 1.1377. Even for $H^{18}ONO_2$, where $\bar{\nu}$ varies by 16% (1808 → 2097) over this temperature range, the errors in extrapolating with the $\bar{\gamma}$ method are not unreasonably large. Extrapolation from 298.1°K. to 500°K. yields $(s_2/s_1)f_{500°K.} \approx 1.0414$, compared with the "exact" value of

Table IV. Application of Approximation Equations

Isotopic Species	$(s_2/s_1)f(298.1°K.)$			
	"exact"	l.t.a.[a]	z.p.e.a.[b]	h.t.a.[c]

A. ^{15}N-Substituted Species

Isotopic Species	"exact"	l.t.a.	z.p.e.a.	h.t.a.
^{15}NO	1.0649	1.0649	1.0843	1.1287
$^{15}NOBr$	1.0784	1.0691	1.1263	1.1384
$^{15}NOCl$	1.0791	1.0717	1.1253	1.1393
$^{15}NO_2^-$	1.0847	1.0833	1.1328	1.1265
^{15}NOF	1.0858	1.0815	1.1316	1.1519
cis-$HO^{15}NO$	1.0863	1.0828	1.1359	1.1402
$trans$-$HO^{15}NO$	1.0894	1.0860	1.1391	1.1488
$^{15}NO_2$	1.1025	1.1008	1.1527	1.1715
$^{15}NO_2Cl$	1.1377	1.1299	1.2263	1.2234
$^{15}NO_2^+$	1.1436	1.1322	1.2155	1.3223
$FO^{15}NO_2$	1.1456	1.1379	1.2357	1.2435
$^{15}NO_3^-$	1.1505	1.1468	1.2414	1.2318
$^{15}NO_2F$	1.1505	1.1448	1.2400	1.2540
$HO^{15}NO_2$	1.1638	1.1594	1.2551	1.2740

B. ^{18}O-Substituted Species

Isotopic Species	"exact"	l.t.a.	z.p.e.a.	h.t.a.
$trans$-$H^{18}ONO$	1.0750	1.0683	1.1261	1.1559
$NO^{18}O^-$	1.0818	1.0795	1.1331	1.1193
$H^{18}ONO_2$	1.0874	1.0761	1.1584	1.1712
cis-$H^{18}ONO$	1.0880	1.0829	1.1445	1.1700
$NO^{18}O$	1.0906	1.0884	1.1411	1.1422
cis-$HON^{18}O$	1.0911	1.0861	1.1461	1.1481
$F^{18}ONO_2$	1.0937	1.0639	1.1943	1.1201
$NO_2^{18}O^-$	1.0938	1.0882	1.1678	1.1292
$trans$-$HON^{18}O$	1.0960	1.0904	1.1503	1.1640
$N^{18}O$	1.0970	1.0970	1.1266	1.1943
$N^{18}OBr$	1.0971	1.0750	1.1510	1.1824
$NO^{18}OCl$	1.0982	1.0825	1.1754	1.1491
$N^{18}OCl$	1.0989	1.0838	1.1521	1.1846
$HONO^{18}O$[d]	1.0991	1.0918	1.1752	1.1441
$FONO^{18}O$[d]	1.1039	1.0838	1.1859	1.1579
$N^{18}OF$	1.1094	1.1028	1.1636	1.2047
$NO^{18}OF$	1.1101	1.1025	1.1868	1.1696
$NO^{18}O^+$	1.1235	1.1192	1.1823	1.2316

[a] Low-temperature approximation.
[b] Zero-point-energy approximation.
[c] High-temperature approximation.

1.0383, while extrapolation from 500°K. to 298.1°K. yields $(s_2/s_1)f_{298.1°K.}$ $\approx$ 1.0781, compared with the "exact" value of 1.0874.

The success of Equation 12 in predicting $\bar{\nu}$ from the frequencies (which can be reasonably estimated) of the isotopic species involved

for Estimating Reduced Partition-Function Ratios

$(s_2/s_1)f(500°K.)$		$(s_2/s_1)f(2000°K.)$		$\bar{\nu}(cm.^{-1})$		
"exact"	h.t.a.	"exact"	h.t.a.	298.1°K.	500°K.	$\bar{\bar{\nu}}$

A. ^{15}N-Substituted Species

1.0312	1.0440	1.0026	1.0027	1860	1860	1843
1.0355	1.0472	1.0028	1.0029	1576	1632	1609
1.0358	1.0475	1.0028	1.0029	1570	1627	1606
1.0363	1.0433	1.0026	1.0027	1207	1215	1202
1.0388	1.0516	1.0031	1.0031	1577	1634	1618
1.0379	1.0477	1.0029	1.0029	1386	1429	1411
1.0396	1.0505	1.0030	1.0031	1437	1482	1466
1.0455	1.0579	1.0035	1.0035	1441	1462	1445
1.0593	1.0743	1.0044	1.0045	1354	1401	1379
1.0676	1.1044	1.0060	1.0062	2071	2158	2151
1.0631	1.0805	1.0048	1.0049	1413	1466	1445
1.0637	1.0769	1.0046	1.0046	1240	1257	1238
1.0654	1.0838	1.0049	1.0050	1429	1482	1464
1.0710	1.0899	1.0053	1.0054	1403	1436	1418

B. ^{18}O-Substituted Species

1.0337	1.0528	1.0030	1.0032	1965	2247	2490
1.0347	1.0409	1.0025	1.0025	1157	1171	1157
1.0383	1.0578	1.0033	1.0035	1808	2097	2316
1.0390	1.0574	1.0033	1.0035	1776	2011	2198
1.0394	1.0484	1.0029	1.0030	1309	1332	1318
1.0400	1.0503	1.0030	1.0031	1385	1427	1407
1.0371	1.0412	1.0025	1.0025	877	900	873
1.0385	1.0441	1.0027	1.0027	1031	1053	1035
1.0428	1.0555	1.0033	1.0034	1490	1532	1510
1.0461	1.0651	1.0038	1.0039	1852	1852	1827
1.0450	1.0614	1.0036	1.0037	1701	1726	1698
1.0418	1.0507	1.0030	1.0031	1237	1282	1258
1.0456	1.0621	1.0037	1.0038	1687	1715	1687
1.0413	1.0490	1.0030	1.0030	1144	1191	1171
1.0441	1.0535	1.0032	1.0033	1234	1281	1258
1.0502	1.0685	1.0040	1.0041	1683	1722	1696
1.0469	1.0573	1.0034	1.0035	1260	1309	1290
1.0560	1.0769	1.0045	1.0046	1675	1740	1752

[a] $(s_2/s_1)f$ values are geometric means of the respective values for the two individual terminal ^{18}O-substituted molecules. $\bar{\nu}$ values were calculated from the average "exact" and h.t.a. $(s_2/s_1)f$ values.

suggests that temperature-extrapolations of partition-function ratios with the $\bar{\gamma}$ method may be carried out with estimated values of $\bar{\nu}$ rather than of $\Sigma(\nu_{1i}^2 - \nu_{2i}^2)$. Estimations of both $\bar{\nu}$ and $\Sigma(\nu_{1i}^2 - \nu_{2i}^2)$ would allow completely *a priori* predictions of $(s_2/s_1)f$ values. The $\overline{\gamma}$ method was, in fact, originally proposed $(4, 9)$ for the *a priori* prediction of isotope effects.

Isotope-Exchange Equilibrium Constants. A more critical test of the approximation methods is the applicability of these methods to the prediction of isotope-exchange equilibrium constants—*i.e.*, ratios of partition-function ratios. The reduced partition-function ratios considered in this work are fairly similar in magnitude to one another at a given temperature, thus resulting in isotope-exchange equilibrium constants, at room temperature and above, on the order of unity. The relative errors of the approximations to the $\ln (s_2/s_1)f$ [$\approx (s_2/s_1)f - 1$] values might, therefore, be expected to be reflected as considerably increased relative errors in the approximations to the $\ln K_{A/B}$ ($\approx K_{A/B} - 1$) values. On the other hand, the errors of a particular approximation to $(s_2/s_1)f$ are always in the same direction (*cf.* Table IV) and one might, therefore, hope for satisfactory cancellation when ratios are taken. In order to test the accuracy of the various approximation methods, we calculated equilibrium constants for all possible ^{15}N-exchange and mono-^{18}O-substituted-exchange equilibria using the values in Table IV. Some representative results are shown in Table V. In comparing results obtained by an approximation with those predicted by the "exact" equation, one must consider the relative error in $\ln K_{A/B} \approx K_{A/B} - 1$, the purpose for which the approximation is being made, and the precision to which the isotope-exchange equilibrium constant can be measured. In the following discussion we have chosen, somewhat arbitrarily, to examine whether approximate results deviate by more than ± 0.003 from the corresponding "exact" result. An error of this magnitude represents roughly 10% of the average $\ln K_{A/B}$ at room temperature, for the equilibria considered, and is considerably larger than the usual present-day experimental error in measuring equilibrium constants for heavy-atom (all but hydrogen) isotope exchange.

At 298.1°K., the l.t.a. values of the equilibrium constants $K_{A/B}$ agreed with the corresponding "exact" values within ± 0.003 for less than one-half of the 91 ^{15}N exchanges considered. For the ^{18}O-exchange equilibrium constants, such agreement between the "exact" and l.t.a. values was achieved in only about one-third of the 153 cases considered. In $\sim 25\%$ of the ^{18}O-exchange cases, the l.t.a. predicted the wrong direction of the isotopic enrichment—*i.e.*, an "exact" $K_{A/B} > 1$ and a corresponding l.t.a. $K_{A/B} < 1$, or *vice versa*. Such reverse enrichment was predicted in 2 of the ^{15}N-exchange cases (^{15}NOF/^{15}NO$_2^-$ and *cis*-HO^{15}NO/^{15}NO$_2^-$), but in these cases the $K_{A/B}$ values were very close to unity and the agreements with the corresponding l.t.a. values were within ± 0.003.

The z.p.e.a., applied at 298.1°K., was usually a much poorer approximation than the l.t.a. The wrong direction of enrichment was predicted by the z.p.e.a. in about the same number of cases as by the l.t.a., but generally for different systems.

The h.t.a. yielded values of $K_{A/B}$ which agreed within ± 0.003 with the corresponding "exact" values in only $\sim 10\%$ of the cases at 298.1°K. and $\sim 35\%$ of the cases at 500°K., with no marked preference for either the ^{15}N- or ^{18}O-exchange systems. At 2000°K., of course, the h.t.a. always performed satisfactorily. At room temperature, the h.t.a. $K_{A/B}$ values were generally poorer approximations to the "exact" values than were the corresponding l.t.a. values, with the fraction of better h.t.a. values being somewhat larger for the ^{18}O- exchanges than for the ^{15}N-exchanges. Only $\sim 10\%$ of the ^{15}N-exchange cases, but about one-third of the ^{18}O-exchange cases, had their directions of enrichment at 298.1°K. predicted incorrectly by the h.t.a. The situation was not very much improved even at 500°K., where $\sim 7\%$ of the ^{15}N-exchange cases and $\sim 20\%$ of the ^{18}O-exchange cases exhibited disagreement in direction of enrichment between the h.t.a. and the "exact" calculations.

In order to investigate the validity of the gamma-bar method for these equilibrium cases, a single fit-producing $\overline{\gamma}$ was calculated for each isotope-exchange equilibrium constant according to

$$\overline{\gamma}_{A/B} = \frac{\ln (K_{A/B})_{\text{"exact"}}}{\ln (K_{A/B})_{\text{h.t.a.}}}. \tag{13}$$

The constancy of the resulting characteristic frequency $\overline{\nu}_{A/B}$, over the temperature range considered, is taken as a criterion of the validity of the gamma-bar approximation. $\overline{\nu}_{A/B}$ should now be characteristic of both exchanging species. In $\sim 25\%$ of the 91 ^{15}N-exchange cases and in $\sim 50\%$ of the 153 ^{18}O-exchange cases, Equation 13 applied at 298.1°K. and at 500°K. led (for at least one of the two temperatures and usually for both) to values of $\overline{\gamma}_{A/B}$ which were outside the range for which γ is defined ($0 < \gamma < 1$). Negative $\overline{\gamma}_{A/B}$ corresponds to a prediction of the wrong direction of isotopic enrichment by the h.t.a. (*vide supra*), while $|\overline{\gamma}_{A/B}| > 1$ corresponds to the h.t.a. predicting a smaller deviation of $K_{A/B}$ from unity than the deviation of the "exact" $K_{A/B}$. Even in the cases where $\overline{\gamma}_{A/B}$ was in the proper range, the corresponding $\overline{\nu}_{A/B}$ bore little, if any, relationship to the $\overline{\nu}$ for the individual $(s_2/s_1)f$ involved, and generally varied, between the temperatures 298.1°K. and 500°K., by much more than did the individual $\overline{\nu}$. For the cases in which the $\overline{\gamma}_{A/B}$ were in the range $0 < \overline{\gamma}_{A/B} < 1$, $\overline{\nu}_{A/B}$ varied by less than $\pm 10\%$ in $\sim 75\%$ of the ^{15}N-exchange systems but in only $\sim 15\%$ of the ^{18}O-exchange systems.

The reason for the general failure of $\bar{\nu}_{A/B}$ to represent a characteristic "average" frequency (analogous to what $\bar{\nu}$ for a single chemical species approximately represents) can be seen from the equation for its approximation. If $\bar{\gamma}_{A/B}$ and the γ_i of all the isotope-dependent frequencies are taken to obey the same linear equation within the temperature range considered, then the same reasoning applied in the derivation of Equation 12 results (*see Appendix*) in an approximate value $\bar{\bar{\nu}}_{A/B}$, which is related to the isotope-dependent frequencies and the $\bar{\nu}$ values of the individual species by

$$\bar{\nu}_{A/B} \approx \frac{\bar{\bar{\nu}}_A \Sigma \Delta (\nu_i{}^2)_A - \bar{\bar{\nu}}_B \Sigma \Delta (\nu_i{}^2)_B}{\Sigma \Delta (\nu_i{}^2)_A - \Sigma \Delta (\nu_i{}^2)_B} \equiv \bar{\bar{\nu}}_{A/B}. \qquad (14)$$

We see that $\bar{\bar{\nu}}_{A/B}$ is not a weighted average of either the isotope-dependent frequencies or of the individual $\bar{\bar{\nu}}$. In fact, unless $\bar{\bar{\nu}}_A$ and $\bar{\bar{\nu}}_B$ are identical, for which case $\bar{\bar{\nu}}_{A/B} = \bar{\bar{\nu}}_A = \bar{\bar{\nu}}_B$, $\bar{\bar{\nu}}_{A/B}$ cannot even lie within the range of $\bar{\bar{\nu}}_A$ and $\bar{\bar{\nu}}_B$. Although Equation 14 is based on the linear approximation for γ, it indicates that the fact that the values of $\bar{\nu}_{A/B}$ calculated through Equation 13 bore little relationship to the individual $\bar{\nu}$ values should not be overly surprising. Further, since the numerator in Equation 14 contains a difference between two weighted $\bar{\bar{\nu}}$ values, it is to be expected that small relative errors in the individual $\bar{\bar{\nu}}$ would be reflected as a larger relative error in $\bar{\bar{\nu}}_{A/B}$. Thus, we might expect to find, as we have found, that the $\bar{\nu}_{A/B}$ for the equilibrium constants were more temperature-dependent than the $\bar{\nu}$ for the individual $(s_2/s_1)f$. We have not felt it worthwhile to calculate $\bar{\bar{\nu}}_{A/B}$ with Equation 14 for all of the isotope-exchange equilibria considered. The cases for which we did calculate $\bar{\bar{\nu}}_{A/B}$, most of which are shown in Table V, indicate that when Equation 13 yields a value of $\bar{\gamma}_{A/B}$ in the range in which γ is defined, the corresponding $\bar{\nu}_{A/B}$, if fairly temperature-independent, can be reasonably approximated by $\bar{\bar{\nu}}_{A/B}$.

None of the approximation methods investigated appears to be very reliable for application, in the room-temperature region, to the (near-unity) isotope-exchange equilibrium constants for the systems considered here. The inadequacy of the approximation methods in the majority of the cases studied arises, for the most part, from "anomalies" in the temperature dependences of the "exact" equilibrium constants. It has been shown (22) that whereas the logarithms of partition-function ratios are always smooth monotonic functions of temperature, plots of the logarithms of ratios of partition-function ratios—*i.e.*, isotope-exchange equilibrium constants—*vs.* T (or *vs.* log T) may exhibit maxima, minima, and inflection points. In addition, equilibrium constants may exhibit the "crossover phenomenon," where they change, with increasing temperature, from values greater than unity to values smaller than unity, or *vice versa*, and thereby reverse the direction of isotopic enrichment. By temperature-dependence "anomaly" we mean any such deviation from a regular monotonic decrease of $|\ln K_{A/B}|$ from some value at low temperature to its infinite-temperature limit of zero. The "exact" equilibrium constants for the exchange systems considered in this work exhibit numerous temperature-dependence "anomalies" which are classified and discussed in our previous publication (22). Fifteen of the 91 ^{15}N-exchange systems considered and 97 of the 153 ^{18}O-exchange systems considered exhibit inflections, maxima, minima, crossovers, or combinations of these. The much more frequent occurrence of "anomalies" in the ^{18}O-exchanges, as compared with the ^{15}N-exchanges, is consistent with the generally poorer performance of the approximation methods when applied to the ^{18}O-exchange cases.

The approximation methods considered in this work do not allow for most of the "anomalies" discussed above. In the z.p.e.a., $\ln K_{A/B}$ is directly proportional to $1/T$, and in the h.t.a., $\ln K_{A/B}$ is directly proportional to $1/T^2$. Thus, these approximations do not allow crossovers, maxima, minima, or inflection points in plots of $\ln K_{A/B}$ *vs.* T (or *vs.* $\log T$). Similarly, the gamma-bar modification of the h.t.a. cannot produce crossovers, since $\overline{\gamma}$ is always positive. It can further be shown (22) that this method excludes the other "anomalies" as well. Finally, the l.t.a., which is of the form $\ln K_{A/B} = a + b/T$, where a and b are temperature-independent, does not allow maxima, minima, or inflection points, but if a and b are of opposite sign, a single crossover is predicted. A prediction of crossover by the l.t.a. should not be generally reliable, however, since in this approximation there is no way for $\ln K_{A/B}$ to return to zero after passing through the crossover point. Occasionally, the crossovers observed for the "exact" $K_{A/B}$ values fall within the range of validity of the l.t.a. For example, for the systems $NO^{18}O^-/N^{18}O$ and $NO^{18}O/N^{18}O$, the l.t.a. predicts crossover temperatures of 78°K. and 185°K., respectively, in excellent agreement with the corresponding "exact" (22) values of 80° ± 10°K. and 190° ± 10°K. However, for the systems $NO^{18}OF/N^{18}O$ and $NO^{18}OF/N^{18}OBr$, with "exact" crossover temperatures of 550° ± 50°K. and 700° ± 50°K., respectively, the l.t.a. predicts crossovers at 330°K. and 1682°K., respectively. Furthermore, a prediction of crossover by the l.t.a. is no guarantee that the "exact" $K_{A/B}$ will indeed exhibit a crossover at any temperature. Thus, for example, for the $N^{18}OF/N^{18}O$ system the l.t.a. predicts a crossover point at 356°K. although no crossover in the "exact" $K_{N^{18}OF/N^{18}O}$ is observed. Conversely, the l.t.a. does not predict any

Table V.   Application of Approximation Equations for

Exchange System	$K_{A/B}$ $(298.1°K.)$			
	"exact"	l.t.a.[a]	z.p.e.a.[b]	h.t.a.[c]

A. ^{15}N-Substituted Species

Exchange System	"exact"	l.t.a.	z.p.e.a.	h.t.a.
$^{15}NO_2^-/^{15}NO$	1.0186	1.0173	1.0447	0.9981
$^{15}NOF/^{15}NO$	1.0196	1.0156	1.0436	1.0206
$^{15}NO_2F/^{15}NO$	1.0804	1.0750	1.1436	1.1110
$HO^{15}NO_2/^{15}NO$	1.0929	1.0887	1.1575	1.1287
$^{15}NO_2^+/^{15}NO_2^-$	1.0543	1.0451	1.0730	1.1738
$cis\text{-}HO^{15}NO/^{15}NO_2^-$	1.0015	0.9995	1.0027	1.0122
$^{15}NO_2Cl/^{15}NOBr$	1.0550	1.0569	1.0888	1.0747
$^{15}NO_2^+/^{15}NOBr$	1.0605	1.0590	1.0792	1.1615
$cis\text{-}HO^{15}NO/^{15}NOBr$	1.0073	1.0128	1.0085	1.0016
$^{15}NO_2^+/^{15}NOCl$	1.0598	1.0565	1.0802	1.1606
$^{15}NO_3^-/^{15}NOF$	1.0596	1.0604	1.0970	1.0694
$FO^{15}NO_2/^{15}NO_2$	1.0391	1.0337	1.0720	1.0615
$trans\text{-}HO^{15}NO/^{15}NO_3^-$	0.9469	0.9470	0.9176	0.9326
$cis\text{-}HO^{15}NO/^{15}NO_2F$	0.9442	0.9458	0.9160	0.9093
$^{51}NO_2^+/HO^{15}NO_2$	0.9826	0.9765	0.9684	1.0379
$FO^{15}NO_2/^{15}NO_2^+$	1.0017	1.0050	1.0166	0.9404
$trans\text{-}HO^{51}NO/FO^{15}NO_2$	0.9509	0.9544	0.9218	0.9238
$cis\text{-}HO^{15}NO/trans\text{-}HO^{15}NO$	0.9972	0.9971	0.9972	0.9925

B. ^{18}O-Substituted Species

Exchange System	"exact"	l.t.a.	z.p.e.a.	h.t.a.
$NO^{18}O^-/N^{18}O$	0.9861	0.9840	1.0058	0.9372
$H^{18}ONO_2/N^{18}O$	0.9912	0.9809	1.0282	0.9807
$trans\text{-}H^{18}ONO/N^{18}O$	0.9799	0.9738	0.9996	0.9678
$cis\text{-}HON^{18}O/N^{18}O$	0.9946	0.9901	1.0173	0.9613
$N^{18}OBr/NO^{18}O^-$	1.0141	0.9958	1.0158	1.0564
$NO_2^{18}O^-/NO^{18}O^-$	1.0111	1.0081	1.0306	1.0088
$H^{18}ONO_2/NO^{18}O^-$	1.0052	0.9969	1.0223	1.0464
$cis\text{-}H^{18}ONO/NO^{18}O^-$	1.0057	1.0031	1.0101	1.0453
$NO^{18}OCl/N^{18}OBr$	1.0010	1.0070	1.0212	0.9718
$NO_2^{18}O^-/N^{18}OBr$	0.9970	1.0123	1.0146	0.9550
$NO^{18}OF/N^{18}OBr$	1.0118	1.0256	1.0311	0.9892
$HONO^{18}O/N^{18}OBr$	1.0018	1.0156	1.0210	0.9676
$F^{18}ONO_2/N^{18}OCl$	0.9953	0.9816	1.0366	0.9456
$NO_2^{18}O^-/N^{18}OF$	0.9859	0.9868	1.0036	0.9373
$trans\text{-}HON^{18}O/N^{18}OF$	0.9879	0.9888	0.9886	0.9662
$NO^{18}OF/NO^{18}O$	1.0179	1.0130	1.0400	1.0240
$H^{18}ONO_2/NO^{18}O$	0.9971	0.9887	1.0152	1.0254
$NO^{18}O^+/NO^{18}O$	1.0302	1.0283	1.0361	1.0783
$FONO^{18}O/NO^{18}O$	1.0122	0.9958	1.0393	1.0137
$cis\text{-}H^{18}ONO/NO^{18}OCl$	0.9907	1.0004	0.9737	1.0182
$trans\text{-}H^{18}ONO/NO_2^{18}O^-$	0.9828	0.9817	0.9643	1.0236
$NO^{18}O^+/NO^{18}OF$	1.0121	1.0151	0.9962	1.0530
$NO^{18}O^+/H^{18}ONO_2$	1.0332	1.0401	1.0206	1.0516
$cis\text{-}H^{18}ONO/H^{18}ONO_2$	1.0006	1.0063	0.9880	0.9990

Estimating Isotope-Exchange Equilibrium Constants

$K_{A/B}$ (500°K.)		$K_{A/B}$ (2000°K.)		$\bar{v}_{A/B}$ $(cm.^{-1})^d$		
"exact"	h.t.a.	"exact"	h.t.a.	298.1°K.	500°K.	$\bar{v}_{A/B}$
A. ^{15}N-Substituted Species						
1.0049	0.9993	1.0000	1.0000	o.r.	o.r.	41,739
1.0074	1.0073	1.0005	1.0004	351	o.r.	283
1.0332	1.0381	1.0023	1.0023	1042	1064	1029
1.0386	1.0440	1.0027	1.0027	1045	1023	993
1.0302	1.0586	1.0034	1.0035	3294	3094	2857
1.0015	1.0042	1.0003	1.0002	>5200	4878	3469
1.0230	1.0259	1.0016	1.0016	1015	975	965
1.0310	1.0546	1.0032	1.0033	2682	2701	2621
1.0023	1.0005	1.0001	1.0000	o.r.	o.r.	−14,235
1.0307	1.0543	1.0032	1.0033	2701	2718	2629
1.0240	1.0241	1.0015	1.0015	661	163	435
1.0168	1.0214	1.0013	1.0014	1343	1470	1446
0.9773	0.9755	0.9984	0.9985	898	790	783
0.9742	0.9667	0.9980	0.9979	1490	1558	1537
0.9968	1.0133	1.0007	1.0008	o.r.	o.r.	6916
0.9958	0.9784	0.9988	0.9987	o.r.	>8700	4654
0.9779	0.9722	0.9982	0.9982	1372	1450	1409
0.9984	0.9973	0.9999	0.9998	2793	2438	2420
B. ^{18}O-Substituted Species						
0.9891	0.9773	0.9987	0.9986	>5200	3508	2990
0.9925	0.9931	0.9995	0.9996	2255	o.r.	−2146
0.9881	0.9885	0.9992	0.9993	1428	o.r.	−1119
0.9942	0.9861	0.9992	0.9992	>5200	4155	3298
1.0100	1.0197	1.0011	1.0012	4398	3221	2808
1.0037	1.0031	1.0002	1.0002	o.r.	o.r.	−519
1.0035	1.0162	1.0008	1.0010	>5200	>8700	5194
1.0042	1.0159	1.0008	1.0010	>5200	7140	4840
0.9969	0.9899	0.9994	0.9994	o.r.	6107	3844
0.9938	0.9837	0.9991	0.9990	>5200	4677	3450
1.0018	0.9961	0.9998	0.9998	o.r.	o.r.	7566
0.9965	0.9883	0.9994	0.9993	o.r.	6127	3848
0.9919	0.9803	0.9988	0.9987	>5200	4246	3338
0.9889	0.9772	0.9987	0.9986	>5200	3429	2939
0.9930	0.9878	0.9993	0.9993	3037	2676	2519
1.0072	1.0085	1.0005	1.0005	1002	1172	1133
0.9989	1.0090	1.0004	1.0005	o.r.	o.r.	7603
1.0160	1.0272	1.0016	1.0016	2662	2585	2518
1.0045	1.0049	1.0003	1.0003	586	751	674
0.9973	1.0064	1.0003	1.0004	o.r.	o.r.	9457
0.9954	1.0083	1.0003	1.0005	o.r.	o.r.	10,054
1.0087	1.0185	1.0011	1.0011	4900	3563	3153
1.0170	1.0181	1.0012	1.0011	1320	660	−22
1.0007	0.9996	1.0000	1.0000	o.r.	o.r.	20,687

Table V.

Exchange System	$K_{A/B}$ (298.1°K.)			
	"exact"	l.t.a.[a]	z.p.e.a.[b]	h.t.a.[c]
	B. ^{18}O-Substituted Species			
FONO^{18}O/HONO^{18}O	1.0044	0.9927	1.0091	1.0121
trans-HON^{18}O/NO^{18}O$^+$	0.9755	0.9743	0.9729	0.9451
trans-H^{18}ONO/F^{18}ONO$_2$	0.9829	1.0041	0.9429	1.0320
cis-HON^{18}O/F^{18}ONO$_2$	0.9976	1.0209	0.9596	1.0250
cis-H^{18}ONO/FONO^{18}O	0.9856	0.9856	.0.9651	1.0104
trans-HON^{18}O/trans-H^{18}ONO	1.0195	1.0207	1.0215	1.0070

[a] Low-temperature approximation.
[b] Zero-point-energy approximation.
[c] High-temperature approximation.
[d] An entry of o.r. indicates that the fit-producing $\overline{\gamma}_{A/B}$, calculated with Equation 13, lies outside the range in which γ is defined ($0 < \gamma < 1$). An entry of > 5200 (at

crossover for the trans-H^{18}ONO/NO^{18}O$^-$ system, whereas the "exact" equilibrium constant exhibits crossover at 600° ± 50°K. The fact that very limited temperature dependences are allowed by the approximations investigated, while temperature-dependence "anomalies" in the "exact" equilibrium constants are prevalent for the systems considered, indicates that the validity of these approximations, applied to the $K_{A/B}$ values, will, in general, depend strongly on the particular temperature considered.

Conclusions

It has been shown that gross correlations of reduced partition-function ratios $(s_2/s_1)f$ can be made with the structures of some simple ^{15}N- and ^{18}O-substituted oxynitrogen molecules, but for finer details, more exact calculations need be performed. Several approximation methods for predicting isotope effects (viz., the low-temperature approximation, the high-temperature approximation, and modifications of these) have been tested on these simple molecules. Some of the approximation methods can lead to reasonable estimates of the room-temperature-region $(s_2/s_1)f$ values. The modified high-temperature approximation, or "gamma-bar" method, appears particularly useful for extrapolating the partition-function ratios over limited temperature ranges. The necessary characteristic frequency $\overline{\nu}$ is approximately a weighted average of the isotope-dependent frequencies in the molecule and can, therefore, be reasonably estimated. The fact that a different correction factor must be associated with each chemical species (pair of isotopic molecules) is in

(Continued)

$K_{A/B}$ (500°K.)		$K_{A/B}$ (2000°K.)		$\bar{\nu}_{A/B}$ (cm.$^{-1}$)^d		
"exact"	h.t.a.	"exact"	h.t.a.	298.1°K.	500°K.	$\bar{\bar{\nu}}_{A/B}$

B. ^{18}O-Substituted Species

1.0027	1.0043	1.0002	1.0003	2938	2348	2231
0.9875	0.9801	0.9988	0.9988	2328	2352	2403
0.9967	1.0111	1.0005	1.0007	o.r.	o.r.	8322
1.0028	1.0087	1.0005	1.0006	o.r.	5707	3864
0.9951	1.0037	1.0001	1.0002	o.r.	o.r.	15,405
1.0088	1.0026	1.0003	1.0002	o.r.	o.r.	−18,809

298.1°K.) or > 8700 cm.$^{-1}$ ^{f} at 500°K.) indicates that $\bar{u}_{A/B} (= h\bar{\nu}_{A/B}/kT)$, corresponding to the fit-producing $\bar{\gamma}_{A/B}$, is greater than 25. In the range u > 25, γ decreases toward zero very slowly with increasing u (*4, 9*), so that small variations in $\bar{\gamma}_{A/B}$ are reflected as large variations in $\bar{\nu}_{A/B}$. Thus, the specific values of $\bar{\nu}_{A/B}$ corresponding to the range $\bar{u}_{A/B}$ > 25 are fairly meaningless.

agreement with equations derived by means of finite orthogonal-polynomial expansions (*6, 16*).

Attempted application of these approximation methods to the prediction of the (near-unity) equilibrium constants $K_{A/B}$ [ratios of $(s_2/s_1)f$ values] for isotope-exchange reactions among these oxynitrogen species, at room temperature, usually produced rather poor results, often predicting the wrong direction of the isotopic enrichment. The failures were caused, for the most part, by the prevalence of temperature-dependence "anomalies" in the "exact" equilibrium constants. The failure of a simple —*i.e.*, containing only one characteristic frequency to represent the entire reaction—gamma-bar equation to fit the equilibrium-constant data is particularly disappointing in view of its general success in fitting isotopic rate-constant ratios (*23, 28*), the kinetic analog of isotope-exchange equilibrium constants. The single characteristic frequency of the simple gamma-bar equation describing an isotope-exchange equilibrium is not simply related to the isotope-dependent frequencies of the exchanging chemical species and would be, therefore, extremely difficult to predict, even when the "exact" $K_{A/B}$ values are well fit by this equation. The prevalence of temperature-dependence "anomalies" in isotope-exchange equilibria is probably not restricted to the systems investigated in this work. Thus, an application of one of the approximation methods considered here should not, in general, be considered reliable unless it is known not only that the temperature involved is within the range of validity of the approximation, but also that the equilibrium constant approaches unity regularly with increasing temperature, or that the temperature involved is sufficiently low or sufficiently high to be far from the region of the "anomaly." On the other hand, the success of the gamma-bar method in fitting the individual partition-function ratios suggests that isotope-exchange equilibrium constants can be well-fit or possibly even predicted, over a limited temperature range, by applying the gamma-bar method with a separate characteristic frequency assigned to each chemical species (4).

An isotope-exchange equilibrium constant is equivalent to an isotopic ratio of equilibrium constants for an ordinary chemical reaction. Thus, one might want to use an equilibrium isotope-effect study for determining force-constant changes between reactants and products, in the same manner as one would use a kinetic isotope-effect study to determine force-constant changes between reactants and transition state (9, 29). It is usually assumed, however, that reactants and corresponding transition state are structurally more related than reactants and corresponding products. The results of the present study point out that for equilibria involving simple oxynitrogen compounds, it could be quite dangerous to attempt to correlate isotope effects with force-constant changes through the high-temperature approximation or its one-characteristic-frequency gamma-bar modification. Since there is nothing particularly special about the molecules considered in this study, the danger may be fairly general for equilibria.

Acknowledgments

We wish to thank H. C. Hisatsune, D. L. Bernitt, and G. E. McGraw, Pennsylvania State University, for providing us, prior to publication, with force-field data for many of the molecules considered in this work. We also thank Thomas Hughes for his assistance in carrying out some of the computations. Finally, we thank the Columbia University Computer Center and the N.A.S.A. Institute for Space Studies for generous allotments of free computer time.

APPENDIX

Equations 12 and 14 can be derived as follows:
If γ is represented as $a + bu$, Equation 11 becomes

$$a + b\bar{u} = \frac{\Sigma(a + bu_{2i})\Delta(\nu_i^2)}{\Sigma\Delta(\nu_i^2)} = a + b\frac{\Sigma u_{2i}\Delta(\nu_i^2)}{\Sigma\Delta(\nu_i^2)}.$$

Equating the coefficients of b on both sides of the equation and multiplying by kT/h leads to Equation 12.

Equation 13 can be written

$$\overline{\gamma}_{A/B} = \frac{\ln\left[(s_2/s_1)f\right]_A - \ln\left[(s_2/s_1)f\right]_B}{(1/24)\left[\Sigma\Delta(u_i{}^2)_A - \Sigma\Delta(u_i{}^2)_B\right]} = \frac{\Sigma\gamma_{iA}(\Delta\nu_i{}^2)_A - \Sigma\gamma_{iB}\Delta(\nu_i{}^2)_B}{\Sigma\Delta(\nu_i{}^2)_A - \Sigma\Delta(\nu_i{}^2)_B}.$$

Again representing γ as a $+ bu$ yields

$$a + b\overline{u}_{A/B} = \frac{\Sigma(a + bu_{2i,A})(\Delta\nu_i{}^2)_A - \Sigma(a + bu_{2i,B})\Delta(\nu_i{}^2)_B}{\Sigma\Delta(\nu_i{}^2)_A - \Sigma(\Delta\nu_i{}^2)_B}$$

$$= a + b\,\frac{\Sigma u_{2i,A}\Delta(\nu_i{}^2)_A - \Sigma u_{2i,B}\Delta(\nu_i{}^2)_B}{\Sigma\Delta(\nu_i{}^2)_A - \Sigma\Delta(\nu_i{}^2)_B}.$$

Equating the coefficients of b on both sides of the equation and multiplying by kT/h yields

$$\overline{\nu}_{A/B} = \frac{\Sigma\nu_{2i,A}\Delta(\nu_i{}^2)_A - \Sigma\nu_{2i,B}\Delta(\nu_i{}^2)_B}{\Sigma\Delta(\nu_i{}^2)_A - \Sigma\Delta(\nu_i{}^2)_B},$$

which combines with Equation 12 for $\overline{\nu}_A$ and $\overline{\nu}_B$ to give Equation 14.

Literature Cited

(1) Arakawa, E. T., Nielsen, A. H., *J. Mol. Spectr.* **2**, 413 (1958).
(2) Begun, G. M., Fletcher, W. H., *J. Chem. Phys.* **33**, 1083 (1960).
(3) Bernitt, D. L. (personal communication).
(4) Bigeleisen, J., "Proceedings of the International Symposium on Isotope Separation," p. 121, North-Holland Publishing Co., Amsterdam, 1958.
(5) Bigeleisen, J., Goldstein, P., *Z. Naturforsch.* **18a**, 205 (1963).
(6) Bigeleisen, J., Ishida, T., *J. Chem. Phys.* **48**, 1311 (1968).
(7) Bigeleisen, J., Mayer, M. G., *J. Chem. Phys.* **15**, 261 (1947).
(8) Bigeleisen, J., Weston, R. E., Wolfsberg, M., *Z. Naturforsch.* **18a**, 210 (1963).
(9) Bigeleisen, J., Wolfsberg, M., *Advan. Chem. Phys.* **1**, 15 (1958).
(10) Bird, G. R., *J. Chem. Phys.* **25**, 1040 (1956).
(11) Carpenter, G. B., *Acta Cryst.* **8**, 852 (1955).
(12) Clayton, L., Williams, Q., Weatherly, T. L., *J. Chem. Phys.* **30**, 1328 (1959).
(13) Devlin, J. P., Ph.D. dissertation, Kansas State University (1960).
(14) Herzberg, G., "Infrared and Raman Spectra of Polyatomic Molecules," D. Van Nostrand Co., Inc., New York, 1945.
(15) "Handbook of Chemistry and Physics," 45th ed., Chemical Rubber Co., Cleveland, Ohio, 1964.
(16) Ishida, T., Spindel, W., Bigeleisen, J., ADVAN. CHEM. SER. **89**, 192 (1969).
(17) McGraw, G. E., Bernitt, D. L., Hisatsune, I. C., *J. Chem. Phys.* **42**, 237 (1965).
(18) *Ibid.*, **45**, 1392 (1966).
(19) Pauling, L., Brockway, L. O., *J. Am. Chem. Soc.* **59**, 13 (1937).
(20) Schachtschneider, J. H., Snyder, R. G., *Spectrochim. Acta* **19**, 117 (1963).
(21) Shaw, J. H., *J. Chem. Phys.* **24**, 399 (1956).
(22) Stern, M. J., Spindel, W., Monse, E. U., *J. Chem. Phys.* **48**, 2908 (1968).

(23) Stern, M. J., Wolfsberg, M., *J. Chem. Phys.* **39**, 2776 (1963).
(24) Teranishi, R., Decius, J. C., *J. Chem. Phys.* **22**, 896 (1954).
(25) Urey, H. C., *J. Chem. Soc.* **1947**, 562.
(26) Wilson, E. B., Decius, J. C., Cross, P. C., "Molecular Vibrations," Mc-Graw-Hill Book Co., Inc., New York, 1955.
(27) Wolfsberg, M., Z. *Naturforsch.* **18a**, 216 (1963).
(28) Wolfsberg, M., Stern, M. J., *Pure Appl. Chem.* **8**, 225 (1964).
(29) *Ibid.*, **8**, 325 (1964).

RECEIVED December 4, 1967. This work was supported in part by the U. S. Atomic Energy Commission under Contracts AT (30-1)-3462 and AT (30-1)-3663.

10

Correction to the Effect of Anharmonicity on Isotopic Exchange Equilibria

MAX WOLFSBERG

Departments of Chemistry, Brookhaven National Laboratory, Upton, N. Y. 11973 and State University of New York at Stony Brook, Stony Brook, N. Y. 11790

It is demonstrated that the formula for the vibrational energy states of a diatomic molecule should be written as $E_n/hc = G_o + \omega_e(n + 1/2) - \omega_e x_e(n + 1/2)^2$ with non-zero G_o. G_o values are evaluated for some diatomic hydrides and the effect of G_o on the theoretical calculation of isotopic exchange equilibrium constants is shown.

In calculations of the vibrational contribution to isotope effects on partition functions for diatomic molecules it is usual to employ the expression

$$E_n/hc = \omega_e(n + \tfrac{1}{2}) - \omega_e x_e(n + \tfrac{1}{2})^2 \qquad n = 0, 1, 2 \ldots \qquad (1)$$

for the vibrational energy levels. Terms in higher powers of $(n + 1/2)$ are usually omitted because they tend to be unimportant. Here ω_e is the harmonic frequency of the molecule (in cm.$^{-1}$), which depends on the inverse of the square root of the reduced mass μ of the molecule. $\omega_e x_e$ is the so-called first anharmonic correction (in cm.$^{-1}$), which has a μ^{-1} mass dependence. The vibrational zero-point energy of the molecule is then given by

$$E_o/hc = \tfrac{1}{2}\omega_e - \tfrac{1}{4}\omega_e x_e \qquad (2)$$

When one takes into account anharmonicity in the theoretical calculation of isotopic exchange equilibrium constants, one usually employs only the anharmonic correction to the zero-point energy ($-1/4\omega_e x_e$).

A formula of the type of Equation 1 can be obtained for a diatomic molecule oscillator subject to the well-known Morse potential $V = D_e\{1 - e^{-\beta(r-r_e)}\}^2$ where D_e is the dissociation energy, $r - r_e$ is the displacement of the internuclear distance from its equilibrium value r_e, and β is a potential parameter (*see* Reference 3).

185

Perturbation Theory Calculation for the Anharmonic Oscillator

The problem considered is the one-dimensional harmonic oscillator perturbed by cubic and quartic potential terms. Thus, the unperturbed Hamiltonian operator is

$$H = (-\hbar^2/2\mu)(\delta^2/\delta r^2) + \tfrac{1}{2}k(r - r_e)^2$$
$$= (-\hbar^2/2)(\delta^2/\delta Q^2) + \tfrac{1}{2}(k/\mu)Q^2 \tag{3}$$

where k is the harmonic force constant and Q, the normal coordinate, equals $\mu^{1/2}(r - r_e)$ [see Reference 13]. The energy levels corresponding to this Hamiltonian are, of course,

$$E_n^0/hc = (n + \tfrac{1}{2})\omega_e \tag{4}$$

where $\omega_e = (2\pi c)^{-1}(k/\mu)^{1/2}$. The perturbation is given by

$$V = a(r - r_e)^3 + b(r - r_e)^4 = (a/\mu^{3/2})Q^3 + (b/\mu^2)Q^4 \tag{5}$$

The potential constants k, a, and b are independent of isotopic substitution (within the framework of the Born-Oppenheimer approximation). The isotopic mass dependence is completely situated in the reduced mass μ. It is physically reasonable to assume for the diatomic molecule-oscillator that a and b are sufficiently small so that V can be regarded as a perturbation to Equation 3 and that it is necessary to consider no terms in the perturbation energy higher than the second power in a and higher than the first power in b. The term Q^3 only yields a non-vanishing contribution in second order while the Q^4 term yields a first-order contribution to the energy. One obtains by standard methods

$$\Delta E_n/hc = \gamma(90n^2 + 90n + 33) + \delta(2n^2 + 2n + 1)$$

where

$$\gamma = \frac{-\hbar a^2}{24(2\pi)^5 c^5 \omega_e^4 \mu^3} \qquad \delta = \frac{3\hbar b}{4(2\pi)^3 c^3 \omega_e^2 \mu^2} \tag{6}$$

It is obvious that a series in powers of $(n + 1/2)$ for the energy can be obtained only by adding an n-independent term to Expression 1. Thus,

$$E_n/hc = E_n^0/hc + \Delta E_n/hc = G_0 + (n + \tfrac{1}{2})\omega_e - (n + \tfrac{1}{2})^2 \omega_e x_e \tag{7}$$

where the coefficient of $(n + 1/2)^2$ has been designated $\omega_e x_e$ in the standard manner and

$$G_0 = \frac{21}{2}\gamma + \tfrac{1}{2}\delta \tag{8}$$

$$\omega_e x_e = -90\gamma - 2\delta \tag{9}$$

Special attention is drawn to the existence of the term G_0, independent of n but dependent on isotopic substitution. This term appeared in Dunham's WBK calculation on the rotating oscillator (2) and also in other perturbation theory calculations on polyatomic molecules [*see*, for instance, the expression for the bent XYZ molecule (*12*), where, in addition to the anharmonic vibration contribution to G_o, there is also a contribution from rotational-vibrational interaction (no similar contribution present for diatomic molecules)]. The term G_o does not enter into the energy differences between bound levels of molecules and it has therefore usually been dropped from consideration. In calculating the dissociation energies of H_2, D_2, and HD from experimental data, Herzberg and Monfils (*8*) did take this term into account. (They wrongly described it as a rotation-vibration interaction term.) To the best knowledge of the author, this isotope dependent term which contributes to the zero-point energy has always been neglected in calculations of thermodynamic isotope effects.

It is of interest, if the Morse potential is expanded to obtain the parameters k, a, and b, that ω_e and $\omega_e x_e$ obtained in this perturbation development agree with the values obtained by solving the Schroedinger equation with the Morse potential [*see* Reference 3] and that, as already pointed out by Dunham, G_o is equal to zero.

Calculation of G_o

In order to calculate G_o, one needs to know the potential parameters k, a, and b. These should be obtainable from spectroscopically observed quantities. Thus, k can be obtained from observed ω_e. Teller has shown that the rotational-vibrational constant α_e (in cm.$^{-1}$) can be expressed in terms of the cubic potential constant a and other parameters in the following manner [*see* Reference 6].

$$\alpha_e = \frac{24B_e{}^3r_e{}^3a}{hc\omega_e{}^3} - \frac{6B_e{}^2}{\omega_e} \tag{10}$$

where B_e is the rotational constant $h/(8\pi^2c\mu r_e{}^2)$. If one relates experimentally observed $\omega_e x_e$ to the parameters a and b as in Equation 9, one then obtains G_o expressed in terms of experimental observables

$$G_o = \frac{B_e}{4} + \frac{\alpha_e\omega_e}{12B_e} + \frac{\alpha_e{}^2\omega_e{}^2}{144B_e{}^3} - \frac{\omega_e x_e}{4}. \tag{11}$$

This formula agrees with the corresponding formula obtainable from Dunham (*2*) [*see* Reference 6, where the formula contains a typographical error]. G_o should theoretically, within this treatment, depend on isotopic substitution because it has a mass dependence μ^{-1}. The calculated value of G_o tends to be quite sensitive to the precise values of the experimentally observed quantities since it is the difference between the first three terms and the last term in Formula 11.

Discussion of G_0

Table I lists G_0 (Formula 11) and $\omega_e x_e/4$ evaluated from a standard compilation and also evaluated from more recent data for some isotopically substituted hydrogen molecules. It is seen that the G_0 values are by no means negligible compared with $-\omega_e x_e/4$, the usual anharmonicity correction to the zero-point energy. Even the G_0 and $\omega_e x_e/4$ values calculated from the more recent data do not precisely follow the theoretically expected μ^{-1} mass dependence. If one adjusts the more recently obtained $\omega_e x_e/4$ for D_2 so that the value may follow the μ^{-1} dependence, G_0 for D_2 becomes equal to 4.7 cm.$^{-1}$. In order to obtain the "best values" of G_0 and $\omega_e x_e/4$ for D_2, these are adjusted to 4.6 cm.$^{-1}$ and 15.1 cm.$^{-1}$ respectively (both following the μ^{-1} dependence with respect to the H_2 values). The HD values obtained from the more recent data already exhibit the expected mass dependence. Obviously, within the present framework, there is no anharmonicity zero-point energy contribution to the theoretically calculated equilibrium constant for $H_2 + D_2 = 2HD$.

Table I. G_0 and $\omega_e x_e/4$ (both in cm.$^{-1}$) for Isotopically Substituted Hydrogen Molecules

Species	Values Based on Old Compilation of Herzberg[a]		Values Based on New Data of Herzberg[b]		"Best Values"	
	G_0	$\omega_e x_e/4$	G_0	$\omega_e x_e/4$	G_0	$\omega_e x_e/4$
H_2	9.1	29.5	9.2	30.2	9.2	30.2
HD	5.8	23.7	6.9	22.7	6.9	22.7
D_2	3.2	16.0	4.3	15.6	4.6	15.1

[a] Table in Herzberg (6), ground electronic states.
[b] H_2 data from Herzberg and Howe (7); HD from Drurie and Herzberg (1); D_2 from Herzberg and Monfils (8), (the first set of data was used). (All data for ground electronic states.)

G_0 values for other diatomic hydrides have been calculated by means of Formula 11 to obtain an idea about the importance of this quantity in isotopic equilibria among these molecules. The compilation of Herzberg (6) has been employed for these purposes. No attempt has been made to find newer values of experimental data on spectroscopic parameters or to obtain best values of G_0. In many cases where data for the deuteride are listed in Herzberg's table, the calculated G_0 values do not follow the μ^{-1} dependence. Table II lists G_0 values only for a number of hydrides. For the present purposes, the G_0 values of corresponding deuterides and tritides would be calculated by the use of the theoretically expected μ^{-1} dependence.

Table II. G_o and $\omega_e x_e/4$ (both in cm.$^{-1}$) for Hydrides[a, b]

Species	G_o	$\omega_e x_e/4$
LiH	0.9	5.8
NaH	0.5	4.9
KH	−0.4	3.7
RbH	0.2	3.5
CsH	0.0	3.1
CuH	1.0	9.2
AgH	10.7	8.5
AuH	1.1	10.8
BeH	1.1	8.9
MgH	−0.7	7.9
CaH	0.0	4.9
SrH	0.2	4.2
BaH	−0.2	4.0
ZnH	−3.3	13.8
CdH	−1.2	11.6
HgH	−5.3	20.8
BH	1.3	12.2
AlH	1.1	7.3
InH	1.2	6.2
TlH	2.1	5.7
CH	1.7	16.1
PbH	0.4	7.4
BiH	0.7	7.9
OH	3.1	20.7
HF	3.1	22.5
HCl	1.5	13.0
HBr	0.8	11.3
HI	1.5	9.9

[a] Based on data in Table in Herzberg (6), ground electronic states.
[b] This list of molecules includes the same molecules for which Haar *et al.* (5) carried out their calculations of thermodynamic functions. These authors did not, however, use Reference 6 exclusively for their spectroscopic data.

One notices that G_o tends to be positive. The values for the hydrides in Table II range from 10.7 cm.$^{-1}$ to −5.3 cm.$^{-1}$. For many molecules, G_o is less than 1 cm.$^{-1}$ in magnitude. With the values given in Table II, the G_o contribution to the zero-point energy change of the equilibrium

$$\text{AgH} + \text{HgD} = \text{AgD} + \text{HgH} \tag{12}$$

is

$$G_{oHgH}(1 - \mu_{HgH}/\mu_{HgD}) - G_{oAgH}(1 - \mu_{AgH}/\mu_{AgD}) = -8.0 \text{ cm.}^{-1} \tag{13}$$

Thus, the contribution of the G_o factor to the equilibrium constant is $e^{11.5/T}$. The G_o contribution to the zero-point energy change of the equilibrium

$$\text{H}_2 + \text{DBr} = \text{HD} + \text{HBr} \tag{14}$$

is -1.9 cm.$^{-1}$ and the contribution to the equilibrium constant is $e^{2.7/T}$. Many other examples could be cited, of course, with the aid of Tables I and II. The G_0 corrections are of sufficiently large magnitude in many cases so that they cannot generally be neglected in precision calculations of equilibria involving hydrogen isotopes.

The present discussion has been carried out within the framework of the Born-Oppenheimer approximation, as is usual in the discussion of thermodynamic isotope effects. It is conceivable, however, that correction terms to this approximation could make non-negligible contributions to calculated isotopic exchange equilibrium constants [see References 9 and 10].

Conclusion

Attention has been called to the fact that there exists a usually neglected anharmonic term G_0 for the energy of the diatomic molecule-oscillator which depends on the reduced mass of the molecule. This term makes a contribution to the vibrational zero-point energy. It is shown that this contribution to the equilibrium constant for isotopic exchange reactions involving hydrogen isotopes may be non-negligible.

A G_0 type of factor also appears, as mentioned before, in the formula for the vibrational energies of polyatomic molecules. The contribution of G_0 to isotopic exchange equilibria involving larger molecules will be the subject of a separate communication. It is a pleasure to acknowledge that discussions with L. Friedman and V. J. Shiner, Jr. on their experimental measurement (4) (see Reference 11 for another measurement) of the equilibrium constant for the reaction $H_2O + D_2O = 2HDO$ led the author to look for possible origins of discrepancies between experimental observations and usual theoretical calculations of thermodynamic isotope effects. For this equilibrium, usual calculations (without G_0) yield an equilibrium constant 3.43 at 298°K., which compares poorly with the observed value 3.74–3.76. Calculations, which will be presented in detail elsewhere, show that the G_0 contribution to the zero-point energy change (including the small contribution from the before-mentioned rotational-vibrational interaction) is 23.9 cm.$^{-1}$ and that the correctly calculated value of the equilibrium constant is 3.85 at 298°K.

Literature Cited

(1) Drurie, R. A., Herzberg, G., *Can. J. Phys.* 38, 806 (1960).
(2) Dunham, J. L., *Phys. Rev.* 41, 721 (1932).
(3) Eyring, H., Walter, J., Kimball, G. E., "Quantum Chemistry," p. 272, John Wiley and Sons, Inc., New York, N. Y., 1944.
(4) Friedman, L., Shiner, Jr., V. J., *J. Chem. Phys.* 44, 4639 (1966).

(5) Haar, L., Friedman, A. S., Beckett, C. W., *Natl. Bur. Std. (U.S.) Monograph* **20** (1961).
(6) Herzberg, G., "Molecular Spectra and Molecular Structure," Vol. I, D. Van Nostrand Company, Princeton, N. J., 1950.
(7) Herzberg, G., Howe, L. L., *Can. J. Phys.* **37**, 636 (1959).
(8) Herzberg, G., Monfils, A., *J. Mol. Spectroscopy* **5**, 482 (1960).
(9) Kolos, W., Wolniewicz, L., *J. Chem. Phys.* **41**, 3663 (1964).
(10) *Ibid.*, **41**, 3674 (1964).
(11) Pyper, J. W., Newbury, R. S., Barton, Jr., G. W., *J. Chem. Phys.* **46**, 2253 (1967).
(12) Shaffer, W. H., Schuman, R. P., *J. Chem. Phys.* **12**, 504 (1944).
(13) Wilson, Jr., E. B., Decius, J. C., Cross, P. C., "Molecular Vibrations," McGraw-Hill Book Company, New York, N. Y., 1955.

RECEIVED May 8, 1968. Research at Brookhaven National Laboratory carried out under the auspices of the U. S. Atomic Energy Commission.

11

Theoretical Analysis of Chemical Isotope Fractionation by Orthogonal Polynomial Methods

TAKANOBU ISHIDA[1] and W. SPINDEL

Belfer Graduate School of Science, Yeshiva University,
New York, New York 10033

JACOB BIGELEISEN[2]

Brookhaven National Laboratory, Upton, L. I., New York 11973

The reduced partition functions of isotopic molecules determine the isotope separation factors in all equilibrium and many non-equilibrium processes. Power series expansion of the function in terms of even powers of the molecular vibrations has given explicit relationships between the separation factor and molecular structure and molecular forces. A significant extension to the Bernoulli expansion, developed previously, which has the restriction u = hν/kT < 2π, is developed through truncated series, derived from the hypergeometric function. The finite expansion can be written in the Bernoulli form with determinable modulating coefficients for each term. They are convergent for all values of u and yield better approximations to the reduced partition function than the Bernoulli expansion. The utility of the present method is illustrated through calculations on numerous molecular systems.

The reduced partition function ratio, $s/s'f$, of a pair of isotopic molecules, under the harmonic oscillator approximation, has the form (8)

$$\frac{s}{s'}f = \prod_i \frac{u_i}{u'_i} \frac{e^{-u_i/2}/(1 - e^{-u_i})}{e^{-u'_i/2}/(1 - e^{-u'_i})},\qquad(1)$$

[1] Present address, Brooklyn College, City University of New York, Brooklyn, N. Y.
[2] Present address, The University of Rochester, Rochester, N. Y.

where u_i is a dimensionless quantity defined as

$$u_i = \frac{h\nu_i}{kT}, \tag{2}$$

in which ν_i is the i-th frequency of a molecule. The product in Equation 1 is taken over all the normal vibrations, and u' and u refer to the lighter and heavier isotopic molecules, respectively. For any assembly of harmonic oscillators Equation 1 represents the theoretical basis for equilibrium isotope effects as well as the isotope effect on the population of transition states, which is a major factor in kinetic isotope effects.

Various methods of approximation for the function (Equation 1) have been developed in the last two decades ($4, 6; 8, 24, 25, 27$), some of them primarily designed to permit quick and accurate numerical evaluation of the function, and others are particularly suited to give insight into the understanding of isotope effects. The $G(u)$ expansion developed by Bigeleisen and Mayer (8) and the approximations in terms of hyperbolic functions ($24, 27$) belong to the former methods, while the latter include the Bernoulli series (4), the $\bar{\gamma}$-method (4) and the zero-point energy approximation (6). All these approximation methods are based on Taylor expansions of various arguments. Except for the ones designed for numerical evaluation, the existing expansion methods have all been subject to rather limited ranges of convergence. Even where they converge, the convergence becomes impractically slow for frequencies u and u' far from the center of expansion. Bigeleisen and Ishida (7) have recently proposed a new method, based on the orthogonal polynomial expansion, which has a flexible range of convergence and provides a more evenly distributed error of approximation throughout the region of convergence. This new method is one of the primary subjects of the present paper.

It is appropriate to review the earlier approximation methods here and to discuss briefly why expansion methods continue to be of interest in this age of the high-speed digital computer.

In the $G(u)$-approximation, introduced by Bigeleisen and Mayer (8) and later extended to higher orders by Bigeleisen (4), the reduced partition function ratio (Equation 1) is expanded in terms of the isotope frequency shifts, $\Delta u_i = u'_i - u_i$. The first three terms are

$$\ln \frac{s}{s'}f = \sum_i G(u_i) \left[1 + \frac{S(u_i)}{2G(u_i)} \frac{\Delta u_i}{u_i} + \frac{C(u_i) - 2S(u_i)}{6G(u_i)} \left(\frac{\Delta u_i}{u_i} \right)^2 \right] \Delta u_i, \tag{3}$$

where

$$G(u) = \tfrac{1}{2} - \frac{1}{u} + \frac{1}{e^u - 1}, \tag{4}$$

$$S(u) = \frac{1}{u} - \frac{ue^u}{(e^u - 1)^2}, \tag{5}$$

and

$$C(u) = \frac{2u^2\, e^{2u}}{(e^u - 1)^3} - \frac{u(u + 2)e^u}{(e^u - 1)^2}. \tag{6}$$

The functions $G(u)$, $S(u)$, and $C(u)$ have been tabulated $(1, 8)$ for u up to 25.00. Use of these tables provides an easy method for evaluating $\ln s/s'f$ and leaves little to be desired with respect to the rate of convergence. For the pair of isotopic molecules HD/H_2, for example, the first, second, and third order approximations of Equation 3 compute $\ln s/s'f$ to -0.15, 0.088, and -0.010%, respectively, at room temperature. Vojta (25) later extended this expansion to an infinite series

$$\ln \frac{s}{s'}f = \sum_i \left[G(u_i)\Delta u_i + \sum_{k=2}^{\infty} (-1)^k \left(\frac{1}{ku_i{}^k} - \frac{1}{k!} \sum_{n=1}^{\infty} n^{k-1}e^{-nu_i} \right)(\Delta u_i)^k \right], \tag{7}$$

and showed that the series converges if $\Delta u_i/u_i < 1$. This condition is automatically fulfilled for all known isotopes of all elements in all molecules (4). From the fact that the series (Equation 7) is alternating and absolutely convergent when $\Delta u_i < u_i$, one can set the following upper limits to the error inherent in the two term expansion for any molecule at any temperature whatsoever: substitution of deuterium for protium 8%, substitution of tritium for protium 25%, first row elements 0.5%.

An expansion related to Equation 3 is obtained by expanding

$$\ln \frac{s}{s'}f = \sum_i \ln \frac{u_i}{u'_i} + \sum_i \ln \frac{\sinh u'_i/2}{\sinh u_i/2} \tag{8}$$

in terms of the frequency shift (27) to give (24)

$$\ln \frac{s}{s'}f = \sum_i \ln \frac{u_i}{u'_i} + \sum_i \left[\delta_i \coth x_i + \frac{\delta_i{}^3}{12} \coth x_i (\coth^2 x_i - 1) + \dots \right], \tag{9}$$

where

$$\delta_i = \frac{u'_i - u_i}{2} \tag{10a}$$

and

$$x_i = \frac{u'_i + u_i}{4}. \tag{10b}$$

An expansion of $\ln \frac{s}{s'}f$ in an infinite series of the even powers of frequencies was introduced by Bigeleisen (4):

$$\ln \frac{s}{s'}f = \sum_i \sum_{j=1}^{\infty} \frac{(-1)^{j+1}B_{2j-1}\delta_i{}^{2j}}{2j\,(2j)!}$$

$$= \sum_i \left(\frac{\delta u_i{}^2}{24} - \frac{\delta u_i{}^4}{2880} + \frac{\delta u_i{}^6}{181440} - \dots \right)[u'_i < 2\pi] \tag{11}$$

where

$$\delta u_i^{2j} = u'^{2j}_i - u_i^{2j},\tag{12}$$

and B's are the Bernoulli numbers ($B_1 = \dfrac{1}{6}$, $B_3 = \dfrac{1}{30}$, $B_5 = \dfrac{1}{42}$, etc.). This approximation has been called a Bernoulli expansion because of its relation to a series expansion of the Bernoulli function. As recently pointed out by Vojta (*26*), it is essentially a Taylor expansion around $u = 0$. The series (Equation 11) converges only when $u'_i < 2\pi$; this is a direct consequence of the fact that the Taylor series of $\ln (1 + x)$ is absolutely convergent only when $|x| < 1$. The first term in Equation 11 is the first quantum correction to the reduced partition function of a pair of isotopic molecules, from which one obtains (*2, 4, 8*)

$$\ln \frac{s}{s'} f = \frac{1}{24} \left(\frac{\hbar}{kT} \right)^2 \sum_i \left(\frac{1}{m'_i} - \frac{1}{m_i} \right) a_{ii},$$

the fundamental law of isotope effects in equilibrium systems. Only the masses m'_i and m_i of the atom for which isotopic substitution is made contribute to the isotope effect. The properties of the other atoms in the molecule enter only through their contribution to the Cartesian force constants a_{ii}. It is these properties of the first quantum correction that lead to the rule of the geometric mean, the similar behavior of equivalent isotopic isomers, and the additivity of multiple isotopic substitution (*2*).

We now raise the question as to whether these fundamental laws are restricted to systems in which the temperature and frequencies involved are such that all u's are smaller than 2π. A bond-stretching frequency of 3000 cm.$^{-1}$ corresponds to $u = 15$ at room temperature, so that the Bernoulli series is divergent at room temperature, for any molecule containing such a frequency. In order for the Bernoulli series to converge at room temperature, the highest frequency must be smaller than 1300 cm.$^{-1}$. Thus, the series is inapplicable to all hydrogenous molecules at room temperature. Nevertheless, experimental results, as well as theoretical calculations, indicate that the fundamental laws obtainable from the Bernoulli series apply over a much wider range of the variable than $0 < u < 2\pi$. For example, it has recently been shown experimentally (*11*), that the equilibrium constant for the reaction

$$H_2O + D_2O = 2HDO$$

is $4(0.94_0 \pm 0.005)$ at $25°C$. At this temperature, the O–H stretching frequency corresponds to $u = 19$. The 6%-deviation from the value predicted by the first order rule of the mean can be accounted for by anharmonicities, and by the higher-order correction terms. As a further example, by exact calculation, within the harmonic approximation, one finds $\ln \frac{s}{s'} f$ at $300°$K. for ortho, meta, and para dideutero-benzenes, relative to ordinary benzene, to be 4.79080, 4.79034, and 4.79040, respectively. At this temperature the highest frequency corresponds to $u = 15$. Again, most of the small deviation of 0.01% among these equivalent isotopic isomers has been shown (7) to arise from out-of-plane vibrations, and from that part of the effect of ortho-deuterium substitution associated with the relative motion of two adjacent non-bonded hydrogens. Finally, Wolfsberg and Stern (21, 22, 23, 29, 30) have shown by extensive calculations of secondary isotope effects in model systems that the conclusions of the Bernoulli expansion hold over a much wider range than the region of convergence. The fundamental laws of isotope chemistry which can be derived from the first order Wigner quantum correction were extended to arbitrarily large values of ϵ/kT by Bigeleisen and Ishida (7). They showed that the use of orthogonal polynomials for the expansion of $\ln \frac{s}{s'} f$ leads to a series which is similar in all respects to the Bernoulli series, except for a term by term set of modulating coefficients. The modulating coefficients approach unity as the order of the expansion increases, thus making the new series asymptotically approach the Bernoulli series, term by term. The modulating coefficients also permit adapting the range of convergence to any problem at hand, thus effectively removing the barrier $u < 2\pi$. They also make the new series converge much faster than the Bernoulli series. This orthogonal expansion will be described later in this paper.

The expansions in even powers of normal frequencies are of special interest, because they provide means for obtaining explicit relations between the equations of motion and the thermodynamic quantities, through the use of the method of moments: The sum of $u_1{}^{2n}$ over all the normal vibrations can be expressed as the trace, or the sum of all the diagonal elements, of a matrix $\mathbf{H}^n$ obtained by multiplying the Hamiltonian matrix $\mathbf{H}$ of the system by itself $(n - 1)$ times. Such expansions thus enable us to estimate the thermodynamic functions and their isotope effects from known force fields and structures without solving the secular equations, or alternatively, to estimate the force fields from experimental data on the thermodynamic quantities and their isotope effects. The expansions explicitly correlate the motions of particles with the thermodynamic quantities. They can also be used to evaluate analytically a characteristic temperature associated with the system, such as the cross-over temperature of an isotope exchange equilibrium. Such possible applications, however, are useful only if the expansion yields a sufficiently close approximation. The precision of results obtainable with orthogonal polynomial expansions will be explored later.

An alternate approach to the analysis of isotope effects at large values of u is the low temperature approximation. As the temperature tends to zero, the function (Equation 1) approaches

$$\ln \frac{s}{s'}f = \sum_i \ln \frac{\nu_i}{\nu'_i} + \frac{1}{2} \frac{h}{kT} \sum_i (\nu'_i - \nu_i), \qquad (13)$$

in which the temperature-dependent term represents the isotopic difference in the zero-point energies. Although Equation 13 is satisfactory for most of the bond-stretching and bond-bending frequencies below room temperature, the omission of the excitation terms from Equation 13 greatly increases the error for molecules involving low-frequency normal vibrations such as out-of-plane motions. Thus, at room temperature, the low temperature approximation gives differences between the isomeric dideuterobenzenes one order of magnitude larger than the exact calculations. Bigeleisen and Goldstein (6) developed the zero-point energy difference in a Taylor series of even powers of frequencies around an arbitrary chosen point λ_o in the frequency spectrum:

$$\frac{1}{\omega_0} \sum_i (\omega'_i - \omega_i) = \frac{1}{2} \sum_i \frac{\delta\lambda_i}{\lambda_o} + \sum_{i} \sum_{p=2}^{\infty} \frac{(-1)^{p+1}(2p-2)!}{2^{2p-1}(p-1)!} \sum_{j=0}^{p-1} \frac{(-1)^j}{j!(p-j)!} \frac{\delta\lambda_i^{p-j}}{\lambda_o^{p-j}},$$

where $\qquad\qquad\qquad\qquad\qquad\qquad\qquad\qquad\qquad\qquad\qquad\qquad\qquad\qquad (14)$

$$\lambda_i = 4\pi^2\nu_i^2 = 4\pi^2c^2\omega_i^2, \qquad (15)$$

and

$$\delta\lambda_i^n = \lambda'^n_i - \lambda^n_i. \qquad (16)$$

This series is absolutely convergent when

$$\frac{\lambda'_i - \lambda_o}{\lambda_o} \leqslant 1, \qquad (17)$$

which condition is automatically fulfilled if the point λ_o lies in the upper half of the range of frequency spectrum. They used this series for the study of relationships among the zero-point energies of isotopic homologues—i.e., mono-, di-, tri-, tetra-deutero methane. Coupled with Equation 13, the series (Equation 14) can be used to obtain an explicit relation between $\ln \frac{s}{s'}f$ and the Hamiltonian matrix elements at lower temperatures where formula 13 is applicable.

Another attempt (which in fact was the first attempt) to extend the method of moments to the thermal properties of harmonic oscillators for large values of u was the $\bar{\gamma}$-method (4). This method is based on the first-order approximation of the $G(u)$-expansion, which can be written in the form

$$\ln \frac{s}{s'}f = \sum_i \gamma_i \frac{\delta u_i^2}{24},\tag{18}$$

where

$$\gamma_i = \frac{12\,G(u_i)}{u_i}.\tag{19}$$

Since the function γ is a slowly varying function of u, if all the frequencies of the molecule lie in a narrow range, an average, $\overline{\gamma}$, of all γ_i's, can be used in place of γ_i in Equation 18. Then, Equation 18 becomes

$$\ln \frac{s}{s'}f \cong \frac{\overline{\gamma}}{24} \sum_i \delta u_i^2.\tag{20}$$

This method can naturally be extended to higher terms. The method is successful and powerful (9), if the range of the frequency spectrum is narrow, and if the variation of temperature is limited. It has been successfully used in model-calculations of kinetic isotope effects (20, 29), although there are some difficulties in the choice of $\overline{\gamma}$, or the corresponding characteristic frequency $\overline{\nu}$. As recently shown (16, 18), however, in using the $\overline{\gamma}$-method for estimating equilibrium constants of exchange reactions, it is almost impossible to select a single frequency, characteristic of a pair of exchanging chemical species.

The method of Bigeleisen and Ishida (7), refinements of their method, an analysis of the accuracy obtainable, and some applications to problems of isotope effects will be covered later, as well as additional possible applications.

Orthogonal Expansions

All the earlier expansions of $\ln \frac{s}{s'}f$ are Taylor expansions. The Taylor series is an extrapolating series; all the information needed for a Taylor expansion is obtained at a point around which the function is to be expanded, and values of the function at other points are estimated, based on this information. Approximations by a truncated Taylor series generally become poorer as the point moves away from the center of expansion. In this section, the orthogonal expansions of $\ln \frac{s}{s'}f$ using Jacobi polynomials are discussed in detail. It will be shown that the orthogonal expansion provides an interpolating, and therefore, a better approximation than a corresponding Taylor expansion.

In an orthogonal expansion, a function $f(x)$ is developed in a series of terms of mutually orthogonal functions. An orthogonal function oscillates within a region of orthogonality; this is a direct consequence of the definition of these functions. Therefore, the error of a truncated series is oscillating, within the region of orthogonality, rather than steadily increasing or decreasing. This results in a more evenly distributed error throughout the range of expansion, rather than yielding an extremely close approximation in one region at the expense of very poor approximation in other regions.

Two functions $P_i(x)$ and $P_j(x)$ are said to be orthogonal to each other in a region $\alpha \leqslant x \leqslant \beta$ (hereafter abbreviated as $[\alpha,\beta]$), if they satisfy the condition,

$$\int_\alpha^\beta P_i(x)P_j(x)\,dx = 0. \tag{21}$$

More generally, they are said to be orthogonal to each other in $[\alpha,\beta]$ with respect to a weighting function $\rho(x)$, if

$$\int_\alpha^\beta \rho(x)P_i(x)P_j(x)\,dx = \delta_{ij}h_i, \tag{22}$$

where h_i is a normalization constant, and δ_{ij} is the Kronecker delta.

Any absolutely integrable, bounded function, $f(x)$, can be expanded in terms of a set of orthogonal functions (*15*). If one writes

$$f(x) = \sum_{i=0}^\infty c_i P_i(x), \tag{23}$$

where $P_i(x)$ is the i-th member of a set of functions, which are mutually orthogonal in $[\alpha,\beta]$ with respect to $\rho(x)$, then the coefficients c_i of the expansion are given by

$$c_i = \frac{1}{h_i} \int_\alpha^\beta f(x)\rho(x)P_i(x)\,dx. \tag{24}$$

If, further, the functions $P_n(x)$ are polynomials defined as

$$P_n(x) = \sum_{m=0}^n C_n{}^m x^m, \tag{25}$$

where $C_n{}^m$ are known constant coefficients, then a truncated power series of $f(x)$ to the order x^n, can be obtained by collecting similar terms in the first $(n+1)$ terms of Equation 23. The error of the resulting power series oscillates. When the order of such a power series is increased from n to $n+1$, not only is a new term of x^{n+1} added, but also the coefficients of all the lower-order terms are changed. The order-dependent expansion coefficients are advantageous for the purpose of approximation, because they represent an additional flexibility; the coefficients are re-adjusted to the new situation as the order of expansion is increased, to provide a better approximation than is possible with non-varying coefficients.

If one truncates the infinite series (Equation 23) at $i = n$, the error $\epsilon(x)$ is given by the sum of the omitted terms

$$\epsilon(x) = \sum_{i=n+1}^{\infty} c_i P_i(x). \tag{26}$$

When the region of expansion is properly chosen, the error $\epsilon(x)$ oscillates on both sides of the abscissa. Thus, choosing an orthogonal polynomial $P(x)$ is equivalent to demanding that the error of the approximation be zero at a finite set of points. This is in contrast to the Taylor series for which the error is zero only at one point. In this sense the orthogonal expansion is an interpolating approximation.

The Jacobi polynomials, $P_n^{(\gamma, \delta)}(x)$, are defined as

$$P_n^{(\gamma,\delta)}(x) = F(-n, n + \gamma + \delta - 1, \gamma; x)$$

$$= 1 + \sum_{m=1}^{n} x^m \prod_{k=0}^{m-1} \frac{(-n+k)(n+\gamma+\delta-1+k)}{(\gamma+k)(1+k)} \tag{27}$$

where F is the Gaussian hypergeometric function. The parametric variables γ and δ may assume any real values, except that γ cannot be zero or negative. Jacobi polynomials include such well-known polynomials as Legendre ($\gamma = \delta = 1$), Laguerre ($\gamma = 1$, $\delta \to \infty$) and Hermite ($\gamma = \delta \to \infty$). For a given set of γ and δ, two Jacobi polynomials of different order are orthogonal to each other in $[0,1]$ with respect to a weighting function

$$\rho^{(\gamma,\delta)}(x) = x^{\gamma-1}(1-x)^{\delta-1}. \tag{28}$$

For the expansion of $\ln \frac{s}{s'}f$ Bigeleisen and Ishida (7) used the shifted Chebyshev polynomial of the first kind, $T_n^*(x)$, which is a Jacobi polynomial defined as

$$T_n^*(x) = (-1)^n F(-n, n, \tfrac{1}{2}; x)$$

$$= \sum_{m=0}^{n} C_n{}^m x^m, \tag{29}$$

where

$$C_n{}^m = \frac{(-1)^{n+m} 2^{2m} n(n+m-1)!}{(n-m)!\,(2m)!}. \tag{30}$$

For example

$$T_1^*(x) = -1 + 2x,$$

$$T_2^*(x) = 1 - 8x + 8x^2,$$

and

$$T_3^*(x) = -1 + 18x - 48x^2 + 32x^3.$$

As will be shown later, a common factor on F in the definition of Jacobi polynomials, such as $(-1)^n$ in Equation 29, does not affect the expansion.

The present authors have explored possibilities of using other Jacobi polynomials for expanding $\ln \frac{s}{s'} f$.

Method of Bigeleisen and Ishida. For convenience, we write $\frac{s}{s'} f$ of Equation 1 as

$$\ln \frac{s}{s'} f = \sum_i [\ln b(u'_i) - \ln b(u_i)], \tag{31}$$

where

$$\ln b(u) = -\ln u + \frac{u}{2} + \ln (1 - e^{-u})$$

$$= -\ln \frac{u}{2} + \ln \sinh \frac{u}{2}$$

$$= \sum_{k=1}^{\infty} \ln \left[1 + \left(\frac{u}{2\pi k} \right)^2 \right]. \tag{32}$$

The infinite series of Equation 32 is absolutely convergent for any value of u.

The Taylor series of $\ln (1 + x)$,

$$\ln (1 + x) = \sum_{m=1}^{\infty} (-1)^{m+1} \frac{x^m}{m}, \tag{33}$$

is absolutely convergent when $|x| < 1$. If we substitute Equation 33 into Equation 32 and collect similar terms by using a relation for the Riemann zeta function,

$$z(m) \equiv \sum_{k=1}^{\infty} \frac{1}{k^{2m}} = \frac{2^{2m-1} \pi^{2m} B_{2m-1}}{(2m)!}, \tag{34}$$

we obtain (25)

$$\ln b(u) = \sum_{m=1}^{\infty} \frac{(-1)^{m+1} B_{2m-1} u^{2m}}{2m (2m)!}. \tag{35}$$

The convergence condition of the Taylor expansion (Equation 33) makes the series (Equation 35) convergent when

$$\left(\frac{u}{2\pi k} \right)^2 < 1 \tag{36}$$

for all integer values of k. Equation 35 leads to the Bernoulli series for $\ln \frac{s}{s'} f$ which according to Equation 36 is convergent whenever $u_i < 2\pi$ for all vibrations.

Bigeleisen and Ishida (7) obtained an orthogonal expansion of the logarithmic function,

$$y(x) = \ln (1 + x).\tag{37}$$

Instead of using the procedure of Equations 23, 24, and 25, however, they applied the τ-method (15) to the differential equation

$$(1 + x)\frac{dy}{dx} = 1.\tag{38}$$

In the τ-method one admits that one cannot solve the linear differential equation exactly, and inserts an error term $\tau P_n(x)$, where τ is an *a priori* undetermined coefficient, and $P_n(x)$ is a known orthogonal polynomial of order n. Thus, one writes

$$(1 + x)\frac{dy}{dx} = 1 + \tau P_n(x).\tag{39}$$

The use of one term $\tau P_n(x)$ in Equation 39 is equivalent to assuming that the error $\epsilon(x)$ of Equation 26 can be represented by its first term, the higher terms being negligible. Let $y(x)$ be a finite polynomial of order n:

$$y(x) = \sum_{m=0}^{n} a_m x^m.\tag{40}$$

Substitution of Equation 40 in Equation 39 and comparison of coefficients of x^m gives the coefficients $a_1, a_2, \ldots, a_n$, and τ in terms of the coefficients of $P_n(x)$. The remaining unknown a_o can be determined from a boundary condition, but its magnitude does not affect the expansion of $\ln \frac{s}{s'} f$. The result, obtained with the boundary condition $y(0) = 0$, is

$$\ln (1 + x) = \sum_{m=1}^{n} \frac{(-1)^{m+1} x^m}{m} \frac{\sum\limits_{p=m}^{n} (-1)^p C_n{}^p}{\sum\limits_{p=0}^{n} (-1)^p C_n{}^p},\tag{41}$$

where $C_n{}^m$ are the coefficients of $P_n(x)$ (Equation 25). This is an approximate solution of the differential Equation 38. The error oscillates, because the error term in Equation 39 is an oscillating function.

The τ-method gives as good an approximation as one can arrive at by the procedure of Equations 23, 24, and 25. The latter procedure, however, involves evaluation of definite integrals of Equation 24 which, for $y(x) = \ln (1 + x)$, can only be carried out by numerical processes. When any of the Jacobi polynomials is used for $P_n(x)$, the expansion (Equation 41) converges in the interval [0,1]. The range can be extended (15) to any positive region, [0,R], by dividing every coefficient $C_n{}^m$ in Equation 41 by R^m, leading to

$$\ln (1 + x) = \sum_{m=1}^{n} \frac{(-1)^{m+1} x^m}{m} \frac{\sum\limits_{p=m}^{n} (-1)^p C_n{}^p / R^p}{\sum\limits_{p=0}^{n} (-1)^p C_n{}^p / R^p}. \tag{42}$$

The error remains oscillatory over the new range $[0,R]$, in a manner similar to that in the old range $[0,1]$, but with expanded amplitudes.

Using a common range R, defined by

$$R = \left(\frac{u}{2\pi}\right)^2, \tag{43}$$

for orthogonal expansions of all the logarithmic terms in Equation 32, Bigeleisen and Ishida (7) obtained

$$\ln b(u) = \sum_{m=1}^{n} \frac{(-1)^{m+1} B_{2m-1} u^{2m}}{2m (2m)!} T(n,m,u) \tag{44}$$

where

$$T(n,m,u) = \frac{\sum\limits_{p=m}^{n} (-1)^p C_n{}^p / R^p}{\sum\limits_{p=0}^{n} (-1)^p C_n{}^p / R^p}. \tag{45}$$

Combining Equations 31 and 44, they obtained

$$\ln \frac{s}{s'} f = \sum_{i} \sum_{m=1}^{n} \frac{(-1)^{m+1} B_{2m-1} \delta u_i{}^{2m}}{2m (2m)!} T(n,m,u'_i), \tag{46}$$

or

$$\ln \frac{s}{s'} f = \sum_{m=1}^{n} \frac{(-1)^{m+1} B_{2m-1} \sum\limits_{i} \delta u_i{}^{2m}}{2m (2m)!} T(n,m,u'_{max}). \tag{47}$$

The range for Equation 47 is defined in terms of the highest frequency for the light isotopic molecule, namely

$$R = \left(\frac{u'_{max}}{2\pi}\right)^2. \tag{48}$$

We note with interest that the use of Jacobi polynomials leads to an expansion of $\ln \frac{s}{s'} f$ which is similar term by term to the Bernoulli series. The significant difference between the two expansions is the set of coefficients $T(n,m,u'_{max})$, which modulate each term in the Bernoulli series. Through these modulating coefficients the restrictions on the range of u values in the Bernoulli expansion are all removed. Since the coefficients $C_n{}^m$ of a given Jacobi polynomial, of a given order, alternate their signs as m is increased, all the terms, both in the numerator and denominator of Equation 45, are of the same sign. Thus, the modulating coefficients are always positive but less than unity. For a given m and R, $T(n,m,R)$ tends to unity as the order of expansion n goes to infinity. For any order n, $T(n,m,R)$ is closer to unity for smaller m and smaller R. Thus, the orthogonal expansion approaches the Bernoulli expansion, asymptotically term by term. All the properties which can be derived from the Bernoulli series by the method of moments are immediately obtained from Equation 47. Thus, using this procedure Bigeleisen and Ishida extended the energy range over which the fundamental theorems of equilibrium isotope effects are applicable. As an example of the asymptotic behavior of $T(n,m,u)$, some values of $T(n,m,u = 2\pi)$ for the Chebyshev polynomial of the first kind are given in Table I.

Table I. Values of the Chebyshev Modulating Function
$$T(n,m,u = 2\pi)$$

n	Denominator of $T(n,m,2\pi)$	Numerator of T(n,m,2π)						
		m = 1	m = 2	m = 3	m = 4	m = 5	m = 6	m = 7
1	3	2						
2	17	16	8					
3	99	98	80	32				
4	577	576	544	384	128			
5	3363	3362	3312	2912	1792	512		
6	19601	19600	19528	18688	15104	8192	2048	
7	114243	114242	114144	112576	103168	76288	36864	8192

Subdivision of the Range of the Expansion Variable. In substituting Equation 42 into the infinite series expression for ln $b(u)$, Equation 32, Bigeleisen and Ishida used a constant range,

$$R = \left(\frac{u}{2\pi}\right)^2, \tag{43}$$

for all values of k, from $k = 1$ to $k \to \infty$. For any given value of u, the argument $\left(\frac{u}{2\pi k}\right)^2$ of the logarithmic function becomes smaller as k increases. Consequently, we may use a smaller range for the expansion of logarithmic terms of higher k value without making the expansion (Equation 42) diverge. Using a constant range for expansion of the higher terms causes unnecessary, and avoidable, approximation errors. Although the relative magnitudes of the higher terms of Equation 32 are smaller compared with the lower terms, the error of approximation to any higher term is not necessarily limited by the magnitude of the term.

We divide the summation of Equation 32 into two parts:

$$\ln b(u) = \sum_{k=1}^{L} \ln\left[1 + \left(\frac{u}{2\pi k}\right)^2\right] + \sum_{k=L+1}^{\infty} \ln\left[1 + \left(\frac{u}{2\pi k}\right)^2\right], \quad (49)$$

where L is a finite, positive integer. When $L = 0$, Equation 49 reduces to Equation 32. For the first sum of Equation 49, a sum of lower terms, we vary the range according to

$$R_k = \frac{R_1}{k^2} = \left(\frac{u}{2\pi k}\right)^2 \quad (k = 1, 2, \ldots, L), \quad (50)$$

and for the second sum, we keep the range constant at

$$R_k = R_{L+1} = \frac{R_1}{(L+1)^2} \quad (\text{all } k \geqslant L + 1). \quad (51)$$

In Equations 50 and 51, R_1 corresponds to R of Equation 43.

This leads to a new expansion formula of $\ln b(u)$;

$$\ln b(u) = \sum_{m=1}^{n} \frac{(-1)^{m+1}}{m} \left(\frac{u}{2\pi}\right)^{2m} W(n,m,u,L), \quad (52)$$

where

$$W(n,m,u,L) = \sum_{k=1}^{L} \frac{T(n,m,R_k)}{k^{2m}} + T(n,m,R_{L+1})\left[z(m) - \sum_{k=1}^{L}\frac{1}{k^{2m}}\right]$$

$$= z(m)\, T(n,m,R_{L+1}) + \sum_{k=1}^{L} \frac{T(n,m,R_k) - T(n,m,R_{L+1})}{k^{2m}}. \quad (53)$$

In the last equation, $z(m)$ is the Riemann zeta function, Equation 34, and $T(n,m,R_k)$ is given by Equation 45, with R's defined by Equation 50 and 51. When $L = 0$, the function W becomes

$$W(n,m,u,0) = T(n,m,R_1)\, z(m), \quad (54)$$

which reduces Equation 52 to Equation 44.

Substituting Equation 52 into Equation 31, one obtains

$$\ln \frac{s}{s'} f = \sum_{i}\sum_{m=1}^{n} \frac{(-1)^{m+1}}{m} \frac{\delta u_i^{2m}}{(2\pi)^{2m}} W(n,m,u'_i,L), \quad (55)$$

or

$$\ln \frac{s}{s'} f = \sum_{m=1}^{n} \frac{(-1)^{m+1}}{m} \frac{\sum_i \delta u_i^{2m}}{(2\pi)^{2m}} W(n,m,u'_{max},L)$$

$$= \sum_{m=1}^{n} \frac{W(n,m,u'_{max},L)}{z(m)} \frac{(-1)^{m+1} B_{2m-1}}{2m\,(2m)!} \sum_i \delta u_i^{2m}. \quad (56)$$

In Equation 56 the coefficients modulating the Bernoulli terms—*i.e.*, $W(n,m,u'_{max},L)/z(m)$, are all in the range between zero and unity, as can be seen from Equation 53. The range for Equation 56 is again defined (*see* Equation 48) as $(u'_{max}/2\pi)^2$. Given an order of expansion n, the highest frequency, u'_{max}, and a value of L, the weighting function $W(n,m,u'_{max},L)$ becomes a function of m only, so that each term $(\delta u_i^{2m} = u'_i^{2m} - u_i^{2m})$ in Equation 56 has a frequency-independent coefficient. The method of moments therefore remains applicable to Equation 56. When $L = 0$, Equations 55 and 56 reduce to Equations 46 and 47, respectively. A preliminary numerical examination shows that increasing the L-value from zero generally improves the approximation of $\ln b(u)$, but going much beyond $L = 5$ does not seem worthwhile. A comparison of these approximations of $\ln b(u)$ will be shown and fully discussed later in this section.

Variation of the Orthogonal Polynomial. Among the Jacobi polynomials, $P_n^{(\gamma,\delta)}(x)$, the Chebyshev polynomials of the first kind ($\gamma = \delta = \frac{1}{2}$) are the only ones that oscillate with a constant amplitude, unity, in the region $[0,1]$. The amplitudes of oscillation of all other Jacobi polynomials either increase or decrease in the range $0 \leqslant x \leqslant 1$. If the prime objective of the expansion of a function by means of a Jacobi polynomial, using the method of Equation 24, is to distribute the error of approximation as evenly as possible throughout the range of expansion, then the Chebyshev polynomial of the first kind $T_n^*(x)$ is the best choice. When the system involves a spectrum of frequencies, other Jacobi polynomials may be more suitable.

Bigeleisen and Ishida used $T_n^*(x)$, defined by Equations 29 and 30, for evaluating the modulating coefficients $T(n,m,u)$ by Equation 45. Percent errors of this approximation of $\ln b(u)$ are plotted in Figure 1 as a function of u, for orders $n = 1, 2$, and 3. The solid curves were obtained by using $R = 9$ ($u_{max} = 6\pi$) for evaluating $T(n,m,u)$ over the whole range. Those labelled "running u" were obtained by using the actual value of u for evaluating $T(n,m,u)$. The "running u" plot shows how the percent error decreases as $u = h\nu/kT$ decreases.

The shifted Chebyshev polynomials of the first kind, $T_n^*(x)$, lead to a constant amplitude of oscillation for the differential equation

$$(1 + x)\, y' = 1 + \tau\, T_n^*(x),$$

but not for the integral

$$y(x) = \ln (1 + x) + \tau \int_0^x \frac{T_n^*(x)\,dx}{1 + x}. \tag{57}$$

the error amplitude for the infinite sum of the terms $\ln \left[1 + \left(\dfrac{u}{2\pi k} \right)^2 \right]$

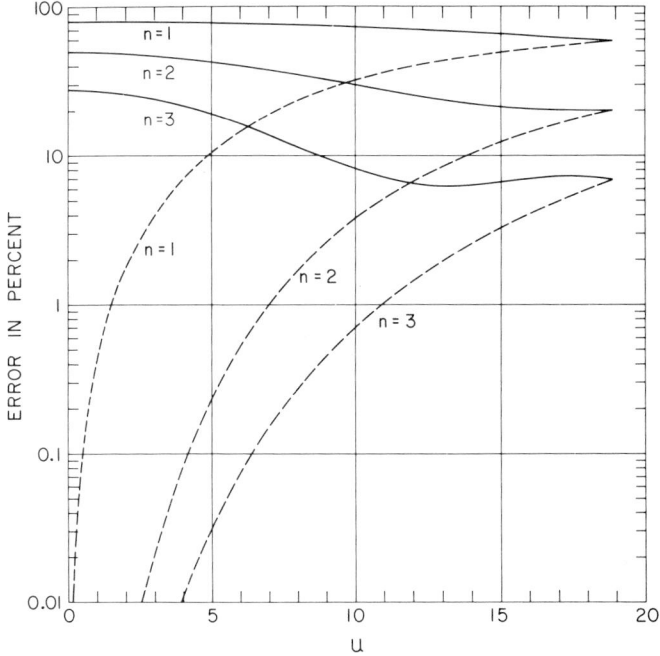

*Figure 1.   Comparison of the accuracy of Chebyshev (L = 0)
expansions of ln* b(u) *with* $u_{max} = 6\pi$ *(——) and running* u
(- - -) for various orders, n, *of the expansion*

—*i.e.*, ln $b(u)$—is therefore not generally uniform. The errors in ln $b(u)$
which one encounters by the Chebyshev approximation are shown in
Figures 2, 3, 4, 5, 6, 7, and 8 for various expansion ranges. In no case is
the amplitude of oscillation uniform.

We have investigated possibilities of using Jacobi polynomials other
than $T_n^*(x)$. Our primary aim was to obtain a good approximation to ln
$\frac{s}{s'}f$ rather than to ln $b(u)$. Ln $\frac{s}{s'}f$ is a sum of differences between pairs
of ln $b(u)$'s, one evaluated at a frequency of one molecule, and the other
at the corresponding frequency of an isotopic molecule. Therefore, if the
absolute error for ln $b(u)$ were constant throughout a range of expansion,
the error for ln $\frac{s}{s'}f$ would become zero, no matter how large the absolute
(constant) error for ln $b(u)$. Thus, what one wants to obtain in an
expansion of ln $b(u)$ is a small amplitude but high frequency in the
oscillation of the absolute error $\epsilon(u)$. The intermixing of positive and
negative $d\epsilon/du$ is advantageous, because it provides opportunities for
mutual cancellation of errors among different pairs of frequencies. The
number of extrema on a plot of $\epsilon(u)$ against u, however, is limited by the

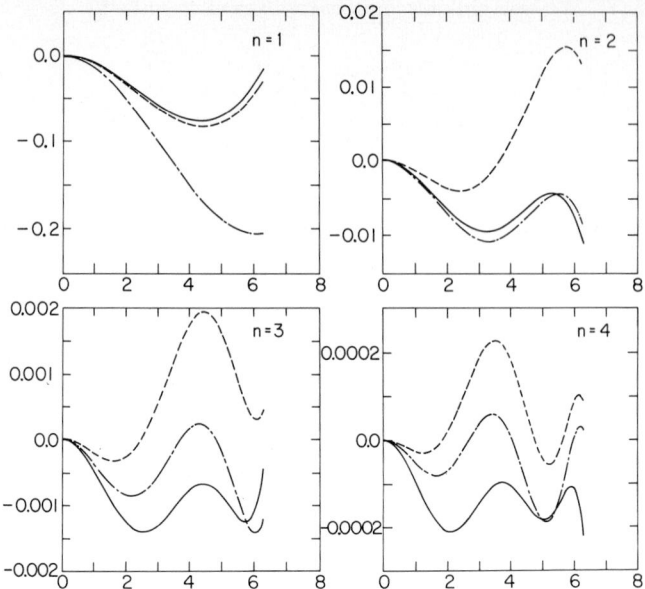

Figure 2.   Absolute error in ln b(u) *obtained by Jacobi polynomial expansions over the range* [0,2π] *as a function of* u *for orders* n = 1 − 4

———— *"Best" polynomial* L = 5
- - - - *Chebyshev polynomial* L = 5
— · — *Chebyshev polynomial* L = 0

order of expansion n; n is the maximum number possible. One is concerned with the absolute error $\epsilon(u)$, rather than the relative error, because $|\epsilon(u_i') - \epsilon(u_i)|$ can be greater at smaller u_i, where $\ln b(u_i') - \ln b(u_i)$ usually makes a small contribution to $\ln \frac{s}{s'}f$. In other words, a low frequency vibration can contribute much to the total error of $\ln \frac{s}{s'}f$, while contributing little to the magnitude of $\ln \frac{s}{s'}f$. Considering the relative error here instead of the absolute error over-emphasizes the relative importance of low frequencies.

A search for the optimal polynomials was made by minimizing a weighted root-mean-square error (RMSE) around the mean of absolute errors of the expansion of $\ln b(u)$:

$$\text{RMSE} = \sqrt{\frac{\int_0^{u_{max}} w(u)\,[\epsilon(u) - \bar{\epsilon}]^2 du}{\int_0^{u_{max}} w(u)\,du}}, \qquad (58)$$

where $w(u)$ is a weight, associated to a point u, and

$$\bar{\epsilon} = \frac{\int_0^{u_{max}} w(u)\, \epsilon(u)\, du}{\int_0^{u_{max}} w(u)\, du}. \tag{59}$$

The weighting function $w(u)$ does not necessarily have to be a continuous one.

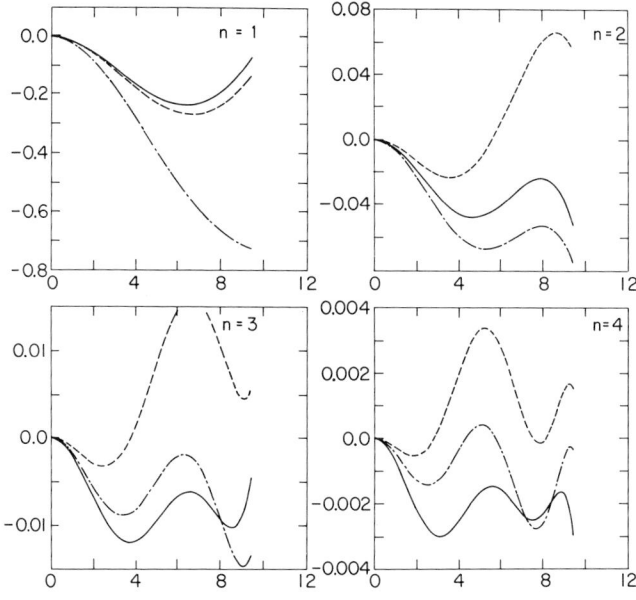

Figure 3. *Absolute error in* ln b(u) *obtained by Jacobi polynomial expansions over the range* $[0, 3\pi]$ *as a function of u for orders* n $= 1 - 4$

——— *"Best" polynomial* L $= 5$
- - - - *Chebyshev polynomial* L $= 5$
— · — *Chebyshev polynomial* L $= 0$

The weighting function $w(u)$ depends on the distribution of frequencies in a system and on the isotope frequency shifts. Indeed, the function $\ln \frac{s}{s'}f$ cannot be determined until all the u'_i and u_i have been specified. Only the relative magnitudes of v'_i and v_i are necessary to specify the weighting function, $w(u)$, as it is used in Equations 58 and 59. Given a specific problem, one can make a reasonable guess as to what region of the frequency spectrum is important. For example, for a heavy atom substitution in a hydrogenous molecule, most of the significant frequency shifts would be located in the middle (and possibly lower) part of the spectrum, while for an isotopic substitution of hydrogen atoms, the largest shifts would be located near u_{max}. Regions of high population of frequencies can be crudely located from the structure of the system, and/or an empirical knowledge (13) of characteristic bond-stretching and bond-bending vibrational frequencies. For instance, the internal normal vibrations of a paraffin, C_nH_{2n+2}, can be divided into three groups: $(2n + 2)$ vibrations essentially corresponding to C–H stretchings, $(n - 1)$ vibrations for C–C stretchings and $(6n - 1)$ frequencies of magnitudes associated with bond-bending vibrations.

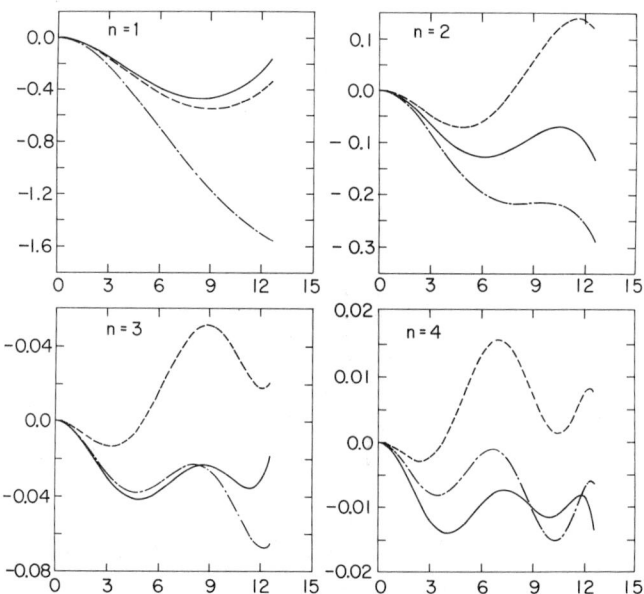

Figure 4. Absolute error in ln b(u) *obtained by Jacobi polynomial expansions over the range* $[0,4\pi]$ *as a function of* u *for orders* n = 1 − 4

——— *"Best" polynomial* L = 5
- - - - *Chebyshev polynomial* L = 5
— · — *Chebyshev polynomial* L = 0

For the present work we assumed that the frequency population is uniform. This situation is approached in large and complicated molecules, for which the expansions in terms of even powers of frequencies are

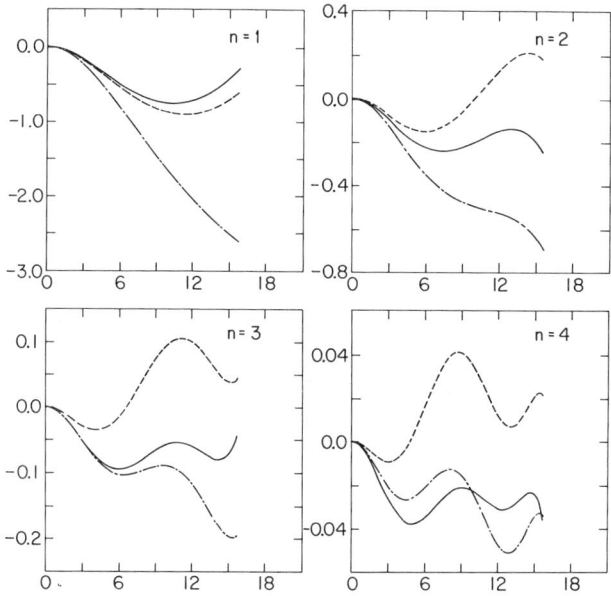

Figure 5. Absolute error in ln b(u) *obtained by Jacobi polynomial expansions over the range* $[0,5\pi]$ *as a function of* u *for orders* n $= 1 - 4$

——— *"Best" polynomial* L $= 5$
- - - - *Chebyshev polynomial* L $= 5$
— · — *Chebyshev polynomial* L $= 0$

especially useful. Here, the method of moments which completely avoids solving secular equations becomes particularly useful for numerical computations. We make the further assumption that the frequency shift is proportional to the frequency. This assumption neglects the difference between the normal coordinates and the internal coordinates, as well as differences between different types of internal coordinates. The net result of these two assumptions is

$$w(u) \propto u. \tag{60}$$

The two parameters γ and δ, which characterize a Jacobi polynomial, were varied, and RMSE values, as defined by Equations 58, 59, and 60, were numerically evaluated using an IBM-360 computer. Preliminary tests showed that satisfactory integrations were achieved by summing over 50 equally spaced points. The RMSE-surface was mapped for both the Bigeleisen-Ishida formula, Equation 44, and the modified one, Equation 52. Naturally, the "best" polynomial may depend on the order and range of the expansion. A set of "best" polynomials was obtained by mapping separately the surface for every combination of fixed range, $u_{max} = 1\pi, 2\pi, \ldots, 8\pi$, and order, $n = 1, 2, 3, 4$, for both $L = 0$ and $L = 5$. In addition, for $L = 5$, "best" polynomials were determined for orders $n = 5$ and 6. For each surface γ was varied from 0.02 to 2.50 in steps of 0.02, and δ from -1.0 to 2.8 in steps of 0.1. After locating the region of the smallest minimum RMSE, a finer mapping was carried out to find the optimum γ and δ to within ± 0.002 and ± 0.05, respectively.

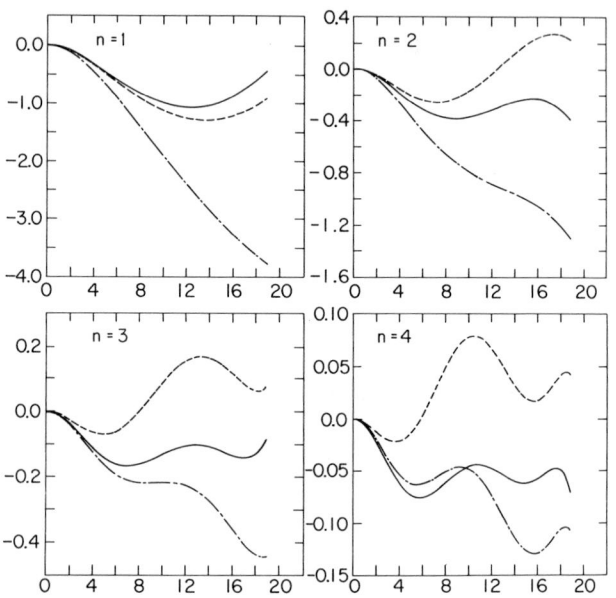

Figure 6. Absolute error in ln b(u) *obtained by Jacobi polynomial expansions over the range* $[0,6\pi]$ *as a function of* u *for orders* n $= 1 - 4$

———— *"Best" polynomial* L $= 5$
- - - - *Chebyshev polynomial* L $= 5$
— · — *Chebyshev polynomial* L $= 0$

Results of Approximations for ln $b(u)$. The optimum (γ, δ) and the corresponding RMSE for the case of $L = 0$ (Equation 44) are tabulated in Tables II and III, respectively. Similar tabulations for the case of $L = 5$ are given in Tables IV and V. In Tables II and IV, the upper and lower numbers for each range and order are the optimum values of γ and δ, respectively. The first order expansion depends only on the ratio γ/δ and not the individual values of γ and δ. For convenience, therefore, the value unity has been entered for δ for all the one-term expansions in

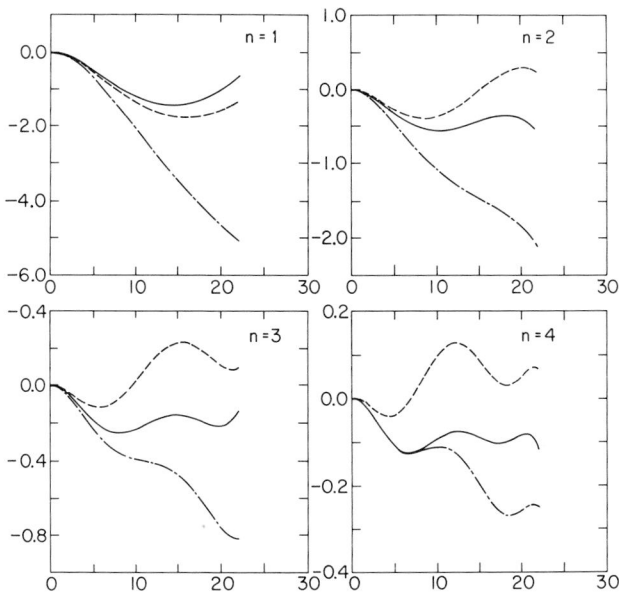

Figure 7.   Absolute error in ln b(u) *obtained by Jacobi polynomial expansions over the range* [0,7π] *as a function of* u *for orders* n = 1 − 4

—— *"Best" polynomial* L = 5
- - - - *Chebyshev polynomial* L = 5
— · — *Chebyshev polynomial* L = 0

these tables. Comparison of Tables III and V shows that the "best" set of polynomials for $L = 5$ yields better RMSE, at every range and order, than the "best" set for $L = 0$.

For comparison, values of the RMSE achieved by the shifted Chebyshev polynomials of the first kind ($\gamma = \delta = \frac{1}{2}$), $T_n^*(x)$, with $L = 0$ and $L = 5$ are shown in Tables VI and VII, respectively. For each value of L, the "best" polynomial naturally gives better RMSE than $T_n^*(x)$ does, for every range and order. Comparison of Tables VI and VIII shows, however, that for smaller ranges and higher orders, $T_n^*(x)$ with $L = 0$ yields lower values of the RMSE than $T_n^*(x)$ with $L = 5$. On the other hand the use of sub-divided ranges of the expansion variable improves the Chebyshev expansion when u covers a wide range and the order of the expansion is less than 2.

The values of the modulating coefficients for the Chebyshev and "best" Jacobi polynomials for both fixed and sub-divided ranges of the expansion variable, $\left(\dfrac{u}{2\pi}\right)^2$ are given in Table VIII.

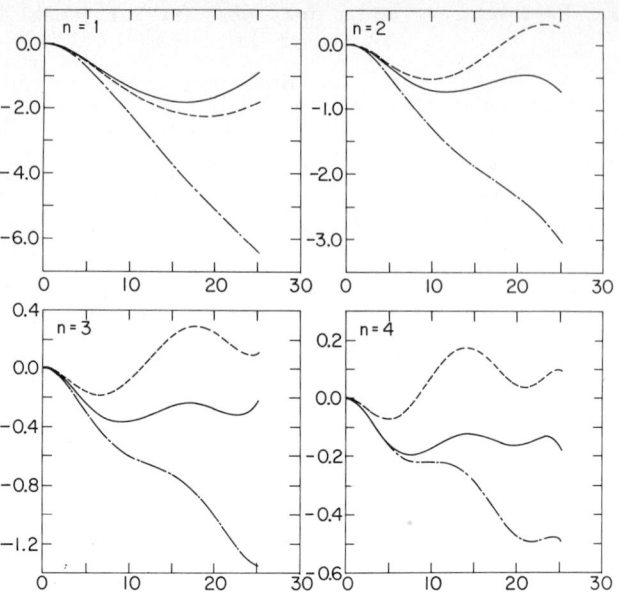

Figure 8. Absolute error in ln b(u) *obtained by Jacobi polynomial expansions over the range* $[0,8\pi]$ *as a function of* u *for orders* n $= 1 - 4$

———— *"Best" polynomial* L $= 5$
- - - - *Chebyshev polynomial* L $= 5$
— · — *Chebyshev polynomial* L $= 0$

A measure of the fidelity of the "best" set polynomial for the approximation of $\ln \frac{s}{s'}f$ can be made through the criterion of least squares. We fit the function $\ln b(u)$ by the principle of least squares to an equation of the form of Equation 44 but with arbitrary coefficients

$$\ln b(u) = \sum_{i=1}^{n} a_i u^{2i}, \tag{61}$$

for the ranges $u = 1\pi, 2\pi, \ldots, 8\pi$. In the least-squares analysis, the RMSE as defined by Equations 58, 59, and 60 was optimized, instead of minimizing the squares of the absolute error, as is ordinarily done. The RMSE thus optimized are tabulated in Table IX. By comparison of Tables V and IX, it is obvious that within the framework of the present set of criteria, Equations 58, 59, and 60, the best possible approximation has already been achieved with the "best" set for $L = 5$. For an imaginary molecule for which the assumptions leading to the present weighting, $w(u) \propto u$, are valid, the set of Jacobi polynomials given in Table IV

Table II.   Parameters γ and δ for "Best Set" of Jacobi Polynomials
($L = 0$)

Order	Range of u							
	1π	2π	3π	4π	5π	6π	7π	8π
1	0.474 [a]	0.395	0.317	0.270	0.223	0.200	0.170	0.151
	1.000	1.000	1.000	1.000	1.000	1.000	1.000	1.000
2	0.628	0.550	0.473	0.404	0.347	0.307	0.270	0.253
	0.800	0.750	0.750	0.700	0.650	0.650	0.600	0.600
3	0.443	0.426	0.412	0.396	0.366	0.307	0.298	0.250
	1.250	1.150	1.100	1.000	−0.220	−0.450	−0.150	−0.500
4	0.650	0.605	0.558	0.511	0.443	0.373	0.345	0.320
	1.450	1.450	1.400	1.250	0.650	0.000	−0.100	−0.150

[a] For each range and order the upper number is the value of γ and the lower one is the value of δ.

yields the best possible approximations for $\ln \frac{s}{s'} f$ when used in Equations 55 or 56 with $L = 5$.

For a specific problem, one could construct a similar table of Jacobi polynomials best suited for the problem, by suitable choice of a weighting function $w(u)$, and modification of the RMSE to be optimized. In some cases it may be of interest to use the polynomial that is "best" at the largest range for all the calculations. Table X provides a crude idea of the degree of approximation obtainable when the polynomial of Table IV that is best at range $= 8\pi$ is used for all the calculations of a given order. A comparison of Tables V and X shows that a simpler "best" set of polynomials used over the entire range of the expansion variable, $\left(\frac{u}{2\pi}\right)^2$, leads to results almost as good as the results obtained by multiple optimization within the range. To simplify the situation even further, one could always use a single polynomial, such as the Chebyshev polynomial, for all ranges and orders.

Figures 2, 3, 4, 5, 6, 7, and 8 show computer-generated plots of the absolute errors of the approximation of $\ln b(u)$ by Equation 52 as functions of u. Plots are shown for ranges 2π, 3π, . . . , 8π, respectively. Each figure consists of four separate frames, one for every order. Each frame contains three error curves: one obtained by the "best" polynomial given in Table IV which has $L = 5$, another by $T_n^*(x)$ with $L = 5$, and the third by $T_n^*(x)$ with $L = 0$. The error curves for $\ln b(u)$ evaluated by the least-squares-analysis are indistinguishable from the curves for the "best" polynomial with $L = 5$. The curves in Figures 2, 3, 4, 5, 6, 7, and 8 clearly illustrate the oscillatory behavior of the error obtained with the expansions; they show error amplitudes, regions of maxima and minima,

Table III.   RMS Error in the Approximation of ln $b(u)$ with

Order	Range			
	1_π	2_π	3_π	4_π
1	2.104×10^{-3}	2.062×10^{-2}	6.043×10^{-2}	1.144×10^{-1}
2	7.499×10^{-5}	2.198×10^{-3}	1.048×10^{-2}	2.550×10^{-2}
3	5.533×10^{-6}	4.925×10^{-4}	3.810×10^{-3}	1.205×10^{-2}
4	2.480×10^{-7}	7.105×10^{-5}	9.522×10^{-4}	4.134×10^{-3}

a Equation 44 is used in calculating ln $b(u)$.

Table IV.   Parameters γ and δ for "Best Set" of Jacobi Polynomials ($L = 5$)

Order	Range of u							
	1_π	2_π	3_π	4_π	5_π	6_π	7_π	8_π
1	0.990*a*	0.905	0.835	0.780	0.735	0.705	0.670	0.645
	1.000	1.000	1.000	1.000	1.000	1.000	1.000	1.000
2	1.930	1.830	1.720	1.620	1.548	1.485	1.430	1.380
	1.900	1.950	1.975	1.975	1.975	1.975	1.950	1.925
3	1.935	1.855	1.775	1.690	1.615	1.555	1.505	1.470
	1.850	1.900	1.950	1.975	1.975	1.975	1.975	1.975
4	1.900	1.845	1.775	1.715	1.650	1.595	1.545	1.500
	1.775	1.850	1.900	1.950	1.970	1.975	1.975	1.950
5	1.895	1.845	1.785	1.735	1.685	1.635	1.585	1.540
	1.725	1.800	1.850	1.900	1.950	1.950	1.950	1.950
6	1.885	1.835	1.790	1.740	1.690	1.650	1.610	1.575
	1.700	1.750	1.825	1.875	1.910	1.940	1.950	1.950

a For each range and order the upper number is the value of γ and the lower one is the value of δ.

and regions where the error is insensitive to change in the variable u. The curves can be used to select a suitable polynomial for use in a limited range of the variable.

Properties of Jacobi-Expansions as Applied to Isotope Effects in Polyatomic Systems

In the preceeding section we have examined the convergence properties of the Jacobi expansions of ln $b(u)$. For the behavior of a system of oscillators with a spectral range, such as a polyatomic molecule, ln $b(u_1)$ must be summed over all vibrations, and then the difference between a pair of isotopic molecules must be taken to obtain ln $\frac{s}{s'}f$. For iso-

"best" Jacobi Polynomials Using Fixed Range Expansions $(L = 0)$ [a]

of u

5π	6π	7π	8π
1.762×10^{-1}	2.425×10^{-1}	3.114×10^{-1}	3.820×10^{-1}
4.555×10^{-2}	6.911×10^{-2}	9.497×10^{-2}	1.224×10^{-1}
2.285×10^{-2}	3.673×10^{-2}	5.576×10^{-2}	7.098×10^{-2}
1.010×10^{-2}	1.878×10^{-2}	2.940×10^{-2}	4.194×10^{-2}

tope effects, such as isotope-exchange equilibria, we further have to take differences between two or more $\ln \frac{s}{s'} f$s.

In this section we present methods and results of applications of the expansions of $\ln b(u)$ for polyatomic molecules and for systems involving more than one chemical species.

The Jacobi expansions of $\ln \frac{s}{s'} f$, Equations 46 and 55, require the use of some molecular property for the evaluation of the range of expansion. Its choice affects the modulating coefficients, $T(n,m,u)$ or $W(n,m,u,L)$. We have chosen the highest frequency of the light molecule as the molecular property which determines the coefficients. A coefficient of given n and m then becomes a common factor for all vibrations, thus reducing Equations 46 and 55 to Equations 47 and 56, respectively. This procedure removes the arbitrariness associated with the application of the $\bar{\gamma}$ method for approximating $\ln \frac{s}{s'} f$ and provides a direct extension of the method to higher terms.

The method of moments is directly applicable with Equations 47 and 56, and the sum rules are automatically satisfied. In the first part of the present section, results of these investigations will be discussed; the various Jacobi expansions will be compared with the Bernoulli series, and with the $G(u)$-method.

The usefulness of the Jacobi expansions would be limited, however, if there were no means of estimating the range of expansion from the equations of motion without solving secular equations. One such method has been used successfully, and will be described later in this section.

Comparison of Numerical Approximations of $\ln \frac{s}{s'} f$. The reduced partition function ratios, $\ln \frac{s}{s'} f$, of various pairs of isotopic molecules, were previously calculated by Bigeleisen and Ishida (7) using the Chebyshev ($\gamma = \delta = \frac{1}{2}$) expansion with $L = 0$ (Equation 47), and the numerical results were compared with those obtained by the Bernoulli series

Table V.   RMS Error in the Approximation of ln $b(u)$ with "best"

Range

Order	1_π	2_π	3_π	4_π
1	2.104×10^{-3}	2.061×10^{-2}	6.043×10^{-2}	1.144×10^{-1}
2	7.486×10^{-5}	2.195×10^{-3}	1.038×10^{-2}	2.534×10^{-2}
3	3.148×10^{-6}	2.815×10^{-4}	2.191×10^{-3}	7.000×10^{-3}
4	1.421×10^{-7}	3.891×10^{-5}	5.018×10^{-4}	2.117×10^{-3}
5	6.688×10^{-9}	5.632×10^{-6}	1.210×10^{-4}	6.783×10^{-4}
6	3.221×10^{-10}	8.352×10^{-7}	2.991×10^{-5}	2.231×10^{-4}

[a] Equation 52 with $L = 5$ is used in calculating ln $b(u)$.

Table VI.   RMS Error in the Approximation of ln $b(u)$ with Shifted Expansions

Range

Order	1_π	2_π	3_π	4_π
1	5.013×10^{-3}	5.939×10^{-2}	2.032×10^{-1}	4.264×10^{-1}
2	1.095×10^{-4}	2.457×10^{-3}	1.323×10^{-2}	5.337×10^{-2}
3	6.422×10^{-6}	5.459×10^{-4}	4.340×10^{-3}	1.642×10^{-2}
4	3.043×10^{-7}	8.080×10^{-5}	1.021×10^{-3}	4.492×10^{-3}

Table VII.   RMS Error in the Approximation of ln $b(u)$ Subdivided Range

Range

Order	1_π	2_π	3_π	4_π
1	2.104×10^{-3}	2.096×10^{-2}	6.362×10^{-2}	1.246×10^{-1}
2	2.543×10^{-4}	7.383×10^{-3}	3.382×10^{-2}	7.878×10^{-2}
3	8.044×10^{-6}	7.426×10^{-4}	6.037×10^{-3}	1.992×10^{-2}
4	3.333×10^{-7}	9.235×10^{-5}	1.213×10^{-3}	5.260×10^{-3}

and the $G(u)$-method. Exact values of ln $\frac{s}{s'} f$ were calculated from complete sets of normal frequencies, obtained by solving secular equations for each isotopic molecule. The Wilson (28) **FG**-matrix method was used, with a potential energy matrix **F** for the gaseous state of the molecule. For the Chebyshev approximation the highest frequency for each molecular species was used to calculate the appropriate coefficients $T(n,m,u'_{max})$.

For our present purposes it suffices to calculate ln $\frac{s}{s'} f$ in the harmonic oscillator approximation over a temperature range larger than that which is experimentally significant.

Jacobi Polynomials Using Subdivided Range Expansion ($L = 5$) [a]

of u

5π	6π	7π	8π
1.762×10^{-1}	2.425×10^{-1}	3.114×10^{-1}	3.820×10^{-1}
4.544×10^{-2}	6.902×10^{-2}	9.491×10^{-2}	1.224×10^{-1}
1.477×10^{-2}	2.495×10^{-2}	3.691×10^{-2}	5.017×10^{-2}
5.302×10^{-3}	1.003×10^{-2}	1.607×10^{-2}	2.314×10^{-2}
2.027×10^{-3}	4.313×10^{-3}	7.504×10^{-3}	1.148×10^{-2}
7.972×10^{-4}	1.915×10^{-3}	3.630×10^{-3}	5.919×10^{-3}

Chebyshev Polynomials of the First Kind Using Fixed Range ($L = 0$)

of u

5π	6π	7π	8π
7.031×10^{-1}	1.013	1.343	1.687
1.412×10^{-1}	2.805×10^{-1}	4.663×10^{-1}	6.924×10^{-1}
4.544×10^{-2}	1.010×10^{-1}	1.894×10^{-1}	3.127×10^{-1}
1.318×10^{-2}	3.205×10^{-2}	6.735×10^{-2}	1.245×10^{-1}

with Shifted Chebyshev Polynomials of the First Kind Using Expansions ($L = 5$)

of u

5π	6π	7π	8π
1.978×10^{-1}	2.802×10^{-1}	3.707×10^{-1}	4.696×10^{-1}
1.343×10^{-1}	1.944×10^{-1}	2.559×10^{-1}	3.172×10^{-1}
4.268×10^{-2}	7.217×10^{-2}	1.060×10^{-1}	1.422×10^{-1}
1.354×10^{-2}	2.619×10^{-2}	4.255×10^{-2}	6.172×10^{-2}

The previous authors (7) calculated $\ln \frac{s}{s'} f$ of Equation 1 for various isotopic substitutions in the molecular species hydrogen, water, methane, ethylene, benzene, carbon dioxide, and nitrous oxide. Their calculations covered temperatures ranging from 100° to 2600°K. Their results for deuterium substitutions in ethylene are reproduced in Table XI. For each deuterium substitution the table compares percentage errors obtained by the $G(u)$-method, the Chebyshev expansion, and the Bernoulli series, for various orders at temperatures 300°, 1200°, and 3000°K. Contributions to $\ln \frac{s}{s'} f$ from the planar and non-planar vibrations are tabulated separately. Two approximations are given for the total $\ln \frac{s}{s'} f$. "Total A" was calculated by using a common value of u_{max} for all the vibrations.

Table VIII.   The Bernoulli-Modulating Coefficients for Various Jacobi Polynomials

Order	Range of $u = \pi$			
n	m = 1	m = 2	m = 3	m = 4
1	0.888889			
	0.926125			
	0.925589			
	0.926458			
2	0.993789	0.795031		
	0.996146	0.806807		
	0.993834	0.803127		
	0.993837	0.803271		
3	0.999654	0.974732	0.708896	
	0.999788	0.976532	0.712452	
	0.999816	0.981447	0.742484	
	0.999509	0.972463	0.707242	
4	0.999981	0.997512	0.948130	0.632087
	0.999989	0.997698	0.948946	0.633125
	0.999985	0.998110	0.956522	0.659390
	0.999964	0.996830	0.944014	0.627106

Order	Range of $u = 3\pi$			
n	m = 1	m = 2	m = 3	m = 4
1	0.470588			
	0.630406			
	0.648689			
	0.648293			
2	0.837022	0.257545		
	0.896594	0.289296		
	0.861282	0.281776		
	0.860452	0.280612		
3	0.953031	0.577282	0.131950	
	0.971002	0.603876	0.138518	
	0.970564	0.636005	0.160862	
	0.945486	0.561880	0.130578	
4	0.986540	0.795114	0.369723	0.067222
	0.991770	0.809649	0.377754	0.068576
	0.989753	0.827890	0.415234	0.082652
	0.979808	0.764287	0.347832	0.063740

"Total B" was obtained by using a separate value of u_{max} for the planar and non-planar vibrations of the molecule.

Orders and Ranges of Expansions of ln $b(u)$ Using Various with $L = 0$ and 5 [a]

	Range of u $= 2\pi$		
m $= 1$	m $= 2$	m $= 3$	m $= 4$
0.666667			
0.773777			
0.779330			
0.781703			
0.941177	0.470588		
0.963169	0.497545		
0.945256	0.487400		
0.945799	0.489246		
0.989899	0.808081	0.323232	
0.993804	0.821142	0.330073	
0.994080	0.844987	0.366551	
0.986972	0.796046	0.320533	
0.998267	0.942808	0.665511	0.221837
0.998943	0.947011	0.670398	0.223535
0.998677	0.954455	0.704208	0.252387
0.997063	0.930755	0.646833	0.215659

	Range of u $= 4\pi$		
m $= 1$	m $= 2$	m $= 3$	m $= 4$
0.333333			
0.519949			
0.540426			
0.545131			
0.714286	0.142857		
0.815775	0.172707		
0.768710	0.166439		
0.768567	0.166242		
0.888889	0.388889	0.055556	
0.930794	0.423440	0.060582	
0.925626	0.447265	0.070676	
0.883088	0.379192	0.055610	
0.957447	0.617021	0.191489	0.021277
0.973857	0.642720	0.199952	0.022136
0.967151	0.661093	0.223503	0.027130
0.943070	0.577991	0.175670	0.019831

Table VIII.

Order	Range of u $= 5_\pi$			
n	m $= 1$	m $= 2$	m $= 3$	m $= 4$
1	0.242424			
	0.437667			
	0.467374			
	0.467571			
2	0.597553	0.824211		
	0.735830	0.108072		
	0.684484	0.103426		
	0.685090	0.103863		
3	0.809156	0.259524	0.025014	
	0.879865	0.296391	0.028561	
	0.797916	0.229167	0.019587	
	0.814315	0.257338	0.025640	
4	0.911882	0.460720	0.099790	0.007392
	0.945521	0.494325	0.107195	0.007897
	0.925174	0.482716	0.107924	0.008216
	0.893542	0.425121	0.090461	0.006852

Order	Range of u $= 7_\pi$			
n	m $= 1$	m $= 2$	m $= 3$	m $= 4$
1	0.140351			
	0.326771			
	0.359723			
	0.361046			
2	0.413961	0.031242		
	0.600489	0.048576		
	0.552585	0.046665		
	0.554543	0.047196		
3	0.643705	0.120169	0.006202	
	0.770179	0.153040	0.007879	
	0.680704	0.117070	0.005481	
	0.688240	0.128360	0.006930	
4	0.792678	0.251102	0.030050	0.001178
	0.869742	0.289787	0.034652	0.001348
	0.815096	0.247203	0.027733	0.001018
	0.785047	0.232984	0.027584	0.001116

[a] The four modulating coefficients listed for each range, order and term, m, are arranged as follows:
      Chebyshev polynomial with $L = 0$
      Chebyshev polynomial with $L = 5$

Continued

Range of u = 6π

m = 1	m = 2	m = 3	m = 4
0.181818			
0.375331			
0.400000			
0.407176			
0.496894	0.049689		
0.663497	0.070925		
0.614588	0.068623		
0.614500	0.068591		
0.725009	0.175028	0.012071	
0.824841	0.210737	0.014511	
0.717221	0.147057	0.008575	
0.748157	0.179074	0.012845	
0.855105	0.339922	0.053709	0.002827
0.909736	0.377567	0.059661	0.003118
0.867182	0.333380	0.050019	0.002494
0.838965	0.312555	0.048670	0.002631

Range of u = 8π

m = 1	m = 2	m = 3	m = 4
0.111111			
0.287910			
0.322680			
0.323162			
0.346939	0.020408		
0.546329	0.034513		
0.495117	0.032889		
0.504437	0.033780		
0.569024	0.084175	0.003367	
0.718356	0.113611	0.004530	
0.599878	0.074717	0.002507	
0.634571	0.094384	0.003966	
0.728957	0.186871	0.017470	0.000529
0.828138	0.224651	0.020970	0.000630
0.766361	0.187741	0.016374	0.000462
0.733770	0.176242	0.016326	0.000511

"Best" polynomial ($L = 0$) with $L = 0$
"Best" polynomial ($L = 5$) with $L = 5$
The coefficients for $L = 5$ are calculated as $W(n,m,u,L)/z(m)$. (*See* Equation 56.)

Table IX. Minimum RMS Error Obtained by

			Range
Order	1_π	2_π	3_π	4_π
---	---	---	---	---
1	2.104×10^{-3}	2.060×10^{-2}	6.043×10^{-2}	1.144×10^{-1}
2	7.486×10^{-5}	2.195×10^{-3}	1.038×10^{-2}	2.534×10^{-2}
3	3.140×10^{-6}	2.799×10^{-4}	2.173×10^{-3}	6.936×10^{-3}
4	1.414×10^{-7}	3.858×10^{-5}	4.959×10^{-4}	2.089×10^{-3}

Table X. RMS Error in the Approximation of

			Range
Order	1_π	2_π	3_π	4_π
---	---	---	---	---
1	2.737×10^{-3}	2.493×10^{-2}	6.814×10^{-2}	1.229×10^{-1}
2	9.050×10^{-5}	2.536×10^{-3}	1.143×10^{-2}	2.677×10^{-2}
3	3.759×10^{-6}	3.208×10^{-4}	2.392×10^{-3}	7.379×10^{-3}
4	1.684×10^{-7}	4.395×10^{-5}	5.440×10^{-4}	2.225×10^{-3}

Comparison of the accuracies of the Chebyshev and Bernoulli approximations in Table XI shows the Chebyshev ($L = 0$) to be better than the Bernoulli by a factor of 5 to 10 at $n = 1$; the improvement increases to about 300 at $n = 4$. This was generally observed for all other isotopic substitutions tested; the rate of convergence of the Chebyshev expansion is better than the Bernoulli expansion at any order, at any temperature. The Chebyshev expansion exists at any temperature, while the Bernoulli series diverges for most of the molecules at room temperature. Table XI also shows that the Bigeleisen-Mayer approximation, Equation 3, computes these $\ln \frac{s}{s'} f$ to 2% by its first term, $G(u)\Delta(u)$, and to 0.5% after two terms. The approximation is even better for heavy-atom substitutions.

Table XI reveals many interesting features of the Chebyshev expansion common to all deuterium-for-protium substitutions in all the hydrocarbons tested: at room temperature where u_{max} is about 15 or higher, $\ln \frac{s}{s'} f$ is calculated by the Chebyshev ($L = 0$) method to about 40% at $n = 1$, 10% at $n = 2$, 4% at $n = 3$ and less than 1% at $n = 4$. As u_{max} decreases with increasing temperature, the error generally drops as T^{-2n}. As more protiums are substituted by deuterium, the frequency shifts generally increase (6) and the Chebyshev approximation slowly becomes less accurate. The non-planar vibrations have a range of frequencies about a third that of the planar ones, and the error in $\ln \frac{s}{s'} f$ for the non-

Least-Squares Fit Around Mean of Absolute Errors

of u

5π	6π	7π	8π
1.762×10^{-1}	2.425×10^{-1}	3.114×10^{-1}	3.819×10^{-1}
4.544×10^{-2}	6.902×10^{-2}	9.491×10^{-2}	1.224×10^{-1}
1.464×10^{-2}	2.475×10^{-2}	3.666×10^{-2}	4.989×10^{-2}
5.229×10^{-3}	9.896×10^{-3}	1.587×10^{-2}	2.288×10^{-2}

ln $b(u)$ with "best" ($L = 5$, 8π) Jacobi Polynomials

of u

5π	6π	7π	8π
1.837×10^{-1}	2.483×10^{-1}	3.157×10^{-1}	3.820×10^{-1}
4.676×10^{-2}	7.001×10^{-2}	9.560×10^{-2}	1.224×10^{-1}
1.519×10^{-2}	2.527×10^{-2}	3.713×10^{-2}	5.017×10^{-2}
5.448×10^{-3}	1.015×10^{-2}	1.614×10^{-2}	2.314×10^{-2}

planar vibrations is smaller than for the planar ones by a factor of more than ten.

A comparison of the approximation of $\ln \frac{s}{s'} f$ by the Chebyshev and "best" Jacobi polynomials for fixed range ($L = 0$) and subdivided range ($L = 5$) expansions, with exact calculations, is given in Tables XII-XV. The molecules studied are benzene, ethylene, methane, and 1-bromobutane. The upper portions of Tables XII, XIII, XIV, and XV intercompare the fixed range ($L = 0$) with the subdivided range expansion ($L = 5$) using Chebyshev polynomials. The use of the subdivided range expansion ($L = 5$) eliminates most of the errors introduced into the expansion of $\ln b(u)$ from the terms $2 \leq k < \infty$ in Equation 32. These become particularly important in dealing with C–H vibrations and are the source of the consistent deviations of 40 to 50% in $\ln \frac{s}{s'} f$ for first order ($n = 1$) expansions of $\ln \frac{s}{s'} f$ at 300°K. for molecules containing hydrogen. The bottom sections of Tables XII, XIII, XIV, and XV show results of similar calculations for the same systems, but using the "best" sets of Jacobi polynomials, tabulated in Tables II and IV, in place of the Chebyshev polynomials. For each "best" set, the calculations were carried out in the following manner using the appropriate equations. For each temperature u'_{max} was computed from the highest frequency of the system, and the "best" polynomial for the range closest to u'_{max} was chosen—i.e., if $u'_{max} = 4.3\pi$ the "best" polynomial for the range $[0,4\pi]$ was selected,

Table XI. Intercomparison of Bigeleisen-Mayer, Chebyshev and

Per

Molecular Pair	Class of Vibrations[b]	T (°K.)	Exact $ln \frac{s}{s'}f$	Bigeleisen-Mayer	
				n = 1	n = 2
C_2H_3D/C_2H_4	Planar	300	2.09490	−2.4	0.41
		1200	0.261075		
		3000	0.0465407		
	Non-planar	300	0.225675	−4.7	0.29
		1200	0.0176614		
		3000	0.00287159		
	Total A	300	2.32057	−2.7	0.40
		1200	0.278736		
		3000	0.0494123		
	Total B	300	2.32057		
		1200	0.278736		
		3000	0.0494123		
cis-$C_2H_2D_2/C_2H_4$	Planar	300	4.19392		
		1200	0.522391		
		3000	0.0930907		
	Non-planar	300	0.453482		
		1200	0.0353384		
		3000	0.00574359		
	Total A	300	4.64740		
		1200	0.557730		
		3000	0.0988343		
	Total B	300			
		1200			
		3000			
$trans$-$C_2H_2D_2/C_2H_4$	Planar	300	4.19273		
		1200	0.522211		
		3000	0.0930835		
	Non-planar	300	0.456029		
		1200	0.0353562		
		3000	0.00574407		
	Total A	300	4.64875		
		1200	0.557567		
		3000	0.0988275		
	Total B	300			
		1200			
		3000			

Bernoulli Expansions of ln $\frac{s}{s'}f$ with Exact Values for Ethylene[a]

cent Error

	Chebyshev				Bernoulli		
n = 1	n = 2	n = 3	n = 4	n = 1	n = 2	n = 3	n = 4
−40.4	−10.5	−3.8	0.58	—	—	—	—
−3.0	−0.031	−0.019	0.001	14.1	−3.5	0.95	−0.27
−0.38	−0.000	−0.000	0.000	2.4	−0.097	0.004	−0.000
−2.3	−0.000	−0.11	0.008	27.6	−12.3	5.9	−3.0
0.017	0.001	−0.000	0.000	1.9	−0.055	0.002	−0.000
0.005	0.000	−0.000	0.000	0.31	−0.001	0.000	−0.000
−42.9	−11.8	−3.9	0.54	—	—	—	—
−3.6	−0.071	−0.019	0.001	13.3	−3.2	0.89	−0.25
−0.50	−0.001	−0.000	0.000	2.3	−0.092	0.004	−0.000
−36.7	−9.5	−3.4	0.52	—	—	—	—
−2.8	−0.029	−0.018	0.001	13.3	−3.2	0.89	−0.25
−0.36	0.000	−0.000	0.000	2.3	−0.092	0.004	−0.000
−40.4	−10.4	−3.8	0.55	—	—	—	—
−3.0	−0.022	−0.020	0.001	14.1	−3.4	0.94	−0.27
−0.39	0.000	−0.000	0.000	2.4	−0.096	0.004	−0.000
−2.8	0.089	−0.11	0.008	27.0	−11.7	5.6	−2.7
−0.027	0.001	−0.000	0.000	1.89	−0.053	0.002	−0.000
−0.002	0.000	−0.000	0.000	0.31	−0.001	0.000	−0.000
−43.0	−11.7	−4.0	0.51	—	—	—	—
−3.7	−0.064	−0.020	0.001	13.3	−3.2	0.88	−0.25
−0.51	−0.001	−0.000	0.000	2.3	−0.091	0.004	−0.000
−36.8	−9.4	−3.5	0.50				
−2.8	−0.020	−0.019	0.001				
−0.37	0.000	−0.000	0.000				
−40.4	−10.5	−3.8	0.59	—	—	—	—
−3.0	−0.031	−0.020	0.001	14.1	−3.5	0.95	−0.27
−0.38	−0.000	−0.000	0.000	2.4	−0.097	0.004	−0.000
−3.4	0.16	−0.11	0.006	26.3	−11.2	5.2	−2.5
−0.078	0.002	−0.000	0.000	1.84	−0.050	0.001	−0.000
−0.010	0.000	−0.000	0.000	0.30	−0.001	0.000	−0.000
−43.0	−11.9	−4.0	0.54	—	—	—	—
−3.6	−0.073	−0.020	0.001	13.3	−3.2	0.89	−0.25
−0.50	−0.001	−0.000	0.000	2.3	−0.091	0.004	−0.000
−36.8	−9.5	−3.4	0.54				
−2.8	−0.029	−0.018	0.001				
−0.36	0.000	−0.000	0.000				

Table XI.

Per

Molecular Pair	Class of Vibrations[b]	T (°K.)	Exact $ln \frac{s}{s'} f$	Bigeleisen-Mayer	
				n = 1	n = 2
gem-$C_2H_2D_2$/C_2H_4	Planar	300	4.19744		
		1200	0.522325		
		3000	0.0930875		
	Non-planar	300	0.451755		
		1200	0.0353247		
		3000	0.00574322		
	Total A	300	4.64920		
		1200	0.557650		
		3000	0.0988307		
	Total B	300			
		1200			
		3000			
C_2HD_3/C_2H_4	Planar	300	6.29919		
		1200	0.783702		
		3000	0.139639		
	Non-planar	300	0.684142		
		1200	0.0530351		
		3000	0.00861612		
	Total A	300	6.98333		
		1200	0.836737		
		3000	0.148256		
	Total B	300			
		1200			
		3000			
C_2D_4/C_2H_4	Planar	300	8.40818		
		1200	1.04525		
		3000	0.186197		
	Non-planar	300	0.916751		
		1200	0.0707474		
		3000	0.0114891		
	Total A	300	9.32493		
		1200	1.11600		
		3000	0.197687		
	Total B	300			
		1200			
		3000			

[a] **F**-matrix elements taken from Stern, Van Hook, and Wolfsberg (19).
Geometry parameters taken from Gallaway and Barker (12): $r(C–C) = 1.353$ A., $r(C–H) = 1.071$ A., <HCH = 119° 55'.

Continued

cent Error

	Chebyshev				Bernoulli		
n = 1	n = 2	n = 3	n = 4	n = 1	n = 2	n = 3	n = 4
−40.5	−10.5	−3.9	0.62	—	—	—	—
−3.0	−0.029	−0.020	0.001	14.1	−3.4	0.94	−0.27
−0.38	0.000	−0.000	0.000	2.4	−0.097	0.004	−0.000
−2.4	−0.023	−0.100	0.009	27.5	−12.2	5.9	−3.0
0.011	0.001	−0.000	0.000	1.93	−0.055	0.002	−0.000
0.004	0.000	−0.000	0.000	0.31	−0.001	0.000	−0.000
−43.0	−11.9	−4.0	0.58	—	—	—	—
−3.7	−0.070	−0.020	0.001	13.3	−3.2	0.88	−0.25
−0.50	−0.001	−0.000	0.000	2.3	−0.091	0.004	−0.000
−36.8	−9.5	−3.5	0.56				
−2.9	−0.027	−0.019	0.001				
−0.36	0.000	−0.000	0.000				
−40.5	−10.5	−3.9	0.60	—	—	—	—
−3.0	−0.024	−0.020	0.001	14.1	−3.4	0.94	−0.27
−0.39	0.000	−0.000	0.000	2.4	−0.096	0.004	−0.000
−3.4	0.17	−0.11	0.006	26.3	−11.2	5.2	−2.5
−0.079	0.002	−0.000	0.000	1.84	−0.050	0.001	−0.000
−0.011	0.000	−0.000	0.000	0.30	−0.001	0.000	−0.000
−43.1	−11.8	−4.0	0.54	—	—	—	—
−3.7	−0.066	−0.020	0.001	13.3	−3.2	0.88	−0.25
−0.51	−0.001	−0.000	0.000	2.3	−0.091	0.004	−0.000
−36.9	−9.4	−3.5	0.54				
−2.8	−0.022	−0.019	0.001				
−0.37	−0.000	−0.000	0.000				
−40.6	−10.4	−3.9	0.60	—	—	—	—
−3.1	−0.020	−0.021	0.001	14.0	−2.4	0.93	−0.26
−0.40	0.000	−0.000	0.000	2.4	−0.096	0.004	−0.000
−3.8	0.27	−0.11	0.004	25.7	−10.6	4.8	−2.3
−0.13	0.003	−0.000	0.000	1.79	−0.047	0.001	−0.000
−0.019	0.000	−0.000	0.000	0.29	−0.001	0.000	−0.000
−43.2	−11.8	−4.1	0.54	—	—	—	—
−3.7	−0.064	−0.021	0.001	13.2	−3.2	0.87	−0.25
−0.52	−0.001	−0.000	0.000	2.3	−0.090	0.004	−0.000
−37.0	−9.4	−3.5	0.54				
−2.9	−0.019	−0.020	0.001				
−0.37	0.000	−0.000	0.000				

[b] ν_{max} for planar vibrations = 3110.38 cm.$^{-1}$, ν_{max} for non-planar vibrations = 1026.96 cm.$^{-1}$.

Total A is Σ (planar + non-planar) using common ν_{max} for all frequencies.
Total B is Σ planar + Σ non-planar each calculated above with its appropriate u_{max}.

Table XII. Intercomparison of Various Jacobi Expansions

Per

T (°K.)	Exact $ln \frac{s}{s'}f$	Chebyshev (L = 0)[b]			
		n = 1	n = 2	n = 3	n = 4
200	3.52605	−57.7	−25.4	−10.8	−0.41
300	2.14408	−40.8	−11.2	−3.8	0.69
400	1.46840	−28.3	−5.1	−1.59	0.39
600	0.822599	−14.0	−1.24	−0.40	0.079
800	0.524540	−7.6	−0.39	−0.127	0.017
1000	0.361470	−4.6	−0.146	−0.046	0.004
1200	0.262944	−3.0	−0.065	−0.019	0.001
3000	0.0467660	−0.38	−0.001	−0.000	0.000

T (°K.)	"Best Set" (L = 0)[d]			
	n = 1	n = 2	n = 3	n = 4
200	8.7	−8.2	−4.8	1.96
300	11.1	−4.9	−2.7	1.05
400	10.3	−3.2	−0.077	0.41
600	4.5	−1.85	0.034	0.040
800	5.2	−0.71	0.010	0.008
1000	2.7	−0.43	0.010	0.002
1200	2.4	−0.23	0.004	0.000
3000	0.59	−0.007	0.000	0.000

[a] **F**-matrix elements taken from Crawford and Miller (10).
   Geometry parameters: $r(C–C) = 1.39$ A., $r(C–H) = 1.08$ A.
   Atomic masses: $m_C = 12.01$, $m_H = 1.008$, $m_D = 2.016$
   $\nu_{max} = 3083.78$ cm.$^{-1}$
[b] Calculated by using Equation 47, and shifted Chebyshev polynomials of the first kind.

if $u'_{max} = 4.7\pi$ the "best" polynomial for range $[0,5\pi]$ was selected. Although the approximation is not improved by using the "best" set ($L = 5$) in place of the "best" set ($L = 0$) at $n = 1$ or 2, using these polynomials with $L = 5$ yields a better than tenfold reduction in error at lower temperatures and higher orders ($n = 3$ and 4).

Intercomparison of the top and bottom sections of Tables XII, XIII, and XIV shows that for the $L = 0$ approximations the "best" set gives much better results than the Chebyshev at low orders, while the Chebyshev at lower temperatures gradually improves as the order increases. It is obvious that the better approximations obtained by the Chebyshev ($L = 5$) for $n = 1$ and 2 are because of accidental cancellation of errors. We do not expect the Chebyshev ($L = 5$) generally to yield as good an approximation as the "best" set for a system. Such an example is illus-

of ln $\frac{s}{s'}f$ for **Planar Vibrations of Benzene (d_1/d_o)** [a]

Cent Error

Chebyshev $(L = 5)$ [c]			
$n = 1$	$n = 2$	$n = 3$	$n = 4$
−0.96	3.5	−1.48	2.7
2.6	2.9	−1.16	1.04
4.1	2.2	−0.78	0.40
4.7	1.08	−0.29	0.068
4.1	0.53	−0.102	0.014
3.3	0.27	−0.039	0.004
2.6	0.152	−0.017	0.001
0.55	0.005	−0.000	0.000

"Best" Set $(L = 5)$ [e]			
$n = 1$	$n = 2$	$n = 3$	$n = 4$
9.5	−8.3	0.048	0.149
9.4	−5.8	−0.037	0.005
8.8	−3.9	−0.019	−0.015
6.0	−1.66	−0.040	−0.006
5.0	−0.81	−0.006	−0.002
3.3	−0.39	−0.005	−0.000
2.7	−0.22	−0.002	−0.000
0.56	−0.008	−0.000	−0.000

[c] Calculated by using Equation 56 with $L = 5$, and shifted Chebyshev polynomials of the first kind.
[d] Calculated by using Equation 47, and the "Best" set of Jacobi polynomials tabulated in Table II.
[e] Calculated by using Equation 56 with $L = 5$, and the "Best" set of Jacobi polynomials tabulated in Table IV.

trated in Table XV, which compares the various Jacobi expansions for a double-deuterium substitution at the α-carbon in 1-bromobutane.

It seems reasonable that the RMSE, as presently defined (Equations 58, 59, and 60), can serve as a general guide in a comparison of two expansions, but it should not be regarded as the final criterion. For any particular system one might re-define the weighting function $w(u)$ for RMSE to reflect more closely the particular frequency distribution and the shifts of the system. With the criterion for choosing polynomials so re-defined the discussion given in the preceeding section regarding the least-squares analysis, shows that the approximations obtained, with such a selected "best" set of polynomials, and Equation 56 with $L = 5$, are the best attainable by any "even-power series."

Table XIII.   Intercomparison of Various Jacobi Expansions

Per

T (°K.)	Exact $ln \frac{s}{s'}f$	Chebyshev $(L=0)$[b]			
		$n=1$	$n=2$	$n=3$	$n=4$
200	3.42613	−57.3	−24.6	−11.0	−0.75
300	2.09490	−40.4	−10.5	−3.8	0.58
400	1.44128	−28.0	−4.6	−1.60	0.35
600	0.812063	−13.9	−0.99	−0.41	0.073
800	0.519383	−7.6	−0.27	−0.129	0.016
1000	0.358527	−4.5	−0.084	−0.047	0.004
1200	0.261075	−3.0	−0.031	−0.019	0.001
3000	0.0465407	−0.38	−0.000	−0.000	0.000

T (°K.)	"Best Set" $(L=0)$[b]			
	$n=1$	$n=2$	$n=3$	$n=4$
200	10.2	−7.1	−4.7	1.58
300	12.2	−4.1	−2.5	0.92
400	11.2	−2.6	−0.178	0.39
600	4.9	−1.62	0.002	0.040
800	5.4	−0.60	−0.001	0.008
1000	2.9	−0.38	0.006	0.002
1200	2.5	−0.196	0.003	0.000
3000	0.61	−0.006	0.000	0.000

[a] *See* the footnote of Table XI for the molecular constants used.

Any expansion of $\ln \frac{s}{s'}f$ in the form,

$$\ln \frac{s}{s'}f = \sum_i \sum_n c_n (u'^{2n}_i - u_i^{2n})$$

$$= \sum_n c_n (\sum_i u'^{2n}_i - \sum_i u_i^{2n}) \qquad (62)$$

cannot be expected adequately to represent an isotopic system by its first one or two terms. This can be seen from the fact that a term of $\sum_i u_i^{2n}$, when combined with the n-th moment of the eigenvalues, relates isotope effects to motions of groups of atoms taken n at a time. Thus, the first order term, when expressed in Cartesian displacement coordinates, becomes

$$c_1 (\sum_i u'^2_i - \sum_i u_i^2) = c_1 \left(\frac{\hbar}{kT}\right)^2 \sum_i \left(\frac{1}{m'_i} - \frac{1}{m_i}\right) a_{ii}, \qquad (63)$$

where m_i is the atomic mass of the i-th atom, and a_{ii} is the harmonic force constant of the i-th Cartesian displacement coordinate. The very

of ln $\frac{s}{s'}f$ for Planar Vibrations of Benzene (d_1/d_o) [a]

Cent Error

	Chebyshev (L = 5) [b]		
n = 1	n = 2	n = 3	n = 4
0.69	5.0	−1.66	2.1
3.8	4.0	−1.23	0.85
5.0	2.9	−0.81	0.33
5.2	1.38	−0.30	0.057
4.3	0.67	−0.106	0.012
3.5	0.35	−0.041	0.003
2.7	0.192	−0.017	0.001
0.57	0.007	−0.000	0.000
	"Best" Set (L = 5) [b]		
n = 1	n = 2	n = 3	n = 4
11.3	−7.0	0.177	0.119
10.8	−4.9	0.061	0.017
9.8	−3.3	0.033	−0.005
6.5	−1.41	−0.023	−0.004
5.3	−0.70	−0.002	−0.001
3.5	−0.33	−0.003	−0.000
2.8	−0.187	−0.001	−0.000
0.58	−0.007	−0.000	−0.000

[b] *See* the footnotes of Table XII.

fact that Equation 63 contains only diagonal elements a_{ii} proves that the first term of Equation 62 describes motions of individual atoms, but fails to take any interactions into account. Such a description of the motion fails to describe the normal modes. The addition of a second term takes into account motions of pairs of atoms, and three terms are needed to describe bending motions adequately. Any attempt to approximate ln $\frac{s}{s'}f$ by a low-order expansion of the form of Equation 62 is equivalent to neglecting the higher-order interactions. As indicated by Tables XII, XIII, XIV, and XV, higher-order interactions and higher order quantum corrections, can be neglected successfully at higher temperatures. As the temperature decreases an adequate description of isotope effects requires progressively higher order quantum corrections. If a certain number of terms satisfactorily describes a system at one temperature, the same number of terms will represent the system more accurately at any higher temperature. These conclusions are valid for any system at any temperature.

An additional useful measure of how well an even-power expansion represents the quantum corrections of order n can be obtained by examining the deviations from "the rules of the mean" (2, 3, 28) of order n. In a molecule containing two or more equivalent atoms, an even-power expansion of the form of Equation 62, for a pair which differ by one isotopic substitution at one of the equivalent positions, is equal to the corresponding term for any other similar pair, up to the term of $\left(\dfrac{h}{kT}\right)^2$. This is the first rule of the mean. It holds if the coefficients c_n are independent of the isotopic substitutions, as they are for the Bernoulli series. The same condition is also satisfied for the Jacobi expansions, when a quantity common to a given molecular species, such as ν'_{max} of the lightest isotopic molecule, is used for evaluating the modulating coefficients. For special combinations of isotopic pairs the rule holds to higher orders and has been given (3) in detail to order $\left(\dfrac{h}{kT}\right)^4$. Thus, the quantum

Table XIV. Intercomparison of Various Jacobi

Per

Γ ($°K.$)	Exact $ln\,\dfrac{s}{s'}$f	Chebyshev (L $= 0$)[b]			
		$n=1$	$n=2$	$n=3$	$n=4$
200	4.00170	-58.3	-24.5	-9.7	-0.52
300	2.45632	-41.7	-10.6	-3.0	0.73
400	1.69197	-29.5	-4.7	-1.15	0.43
600	0.952670	-15.1	-1.07	-0.28	0.089
800	0.608673	-8.4	-0.31	-0.090	0.019
1000	0.419890	-5.2	-0.109	-0.034	0.005
1200	0.305650	-3.4	-0.045	-0.014	0.002
3000	0.0544606	-0.46	-0.001	-0.000	0.000

T ($°K.$)		"Best Set" (L $=0$)[b]			
		$n=1$	$n=2$	$n=3$	$n=4$
200		8.4	-6.3	-3.1	2.2
300		10.4	-3.8	-1.72	1.21
400		9.5	-2.5	0.36	0.36
600		3.8	-1.66	0.148	0.031
800		4.7	-0.64	0.045	0.006
1000		2.4	-0.41	0.022	0.001
1200		2.2	-0.21	0.009	0.000
3000		0.55	-0.007	0.000	0.000

[a] F-matrix elements taken from Jones and McDowell (14).
Geometry parameters (14): r(C–H) $= 1.094$ A.
$\nu'_{max} = 3154.08$ cm.$^{-1}$

correction for the equilibrium constant of the reaction

$$H_2O + D_2O = 2HDO$$

is given by

$$2 \ln \frac{s}{s'} f \left(\frac{HDO}{H_2O} \right) - \ln \frac{s}{s'} f \left(\frac{D_2O}{H_2O} \right).$$

Using a quantity such as ν'_{max} of H_2O for evaluating the modulating coefficients for both isotopic pairs, the one-term Jacobi expansion predicts the quantum correction to be zero, thus satisfying the first rule of the mean. The first contribution to the quantum correction arises from $n = 2$ in the expansion. To describe the bending vibrations adequately, however, we need at least $n = 3$. In Table XVI, quantum corrections predicted by expansion formulae are compared with the "exact" quantum correction for the disproportionation among the isotopic water molecules. No entry is made for the Bernoulli series at 300°K. because the series does not exist at this temperature.

Expansions of ln $\frac{s}{s'} f$ for Methane (d_1/d_o) [a]

Cent Error

Chebyshev $(L = 5)$ [b]

$n = 1$	$n = 2$	$n = 3$	$n = 4$
−0.43	6.2	0.60	2.7
2.5	4.6	−0.017	1.11
3.7	3.2	−0.195	0.44
4.2	1.46	−0.136	0.076
3.7	0.70	−0.059	0.016
3.0	0.36	−0.025	0.004
2.4	0.20	−0.011	0.001
0.52	0.007	−0.000	0.000

"Best" Set $(L = 5)$ [b]

$n = 1$	$n = 2$	$n = 3$	$n = 4$
10.1	−5.8	1.74	0.6
9.4	−4.3	0.89	0.23
8.4	−3.1	0.46	0.078
5.5	−1.42	0.088	0.011
4.6	−0.72	0.033	0.001
3.1	−0.36	0.009	0.000
2.5	−0.20	0.004	0.000
0.53	−0.007	0.000	0.000

[b] *See* the footnotes of Table XII.

Table XV.   Intercomparison of Various Jacobi

Per

T (°K.)	Exact $ln \frac{s}{s'}f$	Chebyshev (L $=$ 0)[b]			
		n $=$ 1	n $=$ 2	n $=$ 3	n $=$ 4
200	8.00774	−58.7	−23.9	−9.3	−0.32
300	4.78225	−41.9	−10.2	−3.0	0.56
400	3.22505	−29.5	−4.5	−1.22	0.30
600	1.76422	−15.2	−1.07	−0.29	0.057
800	1.10700	−8.7	−8.7	−0.33	0.089
1000	0.754707	−5.5	−0.33	−0.089	0.012
1200	0.545030	−3.7	−0.054	−0.013	0.001
3000	0.0951957	−0.54	−0.001	−0.000	0.000

T (°K.)		"Best Set" (L $=$0)[b]			
		n $=$ 1	n $=$ 2	n $=$ 3	n $=$ 4
200		3.8	−6.4	−3.4	1.90
300		−1.43	−6.1	−0.29	0.78
400		1.09	−3.8	−0.000	0.26
600		1.67	−1.48	0.003	0.037
800		2.87	−0.55	−0.001	0.007
1000		1.14	−0.34	0.003	0.002
1200		1.15	−0.174	0.001	0.000
3000		0.33	−0.005	0.000	0.000

[a] Both deuterium atoms substituted in α-position. **F**-matrix elements taken from a model of Wolfsberg and Stern ("normal" diagonal and "normal" interaction force

Table XVII shows similar comparisons of the deviations from the first rule of the mean for an ^{18}O-disproportionation between carbon dioxide species. Here, the normal modes have been divided into 2 linear modes and 2 non-linear modes. The approximations for the non-linear modes are much better than those for the linear modes, simply because v'_{max} for the former is only a quarter of v'_{max} for the latter. Calculations (not shown in the Table) made with the Chebyshev ($L = 5$) yielded ln K's of 2.550×10^{-5} and 2.086×10^{-4} for $n = 2$ and 3, respectively, compared with the exact value of 3.546×10^{-4} at 300°K. "Rule of the Mean" tests are especially useful for examining the suitability of a polynomial to a particular molecule, because they permit an examination of the correspondence between individual terms of the expansion and motions of groups of atoms in the molecule.

Evaluation of Isotope Effects Without Solving Secular Equations. Up to now we have discussed the estimation of isotope effects by the expansion method, starting from a knowledge of exact normal frequencies

Expansions of $\ln \frac{s}{s'}f$ for 1-Bromobutane (d_2/d_0)[a]

Cent Error

Chebyshev $(L = 5)$[b]			
n = 1	n = 2	n = 3	n = 4
−7.2	3.3	−0.165	2.7
−2.8	2.9	−0.39	0.99
−0.43	2.1	−0.35	0.37
1.49	1.04	−0.151	0.057
1.74	0.50	−0.056	0.011
1.55	0.26	−0.022	0.003
1.29	0.142	−0.009	0.001
0.30	0.005	−0.000	0.000
"Best" Set $(L = 5)$[b]			
n = 1	n = 2	n = 3	n = 4
2.4	−7.5	−0.53	0.28
2.2	−5.0	−0.46	0.055
2.6	−3.3	−0.27	0.017
2.7	−1.39	−0.078	0.001
2.6	−0.64	−0.020	0.000
1.6	−0.31	−0.009	0.000
1.34	−0.170	−0.003	0.000
0.31	−0.006	−0.000	0.000

[a] constants) (22, 30). Corresponding frequencies, M. J. Stern, personal communication. $\nu'_{max} = 2924.05$ cm.$^{-1}$
[b] See the footnotes of Table XII.

for the isotopic molecules. We will now describe a method for estimating $\ln \frac{s}{s'}f$ which avoids the need to determine individual vibrational frequencies. The procedure starts with the Wilson kinetic energy and potential energy matrices **G** and **F** applies the method of moments on the Jacobi expansions, and estimates ν'_{max} of a system from the row vectors and column vectors of the **FG** matrix.

Given

$$\mathbf{F} \equiv [f_{ij}] \tag{64}$$

and

$$\mathbf{G} \equiv [g_{ij}], \tag{65}$$

a set of normal frequencies can be obtained by solving a secular equation,

$$\mathbf{H} - \lambda\mathbf{I} = 0 \tag{66}$$

where

$$\mathbf{H} \equiv [h_{ij}]$$

$$\equiv \mathbf{FG} = [\underset{k}{\Sigma} f_{ik} g_{kj}] \tag{67}$$

and $\mathbf{I}$ is a unit matrix. The summation of Equation 67 runs over all the degrees of freedom. Eigenvalues λ_i are related to the normal frequencies ν_i by

$$\lambda_i = 4\pi^2 \nu_i^2 \ . \tag{68}$$

Table XVI. Deviation from the First Rule of the Mean of Water:[a]

T $(°K.)$	Exact	Order n	Bigeleisen-Mayer
300	-3.687×10^{-2}	1	4.900×10^{-3}
		2	-4.906×10^{-2}
		3	-3.410×10^{-2}
1200	-5.741×10^{-4}	1	
		2	
		3	

[a] **F**-matrix elements taken from Papousek and Plíva (17).
    Geometry parameters: $r(\text{O–H}) = 0.9572$ A. $<$ HOH $= 104°30'$

Table XVII. Deviations from the First Rule of the Mean for Carbon

T $(°K.)$	Linear Vibrations				Non-linear	
	Exact	Order n	Chebyshev[b]	Bernoulli	Exact	Order n
300	3.327×10^{-4}	1	0		2.185×10^{-5}	1
		2	1.572×10^{-5}			2
		3	1.806×10^{-4}			3
1200	7.651×10^{-7}	1	0	0	1.263×10^{-7}	1
		2	2.806×10^{-7}	3.385×10^{-7}		2
		3	6.620×10^{-7}	7.748×10^{-7}		3

[a] **F**-matrix elements taken from Herzberg (13).
    Geometry parameters: $r(\text{C–O}) = 1.1615$ A.
[b] The Chebyshev $(L = 0)$ approximations by using Equation 47 with u'_{max} corre-

In any expansion of $\ln \frac{s}{s'}f$ in which every term depends only on an even power of u, the frequency-dependent part of the $2n$-th order term can be expressed as

$$\sum_i (u'^{2n}_i - u^{2n}_i) = \left(\frac{\hbar}{kT}\right)^{2n} \left[\sum_i \lambda'^{n}_i - \sum_i \lambda^{n}_i\right]. \tag{69}$$

$$2\ln \frac{s}{s'}f\left(\frac{HDO}{H_2O}\right) - \ln \frac{s}{s'}f\left(\frac{D_2O}{H_2O}\right)$$

Chebyshev (L = 5)[b]	Chebyshev (L = 0)[b]	Bernoulli
0	0	—
-1.286×10^{-2}	-8.994×10^{-3}	—
-2.630×10^{-2}	-2.181×10^{-2}	—
0	0	0
-4.588×10^{-4}	-4.441×10^{-4}	-7.132×10^{-4}
-5.516×10^{-4}	-5.482×10^{-4}	-5.099×10^{-4}

[b] The Jacobi approximations obtained using u'_{max} corresponding to $\nu'_{max} = 3942.78$ cm.$^{-1}$.

$$\text{Dioxide:}^{a} \ln \frac{s}{s'}f\left(\frac{^{12}C^{18}O_2}{^{12}C^{16}O_2}\right) - 2\ln \frac{s}{s'}f\left(\frac{^{12}C^{16}O^{18}O}{^{12}C^{16}O_2}\right)$$

Vibrations		Total Vibrations			
			Order		
Chebyshev[b]	Bernoulli	Exact	n	Chebyshev[b]	Bernoulli
0	0	3.546×10^{-4}	1	0	
2.631×10^{-5}	3.332×10^{-5}		2	2.167×10^{-5}	
2.125×10^{-5}	1.738×10^{-5}		3	1.946×10^{-4}	
0	0	8.914×10^{-7}	1	0	0
1.280×10^{-7}	1.301×10^{-7}		2	3.884×10^{-7}	4.685×10^{-7}
1.263×10^{-7}	1.262×10^{-7}		3	7.869×10^{-7}	9.010×10^{-7}

sponding to
$\nu'_{max} = 2350.53$ cm.$^{-1}$ for linear vibrations and "total",
666.00 cm.$^{-1}$ for non-linear vibrations.

By the theorem of the n-th moment of eigenvalues,

$$\sum_i \lambda_i{}^n = \sum_i (\mathbf{H}^n)_{ii}, \tag{70}$$

that is, the sum over all the degrees of freedom, of the n-th power of eigenvalues of the $\mathbf{H}$-matrix, is the trace, or the sum of all the diagonal elements of the matrix obtained by multiplying the original $\mathbf{H}$-matrix by itself $(n-1)$ times. Thus,

$$(\mathbf{H}^2)_{ii} = \sum_j h_{ij}h_{ji} = \sum_j \sum_k \sum_l f_{ik}g_{kj}f_{jl}g_{li}, \tag{71}$$

$$(\mathbf{H}^3)_{ii} = \sum_j (\mathbf{H}^2)_{ij}h_{ji}$$

$$= \sum_j \sum_p \sum_q \sum_r \sum_s f_{iq}g_{qp}f_{pr}g_{rj}f_{js}g_{si}, \tag{72}$$

and so on. Combining the Jacobi expansions of $\ln \dfrac{s}{s'}f$, Equation 47 or Equation 56, with Equations 69 and 70, $\ln \dfrac{s}{s'}f$ can be expressed explicitly interms of the elements of the $\mathbf{F}$ and $\mathbf{G}$ matrices.

For such an explicit formula to be useful, we must have a means for estimating ν'_{max} without actually solving the secular equation. This could be done from an empirical knowledge of bond-stretching frequencies, but there are short-comings to this approach. The estimated maximum frequency used for evaluating the modulating coefficients must be equal to or greater than the actual ν'_{max}. Underestimation leads to divergence of the $\ln b(u)$-expansions for the frequencies greater than the estimated ν'_{max} and accordingly less accurate approximations of $\ln \dfrac{s}{s'}f$. An excessive over-estimation would again yield poorer approximations, because the errors are generally greater for a larger range of expansion.

It is a mathematical theorem that the eigenvalue of a matrix (Equation 76), with the largest absolute value, is smaller than the largest of $\sum_i |h_{ij}|$ and also smaller than the largest of $\sum_j |h_{ij}|$. We will call such a sum of the absolute values of all elements in a column of the matrix $\mathbf{H}$ a column-sum, and a similar sum over a row will be called a row-sum. Then it follows, that both the largest row-sum and the largest column-sum of the Hamiltonian matrix of the light isotopic molecule $\mathbf{H}'$ will be greater than the exact value of $4\pi^2 \nu'^2_{max}$. We used the smaller of the two quantities, row-sum-max and column-sum-max, as the basis for estimating ν'_{max}. Although such a range does not usually lead to as good an approximation as an exact range would yield, the difference is usually small, especially if the off-diagonal elements of the Hamiltonian matrix are small compared to the diagonal ones. Since these quantities, the row-sums and column-sums, are not invariant under coordinate transformations, the magnitude of over-estimation of the range, depends upon the particular coordinate system in which the equations of motion are written. If these matrices were given for the normal coordinate system the range based on this method would be exactly equal to ν'_{max}. For other coordinate systems it can be generally stated that the accuracy of estimation increases as the coordinate system being employed approaches the normal coordinate system; the accuracy generally increases in the order: Cartesian coordinates, valence coordinates, "symmetrized" coordinates and normal coordinates.

Combining these principles, a computer program *PEEP* (Partition-function Estimation by Expansion in Polynomials) has been written for estimating $\ln \dfrac{s}{s'}f$ and the related thermodynamic quantities. The program has provisions for the use of various L-values and various sets of Jacobi polynomials. It has been used to examine the temperature-dependence of equilibrium constants for exchange of oxygen and nitrogen isotopes, for which "anomalies" have been discussed by Stern, Spindel, and Monse (*16, 18*). Calculations of the equilibrium constants were performed starting with the **F** and **G** matrices supplied by these authors. The L-value of 5 was used throughout, and the results obtained by the "best" set ($L = 5$) and by the Chebyshev polynomials were compared with exact values obtained by using Equation 1 and exact frequencies. The temperature was varied from 200°K. up to 1600°K. The range for the expansions was evaluated for each isotopic pair at every temperature.

Plots of ln K thus obtained as a function of temperature show that generally expansions of order 4 or higher are required to reproduce the "exact" curves over the entire temperature range. In particular, the polynomials presently used do not produce the inflections where they are expected. Also, the approximations are generally less accurate at lower temperatures. Cross-over temperatures obtained from such plots for various equilibria are compared with "exact" values in Table XVIII. The first column shows the exchange equilibrium considered. As expected from the previous discussion of the physical meaning of each term in an even-power expansion, more than three terms are generally necessary for an adequate prediction of these cross-over temperatures. For less "anomalous" equilibria, such as type A (monotonic) and type D (one cross-over and one extremum) (*16, 18*), lower order approximations by these Jacobi polynomials are already adequate over the entire temperature range. Figures 9 and 10 illustrate such cases. Higher order expansions give extremely close agreement for these equilibria. The breaks in dashed curves, particularly in Figure 9, occur at temperatures where the computer program has called for a shift in the γ, δ values to use a new "best" polynomial.

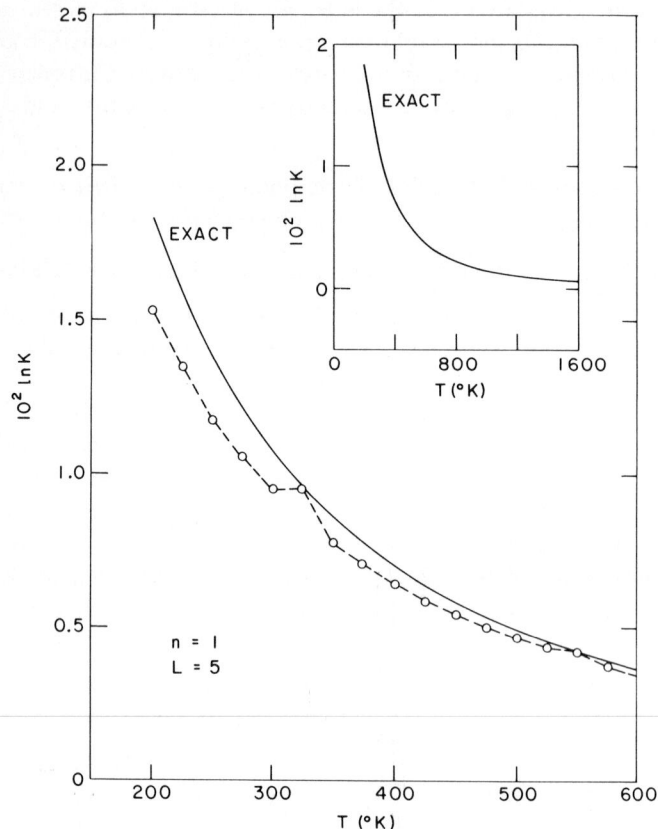

Figure 9.   Approximation of equilibrium constant for the reaction $NO^{18}OCl + NO^{16}OF = NO^{16}OCl + NO^{18}OF$ by "best" Jacobi polynomials ($L = 5$) as a function of temperature

The "row-sum and column-sum" method when applied to these oxynitrogen species, in unsymmetrized internal coordinates (16, 18), overestimates the highest frequencies ν'_{max} as follows: 1.11% for NOBr, 1.01% for NOCl, 0.40% for NO_2, 4.5% for NO_2Cl, 12.4% for NO_3^-, 2.8% for NO_2F, 1.42% for HNO_3, 1.01% for *trans*-HNO_2, 0.70% for *cis*-HNO_2 and 8.2% for $FONO_2$.

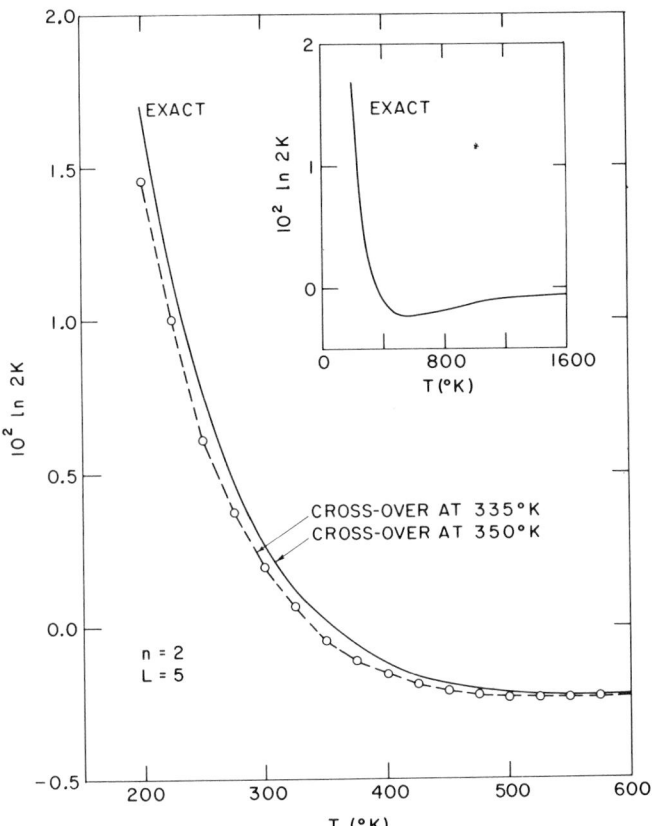

Figure 10.   Approximation of equilibrium constant for the reaction $F^{16}ONO_2 + NO^{18}O = NO^{18}ONO_2 + NO^{16}O$ by "best" Jacobi polynomials ($L = 5$) as a function of temperature

Possible Applications of Jacobi Expansions

It has been shown in the preceding section that, by applying the method of moments and the "row-sum and column-sum" method to the Jacobi expansions of $\ln \frac{s}{s'}f$, the structure and force field of a system can be explicitly related to $\ln \frac{s}{s'}f$ and to its related thermodynamic quantities. This relation can be used in two ways; if the **F** and **G** matrices for a system are known, $\ln \frac{s}{s'}f$ and related thermodynamic quantities can be calculated directly without solving secular equations. Conversely, if a set of data is available for thermodynamic quantities of various isotopic molecules, an effective harmonic force field can be derived through a

Table XVIII. Comparison of Cross-over Temperatures for

Equilibrium	Type[a]	Cross over Exact	n = 2
$F^{18}ONO_2/NO^{18}OCl$	D	210	<200[b]
$F^{18}ONO_2/NO^{18}O$	D	350	335
$F^{18}ONO_2/H^{18}ONO_2$	D	450	605
trans $HON^{18}O/NO_2{}^{18}O^-$	−D	260	365
cis $HON^{18}O/NO_2{}^{18}O^-$	−D	370	505
cis $H^{18}ONO/NO_2{}^{18}O^-$	−D	450	565
trans $H^{18}ONO/NO_2{}^{18}O^-$	−D	900	850
cis $HON^{18}O/$ cis $H^{18}ONO$	E	700	830
$^{15}NO_2F/^{15}NO_3{}^-$	−E	300	460
trans $HON^{18}O/N^{18}OBr$	−F	250[d]	310
cis $H^{18}ONO/NO^{18}O$	−F	550[d]	775
$H^{18}ONO_2/NO^{18}O$	F	650[d]	850
cis $HON^{18}O/H^{18}ONO_2$	−F	800[d]	900

[a] Type classification of "anomaly" as described in Stern, Spindel, and Monse (16, 18).
[b] No cross-over found above 200°K., but the curve heads toward abscissa with decreasing temperature near 200°K.

non-linear least squares process, for those coordinates which involve motion of the isotopically substituted atom.

In the first application, isotope effects on thermodynamic quantities can be predicted as accurately as required by using a sufficiently high order of expansion. Once a certain order of expansion is found to be satisfactory at one temperature, it will generally give even better approximations at higher temperatures. This is in contrast to the $\bar{\gamma}$-method and to its higher order modifications. These methods are based on the $G(u)$-expansion of Bigeleisen and Mayer, Equation 3, and proceed to rearrange every term into a formal function of $\delta u_i{}^{2m}$. The coefficient of every $\delta u_i{}^{2m}$ is then assumed independent, or nearly independent of u, thus arriving at an expansion of $\ln \frac{s}{s'}f$ in terms of $\Sigma \ \delta u_i{}^{2m}$. The coefficient of $\delta u_i{}^2$ obtained from the first order term of the $G(u)$-approximation is γ, as defined by Equation 19. It is related to the first coefficient of Jacobi $(L = 0)$ expansion, $T(1,1,u)$ by

$$\gamma \equiv \frac{12 \ G(u)}{u} = \frac{\partial \ln b(u)}{\partial (u^2/24)} \simeq T(1,1,u). \tag{73}$$

The coefficients $T(n,1,u)$ for the Chebyshev polynomials are shown in Figure 11, and a plot of $\gamma(u)$ is included for comparison with $T(1,1,u)$. Because $\gamma(u)$ and the similar coefficients of higher order terms are not

Exchange Equilibria of Oxygen and Nitrogen Isotopes

Temperatures (°K.)

"Best" Set (L = 5)		Chebyshev (L = 5)		
n = 3	n = 4	n = 2	n = 3	n = 4
220	240	<200[b]	270	250
340	350	355	370	350
475	480	555	460	450
275	260	295	<200[b]	<200[b]
390	370	400	230	320
450	465	615	425	440
900	900	875	900	900
690	710	830	720	705
[c]	310	445	[c]	[c]
[c]	295	420	420	350
550	560	700	520	550
665	660	785	650	650
800	800	900	810	800

[c] No cross-over found above 200°K., and the curve heads away from abscissa with decreasing temperature near 200°K.
[d] The higher of two cross-over temperatures of Type F shown. The lower cross-over occurs below 200°K.

completely independent of u, an average γ must be carefully evaluated for every isotopic pair in every, relatively narrow, range of temperature. An average frequency $\bar{\nu}$, corresponding to such a $\bar{\gamma}$, can be used for a small temperature-extrapolation outside the range in which $\bar{\nu}$ was evaluated. In contrast, in the Jacobi expansion one needs to set only the lower limit of temperature. The $\bar{\gamma}$-approximation becomes poor when one tries to evaluate a single $\bar{\gamma}$ for a system involving more than one chemical species (*16, 18*). One finds a similar situation in Jacobi expansions; use of an excessively large range for a Jacobi expansion generally yields poor approximations. Therefore, use of a single molecular constant for a system involving more than one chemical species (such as the largest ν'_{max} of one species) in the Jacobi expansions leads to large errors contributed from molecules whose ν'_{max} are smaller than the ν'_{max} actually used. Furthermore, the fact that a Jacobi polynomial which is "best" in one range may be very poor in other ranges also leads to the same general conclusion.

In the converse application of the explicit relation between **F** and **G** matrices and thermodynamic quantities, a set of effective harmonic force constants covering a certain range of temperature is derived from experimental data on a strongly temperature-dependent property obtained in the same temperature range. The least-squares process becomes non-linear when more than two terms are used in expanding $\ln \dfrac{s}{s'} f$. The choice of Jacobi polynomials depends on the particular problem at hand. If one is concerned with physical insight into an isotope effect, the expansion should be carried out using the minimum number of terms. That is, a set of polynomials which make the expansion for the system converge as rapidly as possible should be chosen. On the other hand, if the expansion is being used to evaluate thermodynamic quantities numerically, the limitation on the number of terms carried in the expansion is not as critical. For efficiency of computation, one would still like to have reasonably rapid convergence, and as has been demonstrated in the previous sections, this can be achieved by use of a single Jacobi polynomial, such as the shifted Chebyshev of the first kind, for the entire range of u-values.

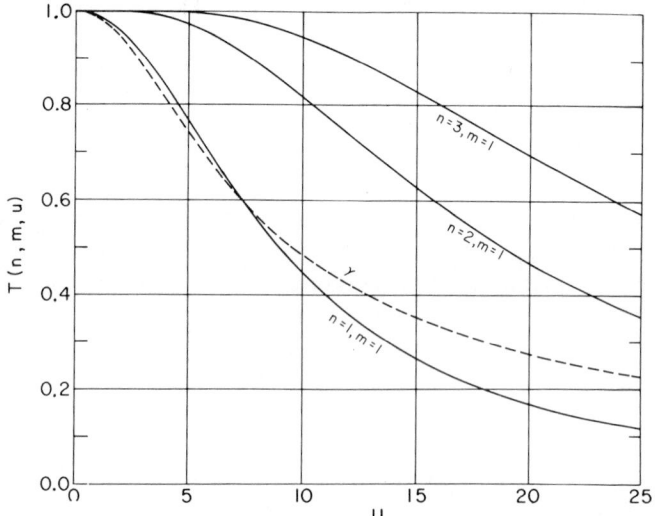

Figure 11.   Plot of γ, 12 G(u)/u, and first Chebyshev coefficients (T(n,1,u)) as a function of u

For a thermodynamic quantity such as heat capacity, which depends upon a derivative of the partition function, rather than on the partition function itself, expanding the exact form of the derivative in Jacobi polynomials, will be more convenient and yield closer approximations, than differentiating the expanded form of the function itself.

Within the framework of the Born-Oppenheimer assumption, studies of isotope effects provide augmental information to a knowledge of force fields. Such information is especially valuable for the condensed states (5), where spectroscopic methods fail to provide accurate information.

The methods described in the present paper also appear to provide a powerful tool in this field of study.

Acknowledgment

We wish to thank the NASA Institute for Space Studies for making the necessary computer facilities and time available to us.

Literature Cited

(1) Bigeleisen, J., *J. Chem. Phys.* **21**, 1333 (1953).
(2) *Ibid.*, **23**, 2264 (1955).
(3) *Ibid.*, **28**, 694 (1958).
(4) Bigeleisen, J., "Proceedings of the Amsterdam Symposium on Isotope Separation," p. 121, North-Holland Publishing Company, Inc., Amsterdam, 1958.
(5) Bigeleisen, J., *J. Chim. Phys.* **61**, 87 (1964).
(6) Bigeleisen, J., Goldstein, P., *Z. fur. Naturforsch.* **18a**, 205 (1963).
(7) Bigeleisen, J., Ishida, T., *J. Chem. Phys.* **48**, 1311 (1968).
(8) Bigeleisen, J., Mayer, M. G., *J. Chem. Phys.* **15**, 261 (1947).
(9) Bigeleisen, J., Wolfsberg, M., "Advances in Chemical Physics," p. 15, I. Prigogine, Ed., Interscience Publishers, Inc., New York, 1958.
(10) Crawford, B. L., Jr., Miller, F. A., *J. Chem. Phys.* **17**, 249, (1949).
(11) Friedman, L., Shiner, V. J., Jr., *J. Chem. Phys.* **44**, 4639 (1966).
(12) Gallaway, W. S., Barker, E. F., *J. Chem. Phys.* **10**, 88 (1942).
(13) Herzberg G., "Molecular Spectra and Molecular Structure II. Infrared and Raman Spectra of Polyatomic Molecules," D. Van Nostrand Company, Inc., Princeton, New Jersey, 1945.
(14) Jones, L. H., McDowell, R. S., *J. Mol. Spectr.* **3**, 632 (1959).
(15) Lanczos, C., "Applied Analysis," Prentice Hall, Inc., Englewood Cliffs, New Jersey, 1956.
(16) Monse, E. U., Spindel, W., Stern, M. J., ADVAN. CHEM. SER. **89**, 148 (1969).
(17) Papousek, D., Plíva, J., *Coll. Czechoslovak Chem. Commun.* **29**, 1973 (1964).
(18) Stern, M. J., Spindel, W., Monse, E. U., *J. Chem. Phys.* **48**, 2908 (1968).
(19) Stern, M. J., Van Hook, W. A., Wolfsberg, M., *J. Chem. Phys.* **39**, 3179 (1963).
(20) Stern, M. J., Wolfsberg, M., *J. Chem. Phys.* **39**, 2776 (1963).
(21) Stern, M. J., Wolfsberg, M., *J. Pharm. Sci.* **54**, 849 (1965).
(22) Stern, M. J., Wolfsberg, M., *J. Chem. Phys.* **45**, 2618 (1966).
(23) *Ibid.*, **45**, 4105 (1966).
(24) Urey, H. C., *J. Chem. Soc.* **1947**, 562.
(25) Vojta, G., *Z. Physik. Chem.* **217**, 337 (1961).
(26) *Ibid.*, **230**, 106 (1965).
(27) Waldmann, L., *Naturwiss.* **31**, 205 (1943).
(28) Wilson, E. B., Decius, J. C., Cross, P. C., "Molecular Vibrations," McGraw-Hill Book Company, Inc., New York, 1955.
(29) Wolfsberg, M., Star, M. J., *Pure Appl. Chem.* **8**, 225 (1964).
(30) *Ibid.*, **8**, 325 (1964).

RECEIVED March 11, 1968. Research carried out under the auspices of the U. S. Atomic Energy Commission.

12

Electromigration in Metals, Salts, and Aqueous Solutions

A. KLEMM and K. HEINZINGER

Max Planck-Institut für Chemie (Otto Hahn-Institut), Mainz, Germany

The progress achieved in the field of isotope electromigra-
tion in metals, salts, and aqueous solutions since the meeting
on isotope separation in Paris in 1963 is reported. It is
shown that the temperature dependence of the isotope effect
in liquid metals leads to the conclusion that it is a result
of classical atom–atom interactions. Isotope effects in
molten salts are smaller than in classical ionic gases. A
three stage model is proposed for an explanation of the
temperature dependences of the isotope effects in molten
salts. The available data of the relative difference in mobili-
ties of isotopes in aqueous solutions are summarized.

The purpose of this article is to report on the progress achieved in the field of isotope electromigration since the 12th annual reunion of the Société de Chimie Physique in Paris in 1963 (*21*). We shall restrict ourselves to the isotope effects themselves and shall not discuss experimental techniques, multiplication of the elementary effects, and technical applications. Earlier work will only be cited occasionally. (*See* References 21, 24, and 49.)

Metals

Isotope electromigration in pure liquid metals ("Haeffner-effect") has been observed up to now in Li (*50*), K (*44*), Rb (*60*), Zn (*43*), Cd (*43*), Ga (*47*), In (*44*), Sn (*43*), and Hg (*5, 15*). Invariably the migration of the lighter isotopes relative to the heavier ones is towards the anode, and the effect increases with rising temperature.

A measure of the effect is the mass effect of electromigration

$$\mu = \frac{N_{12}}{x_1 N_{+-}} \bigg/ \frac{m_1 - m_2}{\frac{1}{2}(m_1 + m_2)}.$$

248

In this expression m_1 and m_2 are the masses of two isotopes 1 and 2, x_1 is the number of isotopes of kind 1 divided by the number of all isotopes present and N_{12} is the number of isotopes 1 transported through a unit cross section attached to isotope 2, if $N_{-+} = -N_{+-}$ electrons ($-$) are transported through a unit cross section attached to the atomic nuclei ($+$). μ has the advantage of being dimensionless and independent of the two isotopes 1 and 2 chosen from a multicomponent isotope mixture—e.g., tin. Typical values of μ are given in Table I.

Table I.

	m.p. °C.	Temp. °C.	$\mu \cdot 10^5$	Ref.
K	63.7	81	1.1	44
		227	3.7	
Rb	39.0	76	2.3	60
		390	9.6	
Ga	29.9	29.9	1.68	47
		300	5.94	
In	156.4	190	1.35	44
		580	8.4	

For Rb and Ga at low temperatures the apparent activation energy $E_\mu = \partial(\ln \mu)/\partial(1/RT)$ agrees with that of self-diffusion (E_D). E_D is approximately 2 kcal./mole for Rb. At higher temperatures $E_\mu > E_D$ (*47, 60*).

Phenomenologically the mass effect of electromigration can be written, in a linear approximation in relative isotopic differences, as (*25*)

$$\mu = \frac{DF^2 c}{RT\kappa} \; z \left(\frac{\Delta z}{z} - \frac{\Delta r_{+-}}{r_{+-}} \right) \frac{m}{\Delta m}$$

where D = self diffusion coefficient, κ = specific electric conductance, F = Faraday's constant, c = molar concentration, z = number of electrons, contributed by an atom to the conduction electrons, r_{+-} = friction coefficient, describing the friction between the conduction electrons and the atoms, m = atomic mass; Δz, Δr_{+-} and Δm are isotopic differences.

From measurements of μ, D, c, T, and κ it follows that $z \left(\frac{\Delta z}{z} - \frac{\Delta r_{+-}}{r_{+-}} \right) \frac{m}{\Delta m}$ is of the order of 10^{-2} to 10^{-1}. Compared with this order of magnitude the term $\Delta z \cdot m/\Delta m$ is negligible, because z for a given atom is a function of its ionization energy which in turn is a function of the reduced mass $m_{red} = m_- m/(m_- + m)$, where m = electronic mass, and because therefore $\Delta z \cdot m/\Delta m$ is of the order $z m_-/m$.

Theory thus has to explain why $-z \dfrac{\Delta r_{+-}}{r_{+-}} \dfrac{m}{\Delta m}$ is of the order of 10^{-2} to 10^{-1}. In a classical theory of electron-atom collisions the reduced mass m_{red} again enters into the calculations and the theoretical isotope effect becomes orders of magnitude smaller than the experimental one. But $\dfrac{\Delta r_{+-}}{r_{+-}} \dfrac{m}{\Delta m}$ could be a quantum isotope effect, having its origin in electron-atom interactions (11) or in atom-atom interactions. If this were the case, it should be proportional to T^{-2} in the high temperature range. In this context it is interesting to look at the temperature dependence of $\dfrac{RT\kappa}{F^2 c} \cdot \dfrac{\mu}{D} = -z \dfrac{\Delta r_{+-}}{r_{+-}} \dfrac{m}{\Delta m}$. From data in the literature one finds that the temperature coefficient of $T\kappa/c$ is small $\left(\left| d \ln \dfrac{T\kappa}{c} \middle/ d \ln T \right| \lesssim \dfrac{1}{3} \right)$. Also, as stated above, for Rb and Ga the temperature coefficient of μ/D is zero at low and positive at high temperatures. Thus, $\dfrac{\Delta r_{+-}}{r_{+-}} \dfrac{m}{\Delta m}$ could only be a quantum isotope effect, if z were proportional to about T^2. Such a strong increase of z with temperature is quite unlikely, and one is led to the conclusion that $\dfrac{\Delta r_{+-}}{r_{+-}} \dfrac{m}{\Delta m}$ is not essentially a quantum isotope effect. Since it is also no classical isotope effect in electron-atom interactions, it must be chiefly a classical isotope effect in atom-atom interactions.

To specify this idea it has been suggested (25) that in liquid metals there exists an electromigration of the more disordered atoms relative to the less disordered atoms towards the anode (electro-self-transport), and that this transport is faster the smaller the mass of the more disordered atoms, because light atoms in an atomic surrounding are generally more mobile than heavy ones.

Electro-self-transport is a well known property of solid metals. In a solid the "less disordered" atoms form a lattice that can be marked—e.g., by a scratch on the surface of the material. If direct current passes the metal, material is transported relative to the mark and can be measured. In most solid metals (Li (48), Na (65), U (10), Ti (69), Zr (69), Ni (16), Cu (64), Ag (17), Au (46), Zn (46), Cd (46), Al (46), In (46), Sn (46), and Pb (46)) self-transport is directed towards the anode. Only W (59), Pt (46), Fe (46), and Co (18) show self-transport towards the cathode.

The nine liquid metals known for their isotope electro-transport chemically belong to the group of metals that show self-transport towards the anode in the solid state, and it is quite probable that in these metals a kind of self-transport towards the anode also happens in the liquid state.

The self-transport number of solid metals is defined as

$$t_{+1} = N_{+1}/N_{+-}$$

where N_{+1} is the number of atomic nuclei ($+$) transported through a unit cross section attached to the lattice (1), if $N_{-+} = -N_{+-}$ electrons ($-$) are transported through a unit cross section attached to the atomic nuclei. By definition $t_{+1} + t_{-1} = 1$, where $t_{-1} (=N_{-1}/N_{-+})$ is the transport number of the electrons with respect to the lattice.

Typical values of t_{+1} in solid metals are given in Table II.

Table II.

	m.p. (°C.)	Temp. (°C.)	$-t_{+1} \cdot 10^9$	Reference
Zn	419.5	350	26.6	46
In	156.4	113	2.76	46
		135	8.90	
Sn	231.9	181	3.4	46
		206	5.6	

The magnitude of the self-transport numbers t_{+1} of liquid metals necessary to explain the observed mass-effects can be estimated by writing

$$\mu = t_{+1} \frac{N_{12}}{x_1 N_{+1}} \bigg/ \frac{m_1 - m_2}{\frac{1}{2}(m_1 + m_2)}$$

and estimating the factor to the right of t_{+i} to be -10^{-1}. For liquid mercury ($\mu \approx 10^{-5}$) this yields $t_{+1} \approx -10^{-4}$. The self-mobility

$$u_{+1} = t_{+1}\kappa/cF$$

of liquid mercury ($\kappa = 10^4\ \Omega^{-1}$ cm.$^{-1}$, $c = 0.067$ moles/cm.^{3}) would then be $u_{+1} \approx -1.5 \cdot 10^{-4}$ cm.^{2}/V sec.

If the *quasi*-lattice of current carrying liquid metals would remain stationary with respect to solid walls contacting the liquid, it would be possible to observe self-transport in liquid metals by studying electro-osmosis of the liquid in capillaries (26, 31) or electrophoresis of small particles suspended in the liquid (36). But the *quasi*-lattice of liquid is itself electro-transported with respect to solid walls, because near walls the forces acting on the *quasi*-lattice, electron friction and electrostatic force, are unbalanced, the electron drift being attenuated owing to inelastic electron scattering at the wall. For example, for liquid mercury at 30°C., the external mobility was found to be $2.5 \cdot 10^{-3}$ cm.^{2}/V sec. (26, 31) as compared with the self-mobility $-1.5 \cdot 10^{-4}$ cm.^{2}/V sec. as estimated from the observed mass effect $\mu \approx 10^{-5}$ of electromigration in mercury. (The external mobility is the velocity of the liquid relative to the wall in a distance from the wall where the velocity becomes uniform, divided by the electric field.) Direct observation of self-transport in liquid metals by studying external electro–transport is thus impossible.

It would be interesting if in a solid metal both the electro–self-transport and the electro–isotope-transport could be measured. Lodding has tried to do this by subjecting In at 137°C. to a direct current of 5000 amps./cm.² for about eight months. He preliminarily reported a self-transport and a transport of the light isotope towards the cathode (45); meanwhile in more elaborate measurements he found the reverse direction for the self-transport in solid indium (46). It remains a question in which direction the isotope migration in solid indium goes, because the isotope effect reported in Reference 45 was at the limit of measurability.

Salts

The low price of separated lithium isotopes ($23 per gram of 99% ^{6}Li; $1 per gram of 99.99% ^{7}Li) permits the study of the transport properties of lithium and its compounds at varying isotopic compositions. The electrical conductances of pure liquid ^{6}LiCl, ^{7}LiCl, ^{6}LiNO$_3$, and ^{7}LiNO$_3$ (42), and of pure solid and liquid ^{6}Li$_2$SO$_4$ and ^{7}Li$_2$SO$_4$ (37) have been measured. The change of the molar volumes of these salts with isotopic composition can be neglected, thus the conductances measured are proportional to the eigen-mobilities u^o_6 and u^o_7 of the isotopes (the attribute "eigen" and the superscript o are adjoined to indicate the presence of only one isotope in the substance.)

The eigen-mass-effects of lithium electromigration, defined by

$$\mu^o{}_{Li} = \frac{(u^o{}_6 - u^o{}_7)}{(u^o{}_{6-} + u^o{}_{7-})} \cdot \frac{(m_6 + m_7)}{(m_6 - m_7)}$$

($u^o{}_{6.7}$ = eigen-mobility of $^{6.7}$Li with respect to the anions, $m_{6.7}$ = mass of $^{6.7}$Li) can be seen in Table III.

Table III.

Substance	Temp. t(°C.)	$\mu^o{}_{Li}$	Ref.
Molten LiCl	620–780	$0{,}335 + 1.38 \cdot 10^{-4}(t - 610)$	22, 42
Solid Li$_2$SO$_4$	575–860	0.28	37
Molten Li$_2$SO$_4$	860–930	0.28	37
Molten LiNO$_3$	280–440	$0{,}167 + 1.63 \cdot 10^{-4}(t - 254)$	22

It is interesting to compare these results with the mobilities of isotopes in classical ionic gases. These can be calculated as follows.

We start with the equations of linear irreversible thermodynamics (27)

$$- \operatorname{grad} \mu_i - e_i \operatorname{grad} \phi = \sum_k^N \gamma_k r_{ik} v_{ik}; \quad r_{ik} = r_{ki}; \quad i, k = 1, \ldots, N$$

These equations imply that in a system of N components i with molar fractions γ_i and friction coefficients r_{ik} a set of relative velocities $v_{ik} = v_i - v_k$ will establish itself in the stationary state, if on a mole of component i the chemical force $- \operatorname{grad} \mu_i$ and the electrical force $- e_i$ grad ϕ is exerted, where μ_i and ϕ are the chemical and electrical potentials, respectively and e_i is the charge per mole. It is typical that the friction coefficients make no distinction between the chemical and electrical force. Therefore, for our model calculation of r_{ik}, we shall choose a situation where grad $\phi = 0$, in order to get rid of accelerations caused by the external electrical force.

Let us now look at a gas so dilute that only two-body collisions must be considered and the distribution of free particles in space is absolutely random, not withstanding their different electrical charges (22). Then evidently the r_{ik} are positive, proportional to the overall particle concentration, and independent of the molar fractions, and each r_{ik} only depends on its corresponding type of collision ik.

We consider spherically symmetric particles of masses m_i and m_k with an interaction potential ϕ_{ik} depending on the particle distance d_{ik} and obeying classical mechanics. Then the collisions ik are governed by the equation of motion

$$\frac{\partial^2}{\partial t^2} d_{ik} = - \left(\frac{1}{m_i} + \frac{1}{m_k} \right) \operatorname{grad} \phi \, (d_{ik})$$

The dependence of r_{ik} on mass may now be obtained from a dimensional analysis. The friction coefficient r_{ik} depends on two parameters defining the state of the system, say kT and the overall particle concentration c, and on the parameters of the cited equation of relative motion. These parameters are the reduced mass $m_{ik} = m_i m_k / (m_i + m_k)$ and a set of ϕ-values corresponding to a set of d_{ik}-values. Planck's constant h does not enter into our classical calculation. The dimensions of the quantities involved are given in Table IV.

Table IV.

r_{ik}	kT	c	m_{ik}	$\phi(d_{ik})$	d_{ik}
$\dfrac{\text{gram}}{\text{sec.}}$	$\dfrac{\text{gram cm.}^2}{\text{sec.}^2}$	$\dfrac{1}{\text{cm.}^3}$	gram	$\dfrac{\text{gram cm.}^2}{\text{sec.}^2}$	cm.

From Table IV, it is seen that no dimensionless combination of parameters including m_{ik} is possible and that any combination of parameters with the dimension gram/sec. involves m_{ik} in the form of the factor $(m_{ik})^{1/2}$. Therefore

$$r_{ik} \sim \left(\frac{m_i m_k}{m_i + m_k} \right)^{1/2}$$

This dependence of r_{ik} on mass must also hold, if instead of a chemical force (concentration gradient) an electrical force is the cause of the transport.

Also, since r_{ik} is independent of the molar fractions, all components of the system save i and k may be removed without changing r_{ik}. If then the components i and k are renamed $+$ and $-$, one finds for the eigen mobility $u^o{}_{+-}$ of the cations with respect to the anions

$$u^o{}_{+-} = (v^o{}_{+-}/-\text{grad } \phi)_{\text{grad } \mu_{+,-} = 0} = e_+/\gamma_- r^o{}_{+-} = A \left(\frac{m_+ m_-}{m_+ + m_-} \right)^{-1/2}$$

where the factor A is independent of the masses. Thus

$$\mu^o{}_+ \equiv \frac{\Delta u^o{}_+}{u^o{}_{+-}} \cdot \frac{m_+}{\Delta m_+} \approx \frac{\partial \ln u^o{}_{+-}}{\partial \ln m_+} = -\frac{1}{2} \frac{m_-}{m_+ + m_-}$$

If, besides the ions, a much greater number of neutral molecules (s) of mass m_s is also present in the gas, the same reasoning as above yields

$$\frac{\partial \ln u_{+s}}{\partial \ln m_+} = -\frac{1}{2} \frac{m_s}{m_+ + m_s}.$$

This formula is consistent with the result obtained by Langevin (40) for the model of smooth hard spheres. It is not consistent with calculations made on the same model in 1919 by Lenard and in 1924 by Lindemann; cf., Reference 57.

If we put the masses of LiCl ($m_+ = 6.5$, $m_- = 35.5$) into the formula for the pure ion gas, we get $\mu^o{}_{\text{Li}} = -0.42$, a value that is only by 20% larger than the experimental value for molten LiCl, $\mu^o{}_{\text{Li}} = -0.34$. Also the temperature independence of $\mu^o{}_+$ in the gas corresponds to the low temperature dependence found in the condensates. Thus, many of the big differences between gases and condensates in structure and transport mechanisms seem to cancel out when relative differences of the eigen mobilities of isotopes are considered.

It is also interesting to compare the eigen mobilities of ^{6}Li and ^{7}Li with the mobilities u_6 and u_7 in mixtures of the lithium isotopes. For liquid LiCl (23, 42) and solid Li$_2$SO$_4$ (51) the difference $u^o{}_6 - u^o{}_7$ is found to be about twice the difference $u_6 - u_7$ in the natural isotopic mixture.

This indicates a cooperative motion of the lithium ions. If the concept is adopted that a lithium ion always moves as a member of a group of n lithium ions, and that the momentary mobility of an ion is the mean of the eigen mobilities of the momentary members of the group it belongs to, the mean isotopic lithium mobilities in a mixture will be

$$u_6 = [u^{\circ}_6 + (n-1)u^{\circ}_{Li}]/n$$
$$u_7 = [u^{\circ}_7 + (n-1)u^{\circ}_{Li}]/n,$$

where $u^{\circ}_{Li} = (\gamma_6 u^{\circ}_6 + \gamma_7 u^{\circ}_7)/(\gamma_6 + \gamma_7)$. Subtraction of these equations yields

$$u^{\circ}_6 - u^{\circ}_7 = n(u_6 - u_7).$$

The findings about the isotope effects thus indicate that in liquid LiCl and solid Li_2SO_4 the groups of lithium ions moving together comprise about two members. The model just described involves that u_6 and u_7 depend linearly on the molar fraction say of ^6Li, a fact that has not yet been checked experimentally.

From the experimental temperature dependence of $(u^{\circ}_6 - u^{\circ}_7)/(u_6 - u_7)$ the dependence of n on temperature may be obtained (*see* Table V).

Table V.

	600	700	800	900°C.	Ref.
n (liquid LiCl)	—	2.37	1.96	1.66	23, 42
n (solid Li_2SO_4)	2.00	2.06	2.12	—	37, 51

As is seen, when the temperature rises, a considerable decoupling of the Li ions in liquid LiCl seems to take place. Decoupling of the cations is likely to help cationic self-diffusion more than cationic conductance, because in self-diffusion cations must interchange positions while in conductance they may move in parallel. In fact, corresponding to the temperature dependence of n in molten LiCl, an increase of $D_+/T\Lambda$ (D_+ = self-diffusion coefficient of the cations, Λ = equivalent conductance) with absolute temperature T has been observed for all molten alkali halides checked (30). (Also work is in progress at Mainz to check LiCl.)

On the other hand the behavior of $D_+/T\Lambda$ in solid Li_2SO_4 corresponds to the increase of n with temperature deduced from the isotope effects in that medium.

Table VI.

	600	700	800°C.	Ref.
$F^2D_+/RT\Lambda$ (solid Li_2SO_4)	0.91	0.77	0.71	38

The temperature dependence of internal mass effects, $\mu = \dfrac{\Delta u}{u} \dfrac{m}{\Delta m}$

(u = mobility of an ion relative to the ions of opposite charge, m = mass, Δ = difference for two isotopes in the isotopic mixture under consideration) has been studied for five pure molten halides. The results, as well as temperature dependences of $D_+/T\Lambda$, are summarized in Table VII.

Table VII.

	$\dfrac{\partial \ln \mu_+}{\partial \ln T}$	$\dfrac{\partial \ln(D_+/T\Lambda)}{\partial \ln T}$	$\dfrac{\partial \ln \mu_-}{\partial \ln T}$	$\dfrac{\partial \ln(D_-/T\Lambda)}{\partial \ln T}$	Ref.
LiCl 750°C.	1.80	—	—	—	23
KCl 850°C.	1.40	0.30	−0.11	0.20	cf. 22
RbCl 825°C.	1.22	0.55	1.37	0.23	cf. 22
RbBr 800°C.	0.32	—	0.11	—	cf. 22
TlCl 500°C.	−0.79	−0.67	−1.31	−0.60	cf. 22
Li$_2$SO$_4$ 700°C. (solid)	−0.3 ± 0.6	−1.20	—	—	38, 51

Although for some measurements the errors are very high or not given in the publications, there seems to be a correlation between the temperature dependences of μ and $D/T\Lambda$. Both dependences agree in sign (with one exception) and the dependence of μ is generally more pronounced than that of $D/T\Lambda$.

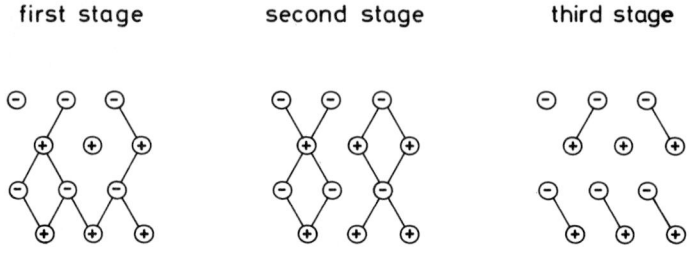

first stage   second stage   third stage

increasing temperature ⟶

Figure 1. Stages of a salt

For an explanation of these facts three stages of an ionic melt, corresponding to three successively more elevated temperatures, may be visualized as shown in Figure 1. In the first stage, a *quasi* crystalline structure is dominating. There is a lattice with a few free ions in between. In the second stage the lattice is broken down into polyionic groups of different electric charge. The third stage is characterized by many neutral ion pairs and a few free ions. Because of the coupling in the second stage of like ions to form rather large mobile charged groups, this stage is less favorable for a big $D_{\pm}/T\Lambda$ and $\mu_{\pm}$ than the first and the third stage, where the mobile charged groups are small. Comparing this scheme with Table VII, one would say that molten TlCl and solid Li_2SO_4 are in a state somewhere between the first and the second stage and the molten alkali halides are in a state between the second and the third stage.

In many salts the transition from the first to the third stage will not be continuous. Thus, on melting the alkali halides seem to shift directly from the first stage to a state between the second and the third stage, and in TlCl the boiling point will possibly be reached before the second stage is passed.

Temperature dependences of internal mass effects and $D_+/T\Lambda$ for two pure molten nitrates are given in Table VIII.

Table VIII.

	$\dfrac{\partial \ln \mu_+}{\partial \ln T}$	$\dfrac{\partial \ln(D_+/T\Lambda)}{\partial \ln T}$	*Ref.*
$LiNO_3$ 300°C.	−0.31	0.49	13, 61
KNO_3 380°C.	2.76	0.34	13, 53

For KNO_3 the same correlation is observed as for the halides (Table VII). In the case of $LiNO_3$ the correlation is violated. This may be owing to quantum effects involved in the magnitude of μ_+ of $LiNO_3$, that is nonclassical isotope exchange equilibria between chemically differing states of lithium in the melt. The low temperature (300°C.) and the low mass of lithium make noticeable quantum effects in $LiNO_3$ more probable than in the other salts mentioned, and quantum effects generally disappear with rising temperature, thus contributing to the negativeness of $\partial \ln \mu / \partial \ln T$.

A decrease with rising temperature has also been observed for the relative differences of the external mobilities (250°–350°C.) of the lithium isotopes in eutectic $NaNO_3$–KNO_3 mixtures (2). On the other hand the relative differences of the external mobilities of the sodium isotopes [22]Na and [24]Na in $LiNO_3$ (305°–359°C.) and in eutectic $NaNO_3$–KNO_3 mixtures (255°–374°C.) rise with rising temperature (in the latter case the increase is followed by a decrease in the range 374°–434°C.) (70).

Table IX is a collection of new data on mass effects of mobilities in salts. (*See* Reference 29 for earlier data.) In Table IX it can be seen that for the series of the chlorides and the nitrates of the alkali metals the internal mass effect μ_+ decreases with increasing mass of the cation. This kind of behavior has been observed in many earlier examples and is qualitatively consistent with almost any model of ion transport including even the ionic gas model mentioned earlier in this article.

Table IX.

System	m.p. °C.	Temp. °C.	Internal $-\mu_+$	$-\mu_-$	Ref.
LiCl	610	610	0.111	—	23
		900	0.087	—	
KCl	770	770	0.0664	0.0623	22
		900	0.0780	0.0615	
RbCl	722	722	0.0464	0.0994	22
		900	0.0566	0.1246	
RbBr	692	692	0.0709	0.1137	22
		900	0.0742	0.1162	
CaJ_2		880	0.0745	—	62
$CdBr_2$		617	0.075	—	19
CdJ_2		580	0.0764	—	62
PbJ_2		600	0.0731	—	62
$LiNO_3$	261	261	0.077	—	61
		450	0.067	—	61
		292	0.089	—	53
$NaNO_3$	308	360	0.045	—	63
KNO_3	333	380	0.041	—	61
		360	0.037	—	53
with some KNO_2		480	0.057	—	53
$RbNO_3$	316	360	0.031	—	61
		350	0.035	—	53
$CsNO_3$	414	450	0.024	—	61
Li_2SO_4	850	600	0.139	—	51
(solid)		790	0.131	—	

Small Quantities of $^{22,24}NaNO_3$ in		External on Asbestos $-\mu_{Na}$	Ref.
$LiNO_3$	305	0.046	70
	355	0.067	
$NaNO_3$	358	0.080	70
KNO_3	358	0.101	70
$CsNO_3$	435	0.065	70
75 gram $NaNO_3$ + 25 gram KNO_3	355	0.082	70
25 gram $NaNO_3$ + 75 gram KNO_3	355	0.092	
45 gram $NaNO_3$ + 55 gram KNO_3	250	0.060	70
	300	0.069	
	370	0.104	
	430	0.083	

The external mass effects deal with mobilities with respect to the container of the salt. They are related to the internal mass effects by external transport numbers $t_\pm$

$$\mu_\pm = t_\pm \, \mu_\pm \text{ (external)}$$

Table IX contains the internal (-0.045) and external (-0.080) mass effects of Na in $NaNO_3$ at 360°C. The external transport number in this case is reported to be $t_+ = 0.7$ (*12*). Evidently these experimental data are not quite consistent.

Aqueous Solutions

In the last few years isotope separation in aqueous solutions by counter-current electromigration has found renewed interest. The reason for this renaissance is the hope that isotope effects in dissociation equilibria might substantially increase the effective relative difference in mobilities and make aqueous solutions a medium for a successful separation of isotopes. In this review we have summarized the available relevant data.

Three different separation tubes have been employed for the counter-current electrolyses in aqueous solutions. They are the diaphragm filled tube, the capillary tube, and the trough. These methods have been steadily improved. The latest stages of development for the diaphragm filled tube are given by Martin and Lübke (*57*) and by Konstantinov and Fiks (*32*), for the capillary tube by Wagener and Bilal (*67*), and for the trough method by Thiemann and Wagener (*66*).

In Figures 2, 3, and 4, the results of the various measurements of the relative difference in mobilities of isotopes in aqueous solutions have been summarized. $\Delta u/u$ always means the effective relative difference in mobilities with respect to water. It includes possible contributions of isotope effects in dissociation equilibria. In judging the results it has to be kept in mind that the errors in $\Delta u/u$ are at least of the order of ± 0.001.

The lithium isotopes, because of their high relative mass difference, are expected to show the largest effects. They have therefore been studied most extensively. All measurements in the concentration range between 1 and 10 moles/liter are reported by Fiks and coworkers (*3, 32, 33*) (Figure 2). The authors claim to have found a stronger increase of $\Delta u/u$ with concentration for Li_2SO_4 compared with LiCl and $LiNO_3$. They conclude that in Li_2SO_4 solutions an isotope effect in the dissociation equilibrium contributes to the measured relative difference of the mobilities. Looking at the distribution of circles in Figure 2 and considering possible errors there remains some doubt as to the justification of this conclusion. What is doubtful in the case of Li_2SO_4 seems to have been clearly established by Behne and Wagener (*4*) for lithium acetate. Figure 3 gives their results. Their measurements at relatively low concentrations show a strong increase with concentration. The measurements of Fiks and coworkers indicate a small linear dependence of $\Delta u/u$ with con-

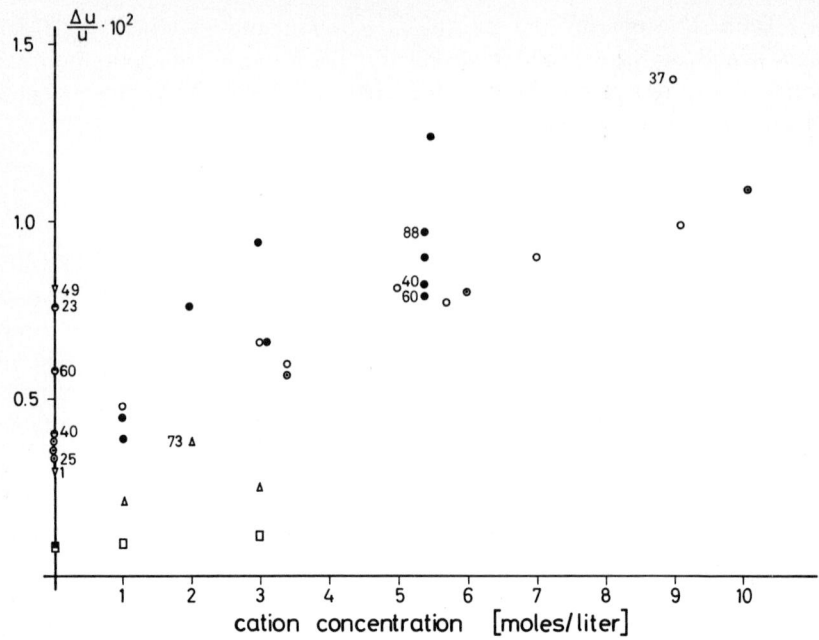

Figure 2.   Relative difference of the mobilities of ^6Li-^7Li, ^{22}Na-^{24}Na, ^{39}K-^{41}K, *and* ^{85}Rb-^{87}Rb *as a function of concentration. The temperature is 20°C. if not otherwise stated by numbers at the points*

○ *LiCl* (32, 33, 35)	△ *KCl* (8, 14)
● *Li₂SO₄* (3, 33)	▽ *NaCl* (7)
⊙ *LiNO₃* (1, 3, 6)	□ *RbCl* (14)
◖ *CH₃COOLi* (4)	▪ *CH₃COORb* (9)

centration. This slope is about the same for LiCl, LiNO₃, and Li₂SO₄. It can not be attributed therefore to equilibrium effects. A possible explanation might be a decrease in hydration with increasing concentration, which would result in a higher difference of the mobilities. An extrapolation to zero concentration gives good agreement with earlier measurements at very dilute solutions (*1, 6*). The point in Figure 2 at 0.35% has been determined by measurements of the electrical conductivity of almost isotopically pure ⁶LiCl and ⁷LiCl solutions (*35*). Bakulin, Troshin, and Fiks (*3*) searched for a temperature dependence of Δu/u in LiCl, LiNO₃, and Li₂SO₄ at various concentrations. They could not find an effect except for Li₂SO₄ at a concentration of 5.4 moles/liter. The temperature dependence is strange and quite small (Figure 2). They found a minimum of Δu/u at about 60°C. A similar temperature effect has been reported for lithium acetate at dilute solutions (*4*). The existence of this temperature dependence can only be established by further and still more accurate measurements.

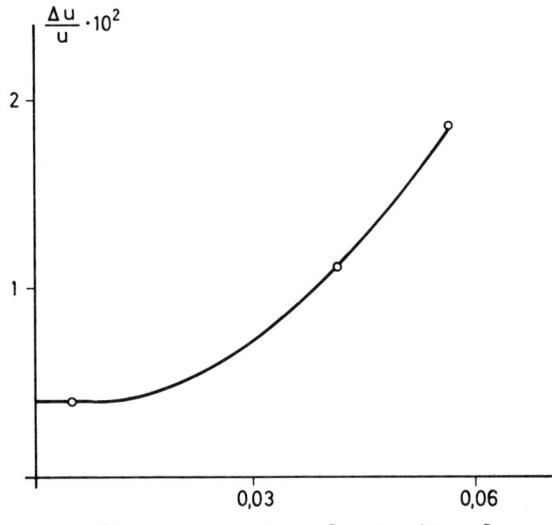

Figure 3. Relative difference of mobilities of
^6Li-^7Li in lithium acetate as a function of concentration at 40°C.

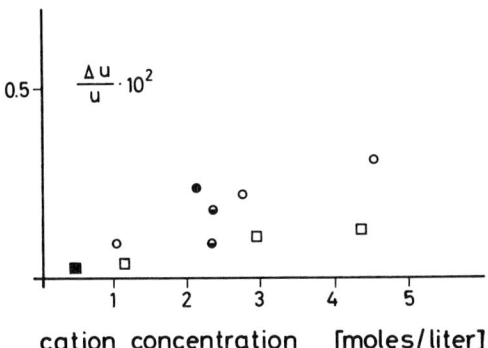

Figure 4. Relative difference of mobilities of
^{24}Mg-^{26}Mg and ^{63}Cu-^{65}Cu

○ $MgCl_2$ (34) 50°C.   □ $CuCl_2$ (34) 50°C.
● $MgSO_4$ (20)   ■ $CuSO_4$ (55) 29°C.
◗ $MgBr_2$ (56) 21°C.

For the sodium isotopes ^{22}Na–^{24}Na, a temperature dependence of $\Delta u/u$ has been found by Bonnin (7). He reports a value of 0.003 for 1°C. and 0.008 for 49°C.

The discussion of the results for all other cations given in Figure 2 and Figure 4 can be summarized. There are indications for a slight increase in $\Delta u/u$ with increasing concentration. Because of the smaller relative mass differences compared with Li, the $\Delta u/u$ values and the concentration dependence are much smaller. The differences for different concentrations are in the limits of error. In addition there is some discrepancy among the results reported by different authors. A temperature dependence has not been measured. It might be interesting to see if rubidium acetate shows a similarly strong concentration dependence as does lithium acetate.

The trough method was employed by Wagener (68) for the separation of the rubidium isotopes in rubidium acetate. The highest enrichment reached (without output) in ^{87}Rb was 40.8% (natural composition 27% ^{87}Rb).

Three $\Delta u/u$ values for anions have been reported in the literature. Madorsky and Straus (54) found a difference in mobilities of ^{35}Cl and ^{37}Cl of 0.0021 in a NaCl-solution. Wagener and Bilal (67) measured in a capillary separation tube a difference between ^{12}C formate and ^{14}C formate of 0.011 in sodium formate. Lamotte (39) gives a $\Delta u/u$ value of 0.022 for $^{10}BO_2{}^--^{11}BO_2{}^-$. It has been shown that this difference depends strongly upon the pH value of the solution. Therefore, it was concluded that the actual difference in mobility is negligible; the effect has almost completely to be attributed to an isotope effect in the dissociation equilibrium $^{11}BO_2{}^- + {}^{10}BO_2H \rightleftarrows {}^{10}BO_2{}^- + {}^{11}BO_2H$.

Literature Cited

(1) Arnikar, H., *J. Inorg. Nucl. Chem.* **11**, 249 (1959).
(2) Arnikar, H., *Ann. Physique, Ser.* **13**(4), 1291 (1959).
(3) Bakulin, E. A., Troshin, V. P., Fiks, V. B., *Russ. J. Phys. Chem.* **38**, 1221 (1964).
(4) Behne, D., Wagener, K., *Ber. Bunsenges. Phys. Chem.* **69**, 378 (1965).
(5) Bogoyavlenski, I. V., Grigoriev, V. N., Rudenko, N. S., *Sov. Phys. J.E.T.P.* **10**, 884 (1960).
(6) Bonnin, A., Chemla, M., *C.R. Acad. Sci. Paris* **243**, 1112 (1956).
(7) Bonnin, A., *C.R. Acad. Sci. Paris* **244**, 2708 (1957).
(8) Brewer, A. K., Madorsky, S. L., Taylor, J. K., Dibeler, V. H., Bradt, P., Parham, O. L., Britten, R. L., Reid Jr., J. G., *J. Res. Nat. Bur. Stds.* **38**, 137 (1947).
(9) Clusius, K., Huber, M., Wagener, K., *J. Chim. Phys.* **60**, 263 (1963).
(10) d'Amico, J. F., *Bull. Am. Phys. Soc.* **12**, 1041 (1967).
(11) de Gennes, P. G., *J. Phys. Rad.* **17**, 343 (1956).
(12) Duke, F. R., Owens, B., *J. Electrochem. Soc.* **105**, 548 (1958).
(13) Dworkin, A. S., Escue, R. B., van Artsdalen, E. R., *J. Phys. Chem.* **64**, 872 (1960).
(14) Fiks, V. B., *Russ. J. Phys. Chem.* **38**, 1218 (1964).
(15) Haeffner, E., *Nature* **172**, 775 (1953).
(16) Hering, H., Wever, H., *Z. Phys. Chem. N.F.* **53**, 310 (1967).
(17) Ho, P. S., Huntington, H. B., *J. Phys. Chem. Solids* **27**, 1319 (1966).
(18) Ho, P. S., *J. Phys. Chem. Solids* **27**, 1331 (1966).
(19) Holmlid, I., *Z. Naturforsch.* **21a**, 270 (1966).

(20) Jack, W., Dissertation Kiel (1951).
(21) *J. Chim. Phys.* **60**, 1 (1963).
(22) Jordan, S., Klemm, A., Z. *Naturforsch.* **21a**, 1584 (1966).
(23) Jordan, S., Lenke, R., Klemm, A., Z. *Naturforsch.* **23a**, 1563 (1968).
(24) Kistemaker, J., Bigeleisen, J., Nier, A. O. C., Eds., "Proceedings of the International Symposium on Isotope Separation," North-Holland Publishing Company, Amsterdam, 1958.
(25) Klemm, A., Z. *Naturforsch.* **9a**, 1031 (1954).
(26) *Ibid.*, **13a**, 1039 (1958).
(27) *Ibid.*, **17a**, 805 (1962).
(28) Klemm, A., *J. Chim. Phys.* **60**, 237 (1963).
(29) Klemm, A., "Molten Salt Chemistry," M. Blander, Ed., Interscience Publishers, New York, 1964.
(30) Klemm, A., Euratom Report **EUR 2466.e** (1965).
(31) Knof, H., Klemm, A., Z. *Naturforsch.* **14a**, 1020 (1959).
(32) Konstantinov, B. P., Fiks, V. B., *Russ. J. Phys. Chem.* **38**, 1038 (1964).
(33) *Ibid.*, **38**, 1216 (1964).
(34) Konstantinov, B. P., Bakulin, E. A., *Russ. J. Phys. Chem.* **39**, 1 (1965).
(35) Kunze, R. W., Fuoss, R. M., *J. Phys. Chem.* **66**, 930 (1962).
(36) Kuz'menko, P. P., Khar'kov, Ye. I., Lozovoy, V. I., *Phys. Metals and Metallography* **21**, 94 (1966).
(37) Kvist, A., Z. *Naturforsch.* **21a**, 487 (1966).
(38) Kvist, A., Trolle, U., Z. *Naturforsch.* **22a**, 213 (1967).
(39) Lamotte, M., Thesis, University of Paris (1967).
(40) Langevin, P., *Ann. Chim. Phys.* **5**, 245 (1905).
(41) Lantelme, F., Chemla, M., *J. Chim. Phys.* **60**, 250 (1963).
(42) Lenke, R., Klemm, A., Z. *Naturforsch.* **20a**, 1723 (1965).
(43) Lodding, A., Z. *Naturforsch.* **12a**, 569 (1957).
(44) *Ibid.*, **16a**, 1252 (1961).
(45) Lodding, A., *J. Chim. Phys.* **60**, 254 (1963).
(46) Lodding, A., *J. Phys. Chem. Solids* **26**, 143 (1965).
(47) *Ibid.*, **28**, 557 (1967).
(48) Lodding, A., Thernqvist, P., Z. *Naturforsch.* **23a**, 629 (1968).
(49) London, H., Ed., "Separation of Isotopes," George Newnes Limited, London, 1961.
(50) Lundén, A., Lodding, A., Fischer, W., Z. *Naturforsch.* **12a**, 268 (1957).
(51) Lundén, A., Z. *Naturforsch.* **17a**, 142 (1962).
(52) Lundén, A., *J. Chim. Phys.* **60**, 259 (1963).
(53) Lundén, A., Z. *Naturforsch.* **21a**, 1510 (1966).
(54) Madorsky, S. L., Straus, S., *J. Res. Natl. Bur. Std.* **38**, 185 (1947).
(55) *Ibid.*, **41**, 41 (1948).
(56) Martin, H., Harmsen, E., Z. *Elektrochem.* **62**, 152 (1958).
(57) Martin, H., Lübke, H.-J., Z. *Naturforsch.* **19a**, 115 (1964).
(58) Menès, F., Dirian, G., Roth, E., *J. Chim. Phys.* **60**, 245 (1963).
(59) Neumann, G. M., Hirschwald, W., Z. *Naturforsch.* **22a**, 388 (1967).
(60) Nordén, A., Lodding, A., Z. *Naturforsch.* **22a**, 215 (1967).
(61) Okada, J., Phd. Thesis, University of Tokyo (1966).
(62) Romanos, J., Klemm, A., Z. *Naturforsch.* **19a**, 1000 (1964).
(63) Saito, N., Tomita, I., Okada, I., *J. Nucl. Sci. Technol.* **3**, 140 (1966).
(64) Sullivan, G. A., *J. Phys. Chem. Solids* **28**, 347 (1967).
(65) Sullivan, G. A., *Phys. Rev.* **154**, 605 (1967).
(66) Thiemann, W., Wagener, K., Z. *Naturforsch.* **18a**, 228 (1963).
(67) Wagener, K., Bilal, B. A., Z. *Naturforsch.* **21a**, 1352 (1966).
(68) Wagener, K., *Ber. Bunsenges. Phys. Chem.* **71**, 627 (1967).
(69) Wever, H., *et al.*, "Physica Status Solidi" (in press).
(70) Wuhl, S., Lantelme, F., Chemla, M., *J. Chim. Phys.* **65**, 488 (1968).

RECEIVED October 12, 1967.

13

Thermotransport in Monatomic and Ionic Liquids

A. LODDING

Department of Physics, Chalmers University of Technology,
Gothenburg, Sweden

The phenomenon of thermotransport in simple liquids is described in a generalized treatment which does not require the adoption of any particular existing model of liquid diffusion. The results of recent isotope experiments in liquid metals are used as illustrations of applicability. The treatment is extended to liquid salts, where electrotransport mobility data under favorable conditions may facilitate the interpretation of thermotransport experiments. The experimental results in the few liquid salt systems, where thermo- as well as electrotransport of isotopes has been measured, are discussed in terms of the above treatment.

Thermotransport ("thermal diffusion," thermomigration) in solids has received considerable attention in recent years. From thermotransport studies it has been possible to derive information concerning—*i.a.*, defect mechanisms, the role of electrons and phonons in atom transport and the energy distribution around an activated configuration. Since the special symposium on the topic in Münster in 1965, literature published on solid state thermotransport has been extensive. Good reviews have been given by Adda and Philibert (*1*), Allnatt and Chadwick (*2*), and Oriani (*24*). As for the evidence of isotope effects in solid state thermotransport, only two instances have been reported (*see* Reference 16).

The usefulness of thermotransport studies, especially isotope studies, in liquids has been pointed out by the present author at the Münster conference and in a paper which appeared in 1966 (*17*). Until recently the basis for a theory applicable to liquids has been rather restricted owing to the scarcity, inexactness, and heterogeneity of available experimental data. However, recent studies of isotope thermotransport in liquid metals (*18, 20, 25, 26*) have allowed the formulation of a theoretical approach (*17*), which also may be applied to other classes of liquids. Further work in this field is greatly encouraged.

The most straightforward liquid thermotransport experiments are performed in leaving a mixture of chemical components or isotopes under a temperature gradient in a closed cylindrical separation tube. The components receive different migration velocities, which tend to enrich them at one or the other end of the tube. After a certain time, given by the length of the tube and the diffusivity of the liquid, a practical steady state is reached, in which further enrichment is prevented by diffusion. The composition along the tube is then analyzed as a function of temperature.

Actual experiments on pure liquid metals have yielded isotope separations of the order of one percent for a temperature interval of 100 degrees. Similar, or slightly smaller, isotope separations have been found in pure liquid salts. In mixtures of cations large chemical separations can be obtained, in optimal cases about a hundred times greater than for isotopes; in other cases the separation can be almost undetectable. While in all liquids the light isotope migrates towards the higher temperatures, hitherto no simple tendency can be seen in the investigated chemical mixtures.

The purpose of the present paper is (a) to give a generalized version of the theoretical approach of Reference *17;* (b) to see whether useful physical information can be extracted from the isotope experiments in liquid metals; (c) to apply the formalism to the results of thermotransport experiments in liquid salts (*10, 11*), which have not hitherto received satisfactory theoretical discussion.

Theoretical Treatment

In our discussion nothing will be assumed initially about the nature of the migrating species, which may be an atom, an ion, or a cluster of particles. We shall also avoid the frequently occurring postulate that the mean displacement length is of the same order as a nearest like-neighbor distance. While the treatment of Reference *17* employed a language adapted from solid-state arguments, the present approach will be based on premises which are not bound to a definite model and do not violate the physical picture of any of the various existing theories of liquid diffusion. It will simply be stated, that the probability of a displacement depends on the energy distribution in the vicinity of the migrating particle in such a way that it can be expressed as the product of an energy function $f(T)$ at the particle site (coordinate x) before displacement, and another energy function, $g(T + \Delta T)$, at an "imperfection" a definite distance away from the particle site—*e.g.*, at the coordinate x + ϕ1. The "imperfection," the presence of which is thus necessary for the displacement of the particle, may be, for example, a void or another density fluctuation. The functions $f(T)$ and $g(T + \Delta T)$ will express the entire temperature-sensitive part of diffusion.

Let us first consider isothermal diffusion. Einstein's diffusion law can be written

$$D = 1/6 \, l^2 \Gamma = 1/6 \, l^2 f(T) g(T) \tag{1}$$

The activation energy—*i.e.*, the slope of the Arrhenius plot (not necessarily a straight line) of D, will be

$$E_D = \frac{\partial \ln D}{\partial \dfrac{1}{RT}} = RT^2 \left[\frac{\partial \ln f(T)}{\partial T} + \frac{\partial \ln g(T)}{\partial T} \right] \tag{2}$$

When a temperature gradient is imposed, the flux velocities in the forward and reverse direction will be, respectively,

$$v_+ = l\Gamma_T = (1/6) f(T) g(T) \left[1 + \phi l \frac{\partial \ln g(T)}{\partial x} \right] \tag{3a}$$

$$v_- = l\Gamma_{T + \Delta T} = (1/6) f(T) \left[1 + \phi l \frac{\partial \ln f(T)}{\partial x} \right] g(T) \tag{3b}$$

The difference gives the net migration velocity (relative to a "pseudo-lattice" of atoms momentarily not engaged in displacement) of the species i,

$$v_i = D_i \phi_i [\partial \ln g(T)/\partial T - \partial \ln f(T)/\partial T] \, \partial T/\partial x \tag{4}$$

The relative velocity of two species will be $\Delta v = v_i - v_j$. At this stage we shall restrict the discussion to the special case of a mixture of two isotopes (denoted by the indices 1 and 2), of one chemical substance. (Chemical de-mixing will be very briefly discussed later.) The velocity difference of two isotopes, which can be assumed to have identical ϕ parameters, will be

$$v_1 - v_2 = (D_1 - D_2) \phi [\partial \ln g(T)/\partial T - \partial \ln f(T)/\partial T] \partial T/\partial x \tag{5}$$

and in combination with Equation 2,

$$v_1 - v_2 = (D_1 - D_2) \phi \frac{\partial T}{\partial x} [(E_D/RT^2) - 2(\partial \ln f(T)/\partial T)] \tag{6}$$

However, in the steady state the gradient of the separation factor $\left(Q = \dfrac{c_1/c_2}{(c_1/c_2)_0} \right)$ is given by

$$v_1 - v_2 = D_{eff}(\partial \ln Q/\partial x) \tag{7}$$

where D_{eff} is the effective diffusion coefficient, consisting of convection as well as molecular self-diffusion. The combination of Equations 6 and 7 yields

$$\frac{\partial \ln Q}{\partial T} = \frac{D_1 - D_2}{D_{eff}} \phi \left[E_D/RT^2 - 2 \frac{\partial \ln f(T)}{\partial T} \right] \qquad (8)$$

In reliable experiments convection is satisfactorily suppressed and one may (insofar as the mechanisms of self-diffusion and thermotransport can be assumed to be identical, *see* Reference 16) put $D_{eff} = D$—i.e., the mean of D_1 and D_2.

Introducing the "isotope factor" of diffusion, defined by

$$a = \frac{D_1 - D_2}{D} \bigg/ \frac{M_1 - M_2}{M} \qquad (9)$$

where M denotes the isotope mass, we can express the variation of istotopic composition with temperature at steady state by

$$\frac{\partial (\ln Q)}{\partial (1/RT)} = -a(\Delta M/M)\phi[E_D - 2RT^2 \, \partial \ln f(T)/\partial T] \qquad (10)$$

(It should be pointed out that the Bardeen-Herring correlation factor has been left out of the present discussion. In rigorous treatment the factor a, as defined by Equation 9, should in Equation 10 be replaced by $a_w = a/f$, where f is the correlation factor (*see* References 5, 16, and 17). The continued use of the term a instead of a_w in this paper will be justified when bearing in mind that the symbols D in our equations denote uncorrelated diffusion coefficients, as measurable—e.g., by NMR—and not tracer diffusion coefficients, as measured in most actual studies.)

The meaning of the term in brackets in Equation 10 (which we will denote by E*) can be illustrated by two examples. The first is the solid-state model, with well-defined and constant activation energies of formation and motion, and $f(T) = $ const. exp $(-E_m/RT)$. This gives a temperature-independent term in the brackets, so that the equation can be integrated from a "cold" to a "hot" temperature, which is convenient in many experiments, where the exact temperature variation along the cell is unknown. The experimentally determined entity will be

$$\frac{Q_{max} - 1}{T_C^{-1} - T_H^{-1}} = -Ra \frac{\Delta M}{M} \phi[E_D - 2E_m] \qquad (11)$$

This is the formula derived in Reference 16. According to practically all recent theories of liquid diffusion, however, to treat E_D and E_m as constants is, at best, a reasonable approximation and actually the integration should be permissible only over short ranges of temperature. The expressions for D in the different theories appear in many different forms (8, 22, 29, 32), depending on the various models employed. In all cases, however, the temperature function at the particle site can be expressed by $f(T) =$ const. T^n, where n ranges between 0 and $+ 3/2$. This simplifies Equation 10 to

$$\frac{\partial (\ln Q)}{\partial (1/RT)} = -a \; \frac{\Delta M}{M} \; \phi (E_D - 2nRT) \tag{12}$$

Discussion of Experimental Results in Liquid Metals

Table I shows the results of isotope thermotransport experiments on a number of liquid metals. In the latest work (20) we have been able to plot ln Q vs. inverse temperature and obtained good straight lines, which indicates that the product $\phi a E^*$ is rather independent of temperature and thus that the second term in E^* is small. Also, in all cases the light isotope is enriched at the high temperature, again showing that E_D is definitely greater than $2nRT$. As seen in Table I, the experiments yield $(-a\phi) \simeq 0.52/(1 - 2nRT/E_D)$. Assuming the temperature dependent term in E^* to be zero gives a minimum value of $-(a\phi)_{min} \simeq 0.5$.

Table I. Thermotransport of Isotopes in Pure Liquid Metals[a]

Metal	$\dfrac{M}{\Delta M} \dfrac{\partial \ln Q}{\partial (1/RT)}$	E_D	$(-a\phi)_{min}$	ϕ_{min}
Li	1440 ± 70	2825 ± 100	0.51 ± 0.04	4.8
K	1130 ± 60	2550 ± 270	0.44 ± 0.08	4.2
Rb	1110 ± 70	1950 ± 300	0.56 ± 0.12	5.4
Ga	1260 ± 80	2350 ± 250	0.54 ± 0.08	5.1
In	1330 ± 130	2430 ± 50	0.55 ± 0.07	5.2

[a] All energies in cal/mole. In the last column, $a = -0.105$. See Reference 20.

The isotope factor $(-a)$ is always smaller than $1/2$ (the maximum value is obtained by putting $w \sim M^{1/2}$ in $a = d \ln w/d \ln M$, which applies only to the ideal solid state case of an atom jumping, without energetic interaction with its neighbors, from one "rigid cage" to another). Actually liquid diffusion is highly cooperative and $(-a)$ is likely to be considerably smaller than the theoretic maximum. Nobody has yet succeeded in measuring the isotope factor in liquid metals, but by comparison with a semi-empirical model first developed by Klemm (12, 19) for electromigration in simple liquid salts, one may assume that in monatomic liquids one should have $a \simeq -0.1$. One then finds (last column in Table I) that $\phi_{min} \simeq 5$ for all metals investigated. The definition of ϕ being (see above)

$$\phi = (d' + 1)/2 \, 1 \tag{13}$$

where d' is the effective particle diameter (measured along jump direction) and l the mean displacement, one obtains the indication that diffusion takes place by position adjustments smaller by about an order of magnitude than the particle diameter.

This result has been quoted in the latest paper by Swalin (*30*) as a support for a cooperative diffusion theory. The physical image is also in agreement with the liquid transport model recently derived by Rahman (*27*) from computer experiments.

The theory as formulated by Equation 12 may in certain cases give evidence against existing diffusion models. An example is the original version (*29*) of Swalin's theory, where it is derived that D should be proportional to T^2—i.e., $E_D = 2RT$. By somewhat arbitrary use of the partition function formalism, Swalin here postulates n = 1. If this treatment is correct, our Equation 12 would predict the thermotransport effect to be zero, which is far from being the case. At the Brookhaven Conference on Liquid Metals in 1967, Nachtrieb and Rice (*22*) pointed out that in the correct treatment of Swalin's theory a T-term should actually cancel out, giving a linear temperature dependence for D and n = 0. This obviously agrees much better with our thermotransport results.

The assumption $a = -0.1$ must be considered as definitely qualitative as long as no directly measured values are available for liquid metals. It may be more interesting to look instead at the product of $a\phi$, as the two entities both express measures of cooperation, and can hardly be expected to be mutually independent. It is tempting to see if the present result, $(-a\phi) \simeq 0.5$, is compatible with the premises of a definite established model. For simplicity a modified form of the Cohen-Turnbull (*8*) model will be chosen. According to this model, displacement is possible only when the redistribution of free volume has produced a sufficiently big void, volume V^*; then a neighbor atom will freely drift into the void. We shall implement the model with the postulate that this atom moves in phase with and ahead of a string of $(n - 1)$ other atoms. Under these hypothetical circumstances ϕ becomes about equal to n and the isotope factor for the independently moving "cluster" becomes $-1/2\ n^{-1}$. Thus, one obtains $\phi a = -1/2$, and that is just what we are getting experimentally.

This stunning agreement does seem somewhat fortuitous. It may be unnecessary to introduce the concept of "clusters," which would also involve the lifetime of such clusters and other complicating factors. It is probably more meaningful and rewarding to interpret (*16*) the isotope factor in terms of Mullen (*21*) and LeClaire (*15*), such that $a = -\Delta K/2$, ΔK denoting the share of the saddle-point kinetic energy, possessed by the diffusing atom itself, rather than its surroundings (*see* Reference *16*). The liquid counterpart of the saddle-point energy can, as a first attempt, be thought to be shared amongst the n' atoms grouped about the critical fluctuation of density (which they have contributed in creating). This would mean $a = 1/(2n')$. When one of these atoms freely drifts into this void, an open void is left behind, so that the motion is correlated. Applying analogous reasoning as for the Bardeen–Herring correlation in the solid state, one may put (*see, e.g.,* Reference *28*)

$$1 \simeq (V^*)^{1/3} \left(1 - \frac{2}{n'} \right) \tag{14}$$

Since the activation energy of motion can be treated as negligible, it is reasonable to substitute the experimental "activation volume" for V^* (*23*) by measuring the pressure dependence of self-diffusion in liquid Hg and Ga. This critical void formation volume has been found to be some 5% of an atomic volume (as compared with 20 to 100% in the solid state). Substituting into Equation 14 and combining with Equation 13, the result $a\phi = -1/2$ corresponds to n' $\simeq$ 4. This means $a = -0.12$ and is in good agreement with our earlier assumption. Also it may be pointed out here, that n' = 4 is a reasonable picture of an "inflated" tetrahedron, in line with the static model of "stacking" spheres introduced by Bernal (*6, 7*).

This part of the discussion may be concluded by pointing out that, in addition to interesting theoretical implications, isotope thermotransport experiments on liquid metals in many cases also offer a rather simple and economical way of obtaining isotope enrichments of the order of a few percent.

Discussion of Experiments in Liquid Salts

In liquid salts the isotope factor is in principle measurable by electrotransport (electromigration). Since many such measurements are available (*13*), it is especially tempting to study thermotransport in molten ionic media. One must bear in mind, however, the possibility of the following complications: (a) the mechanisms of electrotransport, thermotransport, and self-diffusion may be non-identical (*see* Reference *16*); (b) the isotope factors, as determined by electrotransport, are dependent, *via* transport numbers, on the reference system; and (c) severe experimental difficulties may be encountered in liquid salt thermotransport, mainly corrosion and convection effects.

Table II represents the data from the only liquid salts, where both electro- and thermotransport of isotopes have been measured [with the exception of a more recent investigation of LiCl at this laboratory (*31*), which has not yet been evaluated completely]. Up to now, no quantitative discussion of these results has been offered.

Table II.   Thermotransport and Electrotransport in Pure Liquid Nitrates[a]

Salt	$\dfrac{M}{\Delta M}\,R$	$Q_{max}\dfrac{^{-1}}{T_C^{-1} - T_H^{-1}}$	$-\mu^+$	t^+	$-a$	E_D	ϕ_{min}
LiNO$_3$		230	0.08	0.8	0.10	5500	0.42
KNO$_3$		680	0.037	0.6	0.06	5500	2.0
RbNO$_3$		560	0.035	0.6	0.06	5600	1.7

[a] All energies in cal/mole. Thermotransport data recalculated from References *10* and *11*.

The sign of the isotope effect in Table II is the same as for liquid metals—*i.e.*, the light isotope migrates throughout towards the higher temperature. We can infer that it is the energy "outside" the particle that mainly determines its displacement probability. In the discussion it will be assumed that only one transport mechanism is effectively present, and that the experiments have been unhampered by convection. The thermotransport data obtained by Gustafsson (*10, 11*) are recalculated in the second column in the form relevant to the present discussion (*via* Equation 11). The relative isotope mobilities have been measured in electrotransport experiments by Lundén (*see* Reference *13*); which yielded the so-called mass effects, μ, listed in the third column. The fourth column lists the experimental "self-transport numbers," quoted from Reference *13*. The need of introducing the transport numbers t is obvious from the following argument:

The mass effect of the component i of an ion mixture is defined as

$$\mu_i = \Delta b_i / \Sigma (b_+ c_+ z_+ + b_- c_- z_-) \tag{15}$$

where Δ stands for the isotope difference, b for the mobility, c the concentration (mole fraction), z the ionization and the plus–minus suffixes for the sign of all the charge carriers over which the summation takes place. The definition of the transport number is

$$t_i = b_i c_i z_i / \Sigma (b_+ c_+ z_+ + b_- c_- z_-) \tag{16}$$

If the mechanisms are identical, $\Delta D/D = \Delta b/b$ and so

$$a_i = \mu_i c_i z_i / t_i \tag{17}$$

In the fifth column of Table II, in order to obtain the isotope factor, the transport numbers of the previous column have been used, together with $z = c = 1$. Actually, instead of these "external" transport numbers, so-called "internal" or "absolute" transport numbers should have been used.

These cannot be directly measured, however. The experimental, "external," values are, as is well known (14), dependent on the material of the reference container. The a-values in Table II are thus to be regarded as very qualitative. This should not, however, affect the general nature of the conclusions drawn.

Evaluating ϕE^* by the aid of Equation 11, and putting $E^* \simeq E_D$ as in the case of metals (literature values (9) of E_D, with that for $RbNO_3$ interpolated, are listed in the sixth column), we obtain the $\phi_{\min}$ values shown in the last column. For the nitrates of K and Rb, we get about 2, as compared with about 5 in liquid metals. This should not be very surprising in view of other observed differences between the two classes of liquids. Particularly relevant are the diffusivity and conductivity measurements at varying pressures—i.e., the so-called activation volumes. In metals these are, as mentioned above, only about 5% of the atomic volumes. In liquid salts, however, one has found (3) 20% or even more. Very probably this would entail greater displacements, and thus smaller ϕ values, than in the metals. While thus the results in KNO_3 and $RbNO_3$ seem reasonable, the extremely low ϕ value found for $LiNO_3$ seems disconcerting. Any attempt at an explanation must naturally be viewed with great caution, and the possibility of experimental fallacies cannot be quite excluded. Within the frame of the arguments of the present paper, the result suggests that the Li ion is so small that a slight position adjustment within its "cage" does not really constitute a diffusive step. To diffuse, the ion must move into the next cage, the energy required being the opening-up of a ring of anions half-way through, so that ϕ becomes about one-half. The cation participates in a kind of solid-state type diffusion with relatively long "jumps."

The formalism of this paper can also be applied to mixtures other than those of isotopes, such as binary cation systems or liquid alloys. The treatment following Equation 4 can easily be shown for the case of different chemical species A and B, to lead to a counterpart of Equation 11, in the form

$$R \frac{Q_{AB} - 1}{T_C^{-1} - T_H^{-1}} = \frac{(D\phi E^*)_A - (D\phi E^*)_B}{D_{AB}} \tag{18}$$

where D_{AB} is the interdiffusion coefficient of the two species and D_A, D_B the self-diffusion coefficients. The size factors ϕ should depend on ionic radii. On the grounds suggested above, one may for simplicity assume that the same "void formation" energy applies for both species and that the motion energy is small—i.e., $E^*_A \cong E^*_B \cong E_D$. As a further simplification, one may assume the validity of the Darken formula $D_{AB} = c_B D_A + c_A D_B$, and obtains

$$\frac{Q_{AB} - 1}{T_C^{-1} - T_H^{-1}} = E_D \frac{\phi_A - \phi_B \alpha}{c_B + c_A \alpha} \tag{19}$$

where $\alpha = b_B/b_A = D_B/D_A$ is the mobility ratio, obtainable from electromigration. The size parameters are in principle obtainable from isotope effect measurements made in parallel with "chemical" thermotransport. Equation 19 is naturally based on very restricted hypothetical premises; it is intended primarily as an illustration of the interdependence of the various experimental entities and atomistic parameters.

While thermotransport data from experiments on a number of nitrate mixtures are available (*4, 10*), unfortunately no relative electrotransport mobility measurements have been made for these particular systems and diffusion data are scanty. Isotope effects have been seen with cells permitting only qualitative results. Until a more systematic study has been made on all the relevant effects in one well-defined system, the usefulness of the individual transport property investigations in binary liquid systems, however carefully performed, remains relatively limited.

In conclusion, however, one may state that parallel electro- and thermotransport experiments in liquid salts appear to offer useful information concerning the transport mechanism and the distribution of energy around an atom which is about to diffuse. Isotope effect measurements should be combined with reliable transport number investigations in identical environments, or if this cannot be done, with quantitative self-diffusion measurements on both the cations and anions. Investigations of binary salt systems should be accompanied by careful diffusivity measurements and, wherever possible, by determinations of the associated isotope effects.

Acknowledgments

I wish to acknowledge stimulating discussions with Professors C. A. Angell (Purdue University), B. Cleaver (University of Southampton), S. Forcheri (Euratom, Petten), A. Klemm (Otto-Hahn Institute), and N. H. Nachtrieb (University of Chicago).

Literature Cited

(1) Adda, Y., Philibert, J., "La Diffusion dans les Solides," P.U.F., Paris, 1966.
(2) Allnatt, A. R., Chadwick, A. V., *Chem. Rev.* **67**, 681 (1967).
(3) Angell, C. A., Cleaver, B. (private communication).
(4) Backlund, V., Dupuy, J., Gustafsson, S., Lundén, A., *Z. Naturforsch.* **22a**, 471 (1967).
(5) Barr, L. W., LeClaire, A. D., *Proc. Brit. Cer. Soc.* **1**, 109 (1964).
(6) Bernal, J. D., *Nature* **183**, 141 (1959).

 (7) *Ibid.*, **185**, 68 (1960).
 (8) Cohen, M. H., Turnbull, D., *J. Chem. Phys.* **31**, 1164 (1959).
 (9) Dworkin, A. S., Escue, R. B., van Artsdalen, E. R., *J. Phys. Chem.* **64**, 872 (1960).
(10) Gustafsson, S., Z. *Naturforsch.* **18a**, 949 (1963).
(11) *Ibid.*, **21a**, 842 (1966).
(12) Klemm, A., Physikertagung Wiesbaden, p. 73 (1966).
(13) Klemm, A., "Molten Salt Chemistry," M. Blander, Ed., Interscience Pub., New York, 1964.
(14) Klemm, A., Heinzinger, K., ADVAN. CHEM. SER. **89**, 248 (1969).
(15) LeClaire, A. D., *Phil. Mag.* **14**, 1271 (1966).
(16) Lodding, A., *Phys. Stat. Sol.* **22**, 167 (1967).
(17) Lodding, A., Z. *Naturforsch.* **21a**, 1348 (1966).
(18) Lodding, A., Ott, A., Z. *Naturforsch.* **21a**, 1344 (1966).
(19) Lodding, A., *J. Phys. Chem. Solids* **28**, 557 (1967).
(20) Löwenberg, L., Nordén-Ott, A., Lodding, A., Z. *Naturforsch.* **23a**, 1779 (1968).
(21) Mullen, A., *Phys. Rev.* **121**, 1649 (1961).
(22) Nachtrieb, N. H., *Advan. Phys.* **16**, 309 (1967).
(23) Nachtrieb, N. H., "Liquid Metals, and Solidification," p. 49, Am. Soc. Met, Cleveland, 1958.
(24) Oriani, R. A., *J. Phys. Chem. Solids* (in print).
(25) Ott, A., Lundén, A., Z. *Naturforsch.* **19**, 822 (1964).
(26) Ott, A., Löwenberg, L., Lodding, A., Z. *Naturforsch.* **22a**, 2112 (1967).
(27) Rahman, A., *Phys. Rev.* **126**, A405 (1964).
(28) Shewmon, P. G., "Diffusion in Solids," McGraw-Hill, New York, 1963.
(29) Swalin, R. A., *Acta Met.* **7**, 736 (1959).
(30) Swalin, R. A., Z. *Naturforsch.* **23a**, 805 (1968).
(31) Wallin, K. (to be published).
(32) Walls, H. A., Upthegrove, W. R., *Acta Met.* **12**, 461 (1964).

RECEIVED October 23, 1968. The topic of this paper has in part been presented in a lecture given at the Symposium on Molten Salts, Salice Terme (Pavia), May 1968.

INDEX